THE HOMEBUILT, WIND–GENERATED ELECTRICITY HANDBOOK

by Michael A. Hackleman

with contributions by

Vanessa Naumann
Mark Dankoff
Jim DeKorne

1st printing--October, 1975
2nd printing--May, 1976
3rd printing--November, 1976
Library of Congress Catalogue Card Number: 75-36307
ISBN: 0-915238-05-5

Other books by Michael A. Hackleman:

WIND AND WINDSPINNERS—A 'Nuts and Bolts' Approach to Wind/Electric Systems

Additional single copies of both books
may be obtained from
Earthmind
5246 Boyer Rd.
Mariposa, CA 95338
for $8 (includes book rate postage and handling)
or $10 (airmail and foreign orders).   California orders add
6% sales tax.

Earthmind is a non-profit corporation pursuing alternative energy research
in this and related areas. For more information about us and our other publications, send a stamped, self-addressed, long envelope and 50¢ for our
current publications list.   Please use an SASE when corresponding with us.

For wholesale and bulk ordering information,
contact:

PEACE PRESS
—Printing & Publishing—
3828 Willat Avenue
Culver City, California 90230

FOREWORD

Even as Wind and Windspinners was trundled off to the press for printing, this book was at the edge of my mind. That is not to say that I was ready to write another book; I was bone-tired from the first one. But, in the course of writing Wind and Windspinners, I'd discovered more about what I didn't know. And what needed to be "general knowledge" for the alternative energy enthusiast. So, it didn't come as much of a surprise to hear myself (only a few months later) asking Jim DeKorne if he would be interested in co-authoring a book on subjects that all the available literature on wind energy seemed to neglect. Jim was getting wound up to write a book on organic hydroponics, but consented to giving some real support to my objective. His small homestead in New Mexico is the source of (and proving ground for) much of the material in this book. And, besides a write-up on the Jacobs governor breakdown, he's responsible for all these silly cartoons. A welcome gift from a busy man.

Wind and Windspinners took six weeks to write; The Homebuilt Wind-Generated Electricity Handbook has taken a long six months. Not surprising, considering that it is longer and more involved than originally conceived. But, right in the middle of it, I was ready to quit; it was more of a job than I could handle alone. Just then, the cavalry arrived: Mark Dankoff and Vanessa Naumann. Nessie slaved over fuming developer and fixer, miles of film, and piles of print; the book's photos attest to her skill and fortitude. Mark took on the task of the electronic drawings, smoothing out my rough sketches. And he went on to fight with me over all sorts of additions, deletions, revisions, and replacements in the text itself. By virtue of their untiring work and support, this book is a reality, and it speaks of their touch.

There are others to thank: Jim Davis, Bill Hart, William and June House, David House, Win, and the few people that have stopped by and given a hand. A special thanks to Harry Waters for his aid in restoring the wind machines. And Valorie, for handling other things while we dealt with such insanities. And, finally, some recognition to the contribution of The Lone Bandit, who helped us during layout by laying out(stretched) on our final copy, protecting it from pilferage (as any cat-master would).

While the contents of these pages stand as a self-contained whole, the book must be considered as a companion volume to Wind and Windspinners and this accounts for, in part, the frequent reference to it. The reader is advised to seek out other sources and references by making extensive use of the bibliographies listed in both books, and information available from local libraries.

INTRODUCTION

This book is dedicated to the little people of alternative energy, without whose help the whole field of natural energy usage would undoubtedly take one giant step backward. The discussions of the included subjects assume some prior knowledge but, for the most part, this has been minimized. Since it is difficult to ask questions about something you don't know anything about, it is the intent of this book to arm the reader with sufficient information to seek out sources and obtain the detail necessary to complete the picture. Many designs are offered in the text, but inasmuch as the reader will not be under the supervision and direction of the author or Earthmind, no warranty is expressed or implied for the safety and welfare of persons and property involved in the field. Hence, the author and Earthmind disclaim any liability for the use of the material presented in this book.

Wind energy is "popular," and a real "fad" to many who experiment with it. As a hobby, it can be challenging and rewarding--but BEWARE, for danger lurketh, whether you intend to use it for energy self-sufficiency or only to impress others with what you can do. Beyond the inconvenience and cost of losing some part of the system is the danger of "slung" blades, falling towers and wind machines, personal injury, surrounding-property damage, fire, explosion, shock, etc. So, maybe I'm gettin' a few yawns and nods. Well, prop open yer lids and eyeball the two pictures on this page. I don't fancy puttin' my mistakes on display, but I'm trying to deliver a message. I'm personally responsible for the pictured events-- material or design failure were not. And friends, these were not nearly as bad as they could have been, had they gone over in another direction or happened under different circumstances. We were lucky--twice. Take heed! And you won't be taking pictures like these with your own camera.

TABLE OF CONTENTS

An alternative to buying a new wind-electric system or making your own from plans or from your own design, is to go out and find a wind machine. I refer to the wind-electric machines that were manufactured in the USA in the 1930's-1950's. When homes were first electrified, relatively low transmission voltages limited service to the immediate vicinity of the powerhouse and these were only located in the cities and towns. Folks living in the rural areas either did without or they charged batteries with kerosene-fueled generators or . . . used wind machines manufactured by several companies (during this period) to bring power to the people, especially in the "wind corridor"-- the great plains of North America. Ranging in peak output from 200-3000 watts, these machines delivered their power at 12, 32, or 110 volts DC. The biggest wind-electric companies of the era were <u>Wincharger</u> and <u>Jacobs</u>, respectively the Chevrolet and Cadillac of farm wind machines.

Long-distance electricity did, however, finally occur and the REA (<u>R</u>ural <u>E</u>lectrification <u>A</u>dministration) set about the task of convincing the farm owners that Reddy Kilowatt was better than their wind-generated stuff. For some farm owners, this was a welcome substitute to their problem-ridden wind machines. For others, it was no "improvement" at all; bringing in the electricity was going to be expensive and they had grown used to wind-generated electricity and the relative independence that it afforded them. Still others found the decision difficult. The REA offered long-term payments on the installation and this won over most borderline cases. Others held out, waiting until the utility poles were set up for others, and then bought into it. Even to this day some have held out. But most went over to utility. And their wind machines fell into disuse.

Where did they go? Most were sold off as scrap. (These machines have many pounds of copper in them.) Others found their way into barns. Or the nearest junk pile. Or into the nearest garbage hole. (Out in some of the more remote areas, garbage pickup is unheard of so a hole is dug and filled with garbage until the size or smell warrants a proper burial with a plow and another hole is dug.) Or it was left on the tower, disconnected and furled. (This was rare as in many cases the REA would not install utility power until a machine had been taken down . . . if you can believe that!) Or the machines were sold to the "holders-out", who bought a machine (or took it off their neighbors hands) to increase their own generating capacity. The important question is: How many of these machines are still around? The answer? Nobody knows. There were hundreds of thousands of these wind machines manufactured by the half-dozen or so companies that existed!

Well, we didn't know either, but a casual visit with Jim DeKorne indicated that they weren't terrifically scarce; he had four or five of the best of 'em in good shape! This deserved looking into! Jim agreed to go on a wind energy expedition with me; he had the name of one person he'd heard about that had a Jacobs, so we placed a hurried call and, with a tentative buy arranged,

we went north. The result? A few days work and one machine recovered-- a Jacobs. Jim needed some help raising a few towers but I needed to get back to California. A month later I was again in New Mexico and from there mounted another expedition for more wind machines.

We had a month to prepare (at Earthmind) for this second expedition. We knew the names of a few of the wind machines manufactured during the pre-REA period. And we knew what some of them looked like. And we had thought out the various ways to go about finding them. We made decisions to do it this way and that way. We were right on some of them, just so-so on others, and all wet for still others. And after two weeks of truckin' around on back roads, we'd had enuff. The find-a-wind-machine fever had left us. But we'd found a heap of 'em, were happy with the price we paid and what we came home with, and we'd learned a lot to boot. And above all, we had partially answered the question of "how many". There were a lot of these wind machines still around.

There are groups of people in the USA right now engaged in the search for these wind machines. They restore them and sell them for the going price. But . . . there isn't any reason why you can't get one for yourself and avoid the middleman. Don't get the idea that it won't cost you more than the $25 or $50 (if anything) that you'll pay for the machine itself; you might have to invest twice to ten times that amount just to put yourself in the vicinity of the guy who has one that he'll sell. And that price will go up by the day becuz, at some point, those folks will see just what they have and it'll sell high or not at all. BUT . . . if you want a wind machine, this is a way to get one that can save you a few thousand dollars.

The purpose of this chapter will be to take some of the guess work out of the undertaking. The bulk of the information in this chapter comes from firsthand experience-- what we did and why we did it. And what we concluded from the experience. There are a slew of ways that one might go about a search. We didn't try 'em all, for sure, but if I were to go on another expedition, I'd do it another way (or try to, anyway!). Whether you find one of them will work for you, or you choose one of your own, I hope it nets you a wind machine.

Where to Look

The first order of business is to try and figure out where the wind machines are. And the strongest point that can be made here is : Wind machines are where you find 'em! Sound silly? What I mean is summed up in a story I once heard . Late one night, a policeman noticed a small boy crawling around on the sidewalk under a street lamp. Asked what it was that he was doing, the boy replied, " I'm looking for a quarter that I lost. " The policeman observed the search for several moments and, when it appeared unsuccessful, asked the boy where he'd lost the quarter. Slowly the boy raised his hand and pointed to the other end of the darkened block. Puzzled, the policeman asked the boy why he was searching here if he'd lost the quarter a block away. The boy replied, "becuz there's more light here!" So . . . no matter how intensely you search, you won't find wind machines where they aren't to be found.

Here are some factors to help locate an area:

(1) It must be in an area that's fairly rural. Stay away from cities. Look for areas that recieved REA only recently (in the past 5-20 years). Only more recently electrified areas are going to still have a discarded wind machine around that is not now just so much rust and junk, or buried beneath the rubble. As well, they are likely to be of more recent vintage.

2. Check REA records for those areas that were last to go on utility. I don't know if this information is available but it'd be a good source **if** it exists; the REA is still around.

3. The area should be one with good enuff winds to make using wind energy feasible, such as the wind corridor (Texas to Canada). Not a hard and fast rule, though, becuz the folks in the area might not have known they were in a low-wind area, but purchased a wind machine anyway.

4. Look for an area which was wealthy; wind energy systems were not cheap in those days, so the farmer had to shell out enuff to pay for $800-$2000 worth of system. Keep thinkin' back about 10-30 years; you're lookin' for areas that were wealthy <u>then</u>.

5. It helps if you choose a very dry area (of the potential good places). Some of the machines that we found had been outside for 20 years but are quite salvagable becuz of the cold dry climate. In a few instances, we've noticed that these machines only began to rust after they arrived in California.

Once you've spotted a likely area, make some inquiries. Run an ad in the local newspapers. Inquire at service-type facilities--seed and grain companies, utility, sheriff, inspectors, vets-- in the area. What you're lookin' for is someone that visits all the farms or ranches along a route that might remember having seen any wind machines other than the water-pumping type. (Most folks called 'em "winchargers", regardless of their make.) These inquiries have their limitations (as we shall see), but they are worth considering and may work for you.

The method I can personally recommend is the one that we chose . . . just truck on out to the area you have in mind, and begin the search. In our case, we knew one wind machine existed in the area. The only real question in our minds was: Could we find more in the time we had to look for them. It takes a lot of confidence to head out when you face a 1300 mile trip each way!

Our expedition was conducted in Wyoming. Other areas worth considerable attention are Montana, the Dakotas, Iowa, Nebraska, Kansas, Texas, New Mexico, and Colorado. These are the ones I know of, but I'd believe there are other states where a search would be fruitful.

<u>What</u>

It does little good to go out searching for wind machines unless you know what you are looking for. I mean, the chances are good that you will know one when you see it; the problem comes, however, in knowing the parts of the system well enuff to insure that you get them all (or, at least the necessary ones). Without them, the wind machine is next to useless. Lucky for you, this happens to be a byproduct of the next chapter, where we talk about restoring the machines. Look at the pictures well and learn the names, the functions, and the approximate sizes. A lot of the stuff in those pictures is cleaned up, but you'll rarely find that to be the case when you find it out in a junk pile. When it's mixed with a lot of other stuff, it's all one big puzzle that you'll have to work out if you are going to spot the essential governor, slip rings, pull-out arm, etc. It would help to have pictures or drawings of the various pieces to a wind-electric system so that the person you contact will see what in 'tarnation' you're talkin' about. We didn't do this, but I know it would have saved us some time. We had to stand there and explain it and it isn't easy. Remember, you may be talking to second- or third-generation folk on these farms. Chances are they've seen the stuff tucked away back in a corner of the barn or in the overhead of the garage or out there in the junk pile on the north 40, but unless you can draw all of the associations, they've just classified that away as somethin' that Dad, or Grandad, had at one time and is totally worthless and nondescript now.

Another extremely useful need-to-know is the kind of tail that these machines used to sport. They are very distinctive when compared with the water-pumping-type windmill, and they can be an aid in spotting a machine still on a tower from a distance. We saw a few water-pumpers that had Jacobs tails on them; this is a good indicator that at one time there was a wind-electric machine in use and may still be lying around somewhere (minus the tail).

JACOBS TAILVANE

WINCHARGER TOWER STUB

WIND ELECTRIC   JACOBS

JACOBS GENERATOR

JACOBS LOLLY SHAFT

WINCHARGER GEARBOX

JUNK?

The towers that were used for the wind-electric machines of the pre-REA period were substantially different, in most cases, than those used for water pumpers. The Jacobs machine was generally found on a three-leg tower, and all the towers we saw that we later found out had had a Jacobs on them were at least 50 feet high. Occasionally, a three-leg tower sported a Wincharger, but you'll also find the single-leg tower that found frequent use for Winchargers. Many of these towers are now used for TV antennas and, while we were very anxious to also obtain towers, we were unsuccessful. We offered all the way up to $200 for these towers and yet the TV antenna was the main reason they would not sell them. Other towers that we found lying on the ground were destined to provide angle-iron scrap for the varied farm projects as the farmers know well the price of steel.

The Area

If you are actually going to go to an area and search for machines, it is essential that you learn the place well. Try to get a county map which details all of the roads and the farms in the area; these can be obtained from a small-town fire department, sheriff station, or courthouse. With this "tool," you can note the places that you've visited and plan out the expedition's day. In the more remote sections of some of the states, these backroads are not laid out in neat square patterns; if nothing else, the map will just keep you from getting completely lost. We often encountered people who thought they had seen a machine somewhere; with a map handy they were able to pinpoint it for us. (Most of these farm folk know not only the history of their area, but the names of all the neighbors within a 25-mile radius of their own place.)

If you have a map in your possession, you can also note any remarks that people might make in regards to how long ago REA came in, or if there is, or isn't, phone service in the area (which is a good indicator in itself). By the way, you might consider getting several copies of the map; we only got one and it was about ready to fall apart when we got home (I think that we'll frame it as a souvenir of the expedition -- it is certainly a work of art now).

Equipping Yourself

There are all sorts of things that you COULD take on the expedition, but the realities of a small vehicle will necessitate a careful selection of items which are truly essential. From the first expedition, we learned enuff to help the second, but even then we'd not brought along a few things that would have made it easier in one respect or another.

Binoculars are a real help, especially when you are in outlying areas where the farms/ranches are few and far between. From a distance, you can check out farms lying to either side of the road, 3 to 5 miles away. They won't tell you much if you don't see anything . . . but they'll pump adrenalin into the ole bloodstream if you see a tower and can identify the tail shape on it. Unlike the water-pumpers, however, the wind-electric machines are generally very hard to spot on a tower; this is because of the few, and relatively thin blades on them (if the props have not been altogether removed). The Jacobs generator is quite large (looking for all the world like a huge bomb) but the Winchargers and many of the other machines that were manufactured are quite small and are, therefore, not quite as visible. So the binoculars are an asset.

Using binoculars can help, but watch out -- they might get you into some trouble! We conducted both of our expeditions during hunting season, so I imagine that anyone that saw us using them just figured we were looking for antelope. BUT if you are searching during a nonseason, you might find yourself doing some hasty explaining to the sheriff. The folk up in these areas are not necessarily paranoid, but they do watch out for one another. An out-of-state license, and a couple of characters screening off-road farms is sure to catch someone's attention. After a few experiences we learned to use a little bit of discretion when we looked over a nearby spread. On our second expedition, we even went so far as to paint our Volkswagen bus with signs that indicated we were doing solar and wind energy work.

Probably the most essential thing to carry with you is proper and complete identification. Driver's license, a payroll receipt (indication that you are not a vagrant), a picture of Mom and Dad, and maybe even a statement of what it is that you are doing (like a schedule, travel records, etc.). This cannot be over-emphasized, especially if you are from out-of-state. On our first expedition, we were arrested and escorted back to a town by the highway patrol, and detained for a relatively long period of time while they checked us out. Seems someone saw us picking up some broken pieces of wind machine that were lying by the side of the road (this was the only instance where we picked up something without first asking, or buying it). The stuff we'd gathered was unquestionably junk but that didn't make what we did right. Well, they had to check out where we'd gotten the rest of the stuff that we'd put in our truck and, becuz the area did not have phone service, it was a long and drawn out process to contact those folk. This was after the printing of Wind and Windspinners, so I had copies of that in the truck and it helped to show we weren't rip-off artists.

We cooperated fully and the deputies we dealt with at the station reciprocated; they couldn't get hold of the gentleman who owned the property we'd taken the broken wind machine pieces from, but they did just take it all back and allowed us to proceed along our way. Prepare for such an instance and it'll prevent the formation of an absurd and costly nightmare.

"BUT OFFICER - I DIDN'T THINK ANYONE WANTED THAT OL' PIECE OF JUNK!"

We were rather fortunate on our expedition in that we did not have to lower but one of the machines we purchased; we were, however, fully equipped to not only lower wind machines, but towers as well. An inspection of the chapters on these subjects will indicate the necessary equipment for such undertakings. Don't count on being able to rig something up for either of these events. Tower or machine lowering is more dangerous than raising either.

Some consideration must be given to sleeping/eating accommodations. With both of our expeditions, we lived out of the vehicle -- sleeping bags and a cookstove. The towns had both camping facilities and motels, but our method provided us with the option to sleep out in the country (and thereby eliminate a drive into town at night, and a drive back out to the area we were working in the morning). We ended up going to one of the two towns in the area about every two days to gas up, however; There weren't any along-the-side-of-the-road gas stations where we were. If you are camping out and not using a campground provided for this function, insure that you obtain permission from the owner of the property you rest your head on or you might be awakened by an irritated farmer. We found these people to be quite hospitable and generous, but there are limits to making assumptions, so ask!

Whichever area you explore, know where the gas stations are, and when they're open. If you can, take along spare gasoline, oil, and tools. Most of the people in the area we worked had never seen a Volkswagon bus before; this was indication enuff that there weren't any shops or dealerships around for 'em, and that can be scary. After all, how much faith are you going to have in someone that's preparing to work on your vehicle when his first question is, "What is it?" You are, at times, going to be quite distant from anywhere and the inevitable breakdown can be a costly and time-consuming event. In some instances, you might have to wait a few days (especially if there are no phones in the area) just to let someone know that you need to get towed somewhere.

Keeping Records

Both expeditions well proved the necessity for keeping records of all types -- mileage, living expenses, and purchase receipts; one steno notebook (secretarial size) will do adequately for all of these. This will also serve to be proof-of-intent if you receive an unexpected visit from a sheriff. The most important reason for doing this is that it allows you to know just what the expedition cost you. A couple of hundred dollars can evaporate very quickly from your pocket, leaving you to wonder if you didn't just lose some of it. Keeping records will quickly indicate that it went to all sorts of odds-and-ends that add up all too fast. So it serves as kind of a governor, keeping you in touch with the reality of what it is that you are doing so that you budget it and spend it more wisely than you would without it.

Making a record of the purchase of a wind machine or related components should reflect the complete transaction: the date, the name and address of the owner of the property, and a complete listing of the items sold. The amount should also be indicated, as well as (of course) the signature of this person. A sample of this kind of receipt is indicated in the photocopy of one of our receipts from the first expedition. It might be wise to carry along some carbon paper just in case the owner wants a copy, too. If you don't have any, ask. We found it helpful in some instances to give our own mailing address, especially if all the parts to a machine could not be found, or the owner indicated that he might have a manual somewhere but was unable to locate it. On our first expedition, I was not as well informed as to the various parts of the system and received a most welcome "package" at a later date from this one rancher after he'd spotted the overlooked items and mailed them off. It pays to keep thinking.

A notepad will come in handy when conversing with farmers or ranchers who know of other folks in possession (at least at one time) of wind machines. Facts, names, and locations will quickly fill the pages and allow a better scheduling of a day's activities in dawn pow-wows over a cup of coffee (or tea). At every point you will have to be making decisions that could affect the outcome of your efforts; the more information that you have available towards making the decision, the more "right" it will be.

When You Get There

When you've decided to go on an expedition, it is most difficult to keep from just throwing some stuff into the selected mode of transportation and taking off in a cloud of dust. There is always a limit to planning, but the more thought-out the expedition (and hence, prepared for), the more benefit will be achieved from the time, money, and energy spent. This applies, as well, to what you do when you reach the area you intend to search. The overwhelming desire will be to start "goin'-out-and-gettin'-'em." Get the county map (if you did not obtain it by mail already) and check out some possible good sources of information in the town nearest to this area. A stop at the police or sheriff's station is a wise first-thing-to-do. They travel around a lot and if you have some of those pictures ready, they might just be able to turn you on to a few "possibles." The secondary function (or maybe the primary) of visiting the local law enforcement authorities is that you have established contact and this will put you miles ahead when (or if) they see you again. Let them know that you plan to be in the area and, if you know it beforehand, for how long. Tell them who you are, and what you are doing; they probably know everyone on sight for fifty miles around (if it's really a sparsely-populated area). If they don't know of any wind machines, they can probably tell you who might, and would surely know who travels the area a lot. The notepad will come in handy here, so have it ready. If you can walk into a store, shop, or onto a farm and know the first name of the head man, owner, manager, 'tis much better than not knowing.

Remember the deputy's or sheriff's name, too; this is good for "so-and-so told me you might have . . ." when you establish contact. Anyone can be fooled by a first impression; if you were around there for a few weeks, months, or years then everybody would know what kind of a person you really are. But a first, good impression is going to work wonders toward any further communication; so don't underrate it. At first, it might seem to you that you're "puttin' on" but you'll quickly realize that you are developing sensitivity and awareness to other people who might live a very different kind of life, and see things in an entirely different way from your own.

The local newspaper office might be another good place to stop. If you run into an oldtimer here, it could be a pot of gold. Newspapers are the eyes and ears of the community and much can be learned from someone who has worked there a long time. As with anything anyone tells you, you have to take it all with a grain of salt, or you'll end up on a lot of wild goose chases and dead-ends. Jot it all down in the ole notebook, though, and mull over it later.

Looking

If it turns out that you're goin' to have to go down the back roads, pick out a likely-looking area and do it. Most farms are located some distance (1/2 to 3 miles) off the main road. The binoculars will come in handy here, so have 'em ready. If there is just you-all-by-yourself, then you'll have to stop to use them; for chrissakes, don't try it while you're driving--if you spot a Jacobs sittin' pretty on a tower, you'll get so shook that you'll be sittin' not-so-pretty against a tree or sumthin'. If there are two of you, the passenger can probably do the honors while the vehicle is is motion, but 'tain't easy if it's a ruff road. If you do stop, get off the road. If you're movin' slow, stay off (or nearly off) the road. And visualize how you look to folks that go by!

Okay, what are you lookin' at? Well, for a moment, go back 20 years or more. You just bought some property and you've got a house under construction. Ever think about all those trees that are around the house and barn? Well, the guy that bought the place sees all that prairie wilderness around him and what does he see? or feel? Well, it's hot and it's dry and it sure would be nice to have some cool shade. So he plants some trees. Maybe he's got a favorite kind that he likes, so they won't necessarily be indiginous to the area. Pretty soon (after 10 years) he's got lots of shade. Then he sees the city folk with that new-fangled electricity and he's gonna get some for himself. Only they can't bring it in. So, he buys a wind machine. Where does he put it? Well, close to where it's going to be used. Near the house (or barn). Years later, the REA comes in and promises him all the power he wants for pennies a day. So he takes it. He takes the machine down and stores it away (if he hasn't an awful lot of storage space, it'll get moved around until it ends up with all the other scrap metal on the place). He later gets a TV and he puts an antenna up on the tower (nice and handy). Meanwhile, these trees have been growing. Finally, they are above the top of the tower. So . . . don't expect that you'll be able to spot it from the road. But look for that TV antenna stickin' up above the trees; there has to be sumthin' holdin' it up that high!

If you do spot a tower, is it a three- or four-leg? Is there anything on it? How close to the house or barn is it? Does it have a tail? What's the shape? Are there wires leading from the tower?

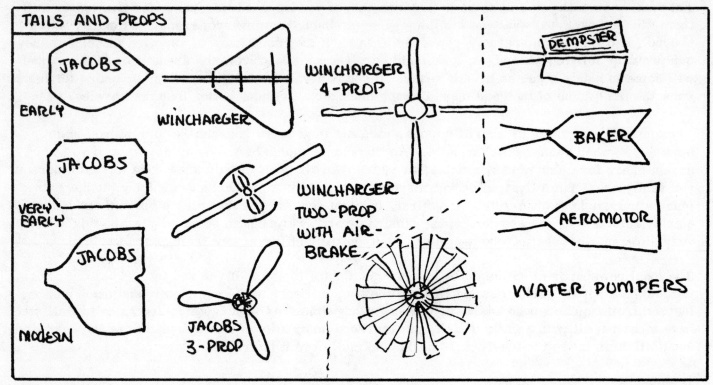

Toward the end of the expedition, we stopped using the binoculars and ignored the "indicators"; they are just what the word says, "indicators." The presence of a tower didn't necessarily mean there was, or had been, a wind machine, and the absence of the tower didn't mean there hadn't been, or wasn't still, a wind machine there. (The folks could have gotten rid of the tower, too, when they hauled the wind machine off to the local scrap yard). And we stopped chasing down leads, too. It got to the point where we'd ignore our schedule and go chasin' off after a machine somebody thought so-and-so had 'bout 10 miles down the road. It wasn't all in vain; we did get some good leads, and they did net us machines. It was just that we covered a lot of ground and time doin' it this way when we could have just as well included it in the next day's schedule when we would have been in that area anyway. And, when you're lookin' from dawn to dusk for machines -- in fact, eatin', sleepin', drinkin' the prairie dust, and thinkin' 'bout wind machines -- it takes its toll on the ole body. It was finally to the point where we had lost all of the excitement (although admittedly not the enthusiasm) and gotten down to the dirty drag-it-out-each-place-be-methodical-take-it-slow-and-steady persistence that we could stay sane with. And whether it was coincidence or not, we found more machines per day at the last.

Driving Into The Farm

There are a number of correct ways to drive into a farm or ranch and there are a number of wrong ways. It will always seem not right to do something in a manner that you're not used to, but the more open you are and, thereby, flexible, the more any situation will tend to work for you and not against you. Some of the things mentioned in this and the next section may go against your grain, but we learned this through experience, so it's in here to help. If you think that it's so much non-sense, you have the option of ignoring it; you'll either find it to be correct, or you'll have no trouble at all.

Whether you've spotted a machine on a tower or see one lying by the side of the road as you come in, curb the urge to stop and look at it. Always drive to the main house. Get out, stretch a little (but refrain from looking around), and walk up to the door. Knock a few times and step back. All of this helps anyone that heard you drive up to look you over a bit. You step back from the door because there happens to be such a thing as distance between strangers, and that's what you are to them. If no one answers, knock again, maybe a little louder, and back away again. If no one answers, that's it. Just get back into your vehicle and drive off . . . and I mean OFF. You've got no business snoopin' around and if you stay and look, that's precisely what you are doing. Don't take pictures, don't go lookin' in the barn, don't pick anything up, and don't loiter. Get out. If you have a notepad, write a note and leave it on the door. (It would probably not be wise to try and open the screen door.)

Of course, if there's genuinely no one around, it won't matter what you do, or don't do. But if there is someone there, you are truly asking for it. You can always come back later, so don't take chances. If you are in that much of a hurry, you're on the wrong foot to begin with.

Making Contact

Of course, the higher probability is that you will make contact with someone. And then you'll be able to get along with what you're doing, but let's get it off to a good start. If you've lived on a farm before, then this will be common knowledge (or sense); it may be necessary, though, for the folks that are goin' onto the land for the first time.

Getting a wind machine may be the most important thing in your life at the moment, but if you get all wound up around these folks, they're sure to think you're a wee bit touched with the heat. Move slowly at all times (disregard this statement in case of a brush fire or stampede) and think about what you're sayin' before it gets past the lips. A good place to start is with what is called the gentle art of "hunkerin"; this describes both a way of approaching people and a kind of kneel/squat when talkin', or bartering. The latter is squatting down until both knees are level (you balance on the balls of your feet) or, from this position, put one knee down until it almost touches the ground. If you're right-handed (and hence, right-footed), you'll be practically sitting on your right heel and your left knee will be high and directly above your left foot. You've probably done this little squat before and not realized that's what it's called. Okay, now you can rest your arms on your knees and sit comfortable like for a long time; a good position to be in when you're conversin' with someone. If there happens to be a little twig around, you can even doodle in the dirt. (This is very difficult to do, however, if you're hunkerin' on cement or tile.) The art of hunkerin' might include this way of holdin' yourself, but it's far more inclusive than this. It could probably be summed up in "gettin' down to earth with other folk." Stop thinking about wind machines for a minute or two and get into what's happenin' around you. So what if you're rushed, or tired, or near broke. They're your problems, not this other person's. So they don't have a place right here, right now. Don't think that you have a ritual to go through; it isn't like that. Just be you, and it will come natural.

Now, if you go up to someone and hunker right down and start talkin' 'bout the weather, you're going to get some funny looks. Hunkerin' will be the first thing that you're going to do if whoever you've walked up to is under a vehicle, or sittin' down, or workin' on a level below you; don't stand there and talk down to them. Farm folk will know you to be "city" if you are, so they might be sensitive enuff to the situation not to do what comes natural for them. If you have been standin' and talkin' for a while, take the initiative and hunker down and they'll follow suit soon enuff.

This will be the approach if you happen to find someone in the "yard" (the area outside the fenced perimeter of the house and fronted with the barns and garages). Generally farms have dogs; they serve primarily as doorbells. If someone is in the barn, or in the general area of the "yard," they'll probably come out. Pull up the vehicle and get out. If there are two of you, just one should get out.

If there are folks in the house, the approach will be different; it also depends on who comes to the door. If it's menfolk, then give the howdy, introduce yourself, and explain away. If it's women-folk, stay on your toes and keep the distance. The same kind of procedure -- explain it to her. She probably doesn't know much about such hardware, but don't make those kinds of assumptions; we did find a few that knew more than the menfolk. Don't ask if the menfolk are around; that's a no-no. If they are, she'll call them to the door. If it appears as though they aren't and she can't help, she'll probably say so and may say when to come back. That's it . . . leave. If she doesn't offer that, but indicates that the menfolk aren't around, then ask when would be a good time to come back. Don't ask when the menfolk will be back; that's also a no-no.

If you run into this a couple of times, you'll learn as we did that the best time to hit the farms is in the early morning, at noon, or five and six (or later) in the evening. If you are working down one road, and no one's home, or the menfolk aren't, it may not be a lot of fun to retrace, but with a notebook, map, and some good timing, you'll get them all checked out. Incidentally, if they do have phone service in the area, you might ask for a phone number; I don't particularly like talking on a phone and even more so when I'm trying to find a wind machine (you can miss a lot of cues and clues), but if it's the only way you can keep from a lot of extra trucking around, then do it. The first machine that we got from an expedition was all but purchased over the phone.

Asking Questions

Unless you are in an area where the REA only recently installed service (like, the last 10 years), you're going to be talking about an antique. Or you're working with, as indicated before, second or third generation, or new owners. Surprisingly enuff, this latter instance is quite rare; in the two instances where we did find it to be the case, both knew about the old wind machines. I guess that comes from having gotten into the dark and dusty corners to see what all was there. Whatever the situation, what you learn will depend on what questions you ask. Rather than trying to say this or say that, I'll provide some examples in the progression they might be used.

"We're looking for old Winchargers; you know, old wind-electric machines, like the ones used out here before REA. Do you know what I'm talking about? Did you ever have one? What happened to it? Did you sell it? To whom? Didn't sell it, huh? Have you seen it lying around here? Maybe in the barn? The junkyard? Have you seen any in this area? Do you know of anyone in the area that used to have one? Where? Can you point it out on the map here? Do you still have the batteries? How about the Delco Light Plant? (That's the standby generator.) When did you get REA? Do you mind if I look in the junkpile over there? Do you have any of the manuals for the Wincharger? The light plant? Any old appliances and light bulbs that were used with it? Motors?"

You may not have to go through this routine. A number of the people we contacted that had machines knew right off what we were talkin' about. They'd saved that infernal machine to use for one thing or another and the "another" just walked up to their door. And they see a chance to get a little more than the junk price they'd get in their own area. But not all the folks knew.

As you're goin' thru it, try to figure out if they don't understand you or they don't know. Or they don't remember. The pictures would come in handy for the first and the last. For all three

WIND GENERATORS?
NOPE! NEVER SEEN ANY
AROUND HERE!

reasons, though, you may have to jog their memories and it can be touchy goin'. Just plow ahead. Which questions and the order you ask them will depend on their response. Don't get in a hurry here, or impatient. You may be a question away from the jackpot. By the time you're finished, even if they still can't remember or if the answer seems to be there isn't one, it has not been a waste of time. You've had a confrontation and you've learned the technique and you've fairly well exhausted the possibility of one being there. Proceed to the next place.

Jackpot

Either first off, or after some questions, you may get some kind of yes, maybe, or let's-go-look-at-sumthin'-that-might-be-what-you're-lookin'-for. And he or she will lead you off to a junkpile, loft, or piled-up-with-junk corner of the garage. And here, beneath the dust, straw, cobwebs and miscellany shows a color of Wincharger red or yellow or Jacobs silver (or other wind machine or color). 'Tis a tuff moment to be curbin' your desire to go rippin' thru the other junk to get at it, but do it. Be gentle with that junk and don't throw it helter-skelter (and don't forget to put it back in neater-than-before order).

Okay, so you've uncovered a wind machine, or parts of a wind machine. Is it all there? What's missin'? Check your list (supposin' you have one) of what is supposed to be there. The generator? The gearbox? The turntable? The tower stub? The slip rings? The control box? The tail? The pulldown cable and winch? The governor? The blades?

If the tower stub is not present, it will probably still be on the tower, and without any luck, they've probably got their TV antenna stuck through it. You need a tower stub, so offer to remove the TV antenna, remove the stub, and secure the TV antenna again. If they say no, that's it! (The Jacobs had its collector brushes mounted on the stub. You may want to ask to remove just that assembly.) If it's the props that are missin', chances are that they're in the loft of garage or barn, or tied up to the underside of the roof, or on the wall. Mention everything that you can think of if the owner doesn't remember where they got to. Handle them with care! If the control box is missin', chances are it's still attached to the wall in whatever was used for a battery room; this may be a separate little house they are now using for a root cellar or bomb shelter, or it may be in the basement of the house. If they don't know where the batteries were kept, find out where the tower was (if it isn't actually there); just look for the foundation, or a likely-lookin' spot, and see if you can see where the wires went to from the tower (they may still be there). If they go into a basement window, ask to go look in the basement; in many instances we found folks that were positive that nothin' like that was there, but when we looked, it was. It looks somewhat like a utility box, so it's easy to confuse for one. As well, the Wincharger boxes are black and blend well into darkened walls. There will be some screws holding it on the wall, so you'll have to open the boxes to get at them. Keep some tools handy, huh? The slip rings, if missing, are probably with the tower stub, or still attached to the machine. If not, your guess is as good as mine as to where they are, so start asking questions. The tail is an unwieldy thing and could be almost any-where. The pull-down cable may be long gone, but the winch will still be on the tower in most cases.

If you're led to a pile of junk and you can't find a machine but the farmer/rancher is sure he's seen "sumthin' like that, " ask where there might be another junk pile, or point to a nearby shed, barn, garage, shack, etc., and ask if it "might be over there." Here you are merely indicating to the man that you are REALLY interested, and are serious (not wishy-washy) about your expedition. Stick to it for as long as he will; the energy spent here is well worth the time you save later on trying to jury-rig or manufacture the piece that "couldn't be found." Twenty-twenty hindsight is frustrating!

If you can't find the totality of parts that should be there, be sure to leave an address just in case they are later found (like 5 minutes after you leave, to a few months). If you have enuff time, ask if you can come back in a few days to check and see if he's found anything. This will be close to useless (unless he offers to keep lookin' and inquires if you can come back in a few days, or tomorrow, etc.) so make it worth his while! Real soon you're going to be talkin' about what it's all worth and that's when you want to indicate HOW important it is to you that he find that missing part!

Before you start talkin' about money, be sure to ask if there are any appliances around that were used with the machine. Obviously, this is not a question worth asking if you've found a 110-volt machine, but for the 32-volt (or 12-volt) wind machines, it can be a real bonus. You should ask about light bulbs, toasters, mixers, inverters, arc welders, skill saws, drills, motors (they generally have a lot of these), and whatever else you'd like to see, or can think of.

What It's Worth

Value and worth are very relative things, so how much the machine and other things that are piled

in front of you will go for depends on a lot of things.   Let's go thru some of the considerations.

1. How much money do you have? Besides travel and living expenses, how much have
   you set aside for buying wind machines (you should already know this) and how
   many machines are you after? Try to determine the maximum you could probably
   spend on any one machine.

2. What kind of shape is the stuff in? Mint? Used, but well stored? Hard to distinguish against all of the other metal that was in the junk pile? Been laying in a
   creek for 10 years? Don't just stand there and look at it -- get down and touch it,
   pull off the dust covers, look at the commutator, brushes, gears in the gearbox.
   Does it rotate? Does it have pieces of the castings chipped off? Is it bent,
   packed with a rat's nest, almost solid mud? Don't just think, "Well, it can be
   repaired." Can you repair it? Do you know someone that can, or will? Are they
   blades or are they sculpture -- twisted from end to end? Are the bearings made
   of sand? Does it look like it was lowered from the tower (if it isn't actually still
   on it), or dropped? Be honest with yourself -- are you hauling away junk, or a
   wind machine that's going to fly for you for years to come?

3. If the wind machine is still on the tower, how does it look? If the blades were
   removed, it will probably have weathered everything just fine. If the blades are
   still on, they probably won't be worth very much, but go up and check; some do
   survive the passage of years with little decay. Is the machine furled, or is the tail
   straight back? If it's the latter, you had better inspect the thing to the hilt,
   especially if the blades aren't turning in a light breeze (you can sing taps if they're
   not turning in a howling gale). An unfurled wind machine will probably have
   extensive damage to the generator which may not be evident (unless the case is
   blackened from that long-ago fire). Remember when you're talking about the
   price that you are going to have to take the thing down!

4. One well-learned caution: Don't price yourself out of the area. This may be your
   first machine, or second, and it may look real good, but don't go higher than what
   you would be willing to pay for any other machine. If you buy a wind machine that's
   rated, say 6 on a scale of 1 to 10 for its condition, then you might have to pay the
   same price to get a machine that's only 3 or 4 on the scale if the word gets out that
   you'll pay that much for a Wincharger. Sure, you might convince the next guy
   (perhaps after you show him the other system that you bought), but it will still
   take a lot of convincin' that you really thought you paid too much for the first and
   really don't want to pay but half of that for his. You're better off talkin' to a wall
   or tree.

5. If these folks knew what the going prices of restored machines are running, they'd
   have either sold the machine already or they'd be using it and trying to get off
   utility. There is no intrinsic value (at least in terms of money) that these machines
   have; the value or worth is, or can be, evaluated only on the basis of what it's worth
   to you. The stuff you're about to bid on may be worth 100 times what you will, or
   can, pay this man; but to him, it's junk (or near junk) and your first offer will
   probably floor him! I'm not kidding! Our first offer in every case was unexpected,
   and some were outright stunned! They really believed they were puttin' one over
   on us! Or that we were outright crazy. I remember almost every one of the
   transactions we made and can honestly feel good about them because both of us

(the owner and ourselves) came away from the "bargainin' table" feelin' good. And that's where it's all at.

6. If, as you found the stuff, it was being hauled out and piled somewhere, chances are real good that the guy really wants to be rid of it altogether. This means the first offer should be half of what it would be if he only points it out to you. At any point, if you are asked, "How much is all of this stuff worth?" remember that he's asking how much it's worth to you (and not what the going price on the international market is). At any rate, you should answer, "Well, that depends on what you have, how much you have, and what kind of shape it's in." You do not want to make any general statement (unless he's not going to go any further without knowing it) or make any comment on $$ until it's all in front of you, just as you'll haul it away.

The Offer

I suppose that it helps to have a poker face thru all of this, but we weren't always able to. If you are alone, you're ready to make a bid. If there are two of you (or more), a pow-wow might be in order. Don't be afraid to do this; just tell the man that you have to talk it over, and walk away a distance. This won't always be necessary, but it does help should one of you (or both) see something that might make a difference. Keep it to the point and reach a decision quickly.

You can make the first offer. Or you can ask the man what he thinks it's worth to him. If he was around when the machine (and the whole system) was bought originally, he'll probably say what it cost originally; this will be a tuff one to bring down becuz it will be very high. Remember here that you don't even know if it works (and won't until you've really torn into it); you are buying it "as is." My preference is to make the first bid. If you suggest a figure that's twice what he wants and he's able to keep from choking, he may ask for a little more. Most farmers and ranchers are good at haggling; it's a way of life to them. Don't worry about insulting anyone (this is very hard to do if you're not used to haggling). You can always go higher, but you can't retract and go lower. If you do go higher, don't go too high too fast. If you are given a counter-offer that is just a little above what you offered, go half the difference, or if it feels real good, think about it and accept it. Keep in mind that you want to make this man feel good about the deal, too (although it must feel good to you); this is not going to happen, though, if you excitedly accept an offer.

If there are parts missing that you need, or the owner thinks might still be around, suggest two prices -- one for the incomplete (as is) and one for the complete system (supplied with the missing parts). Make the difference significant enuff to encourage further looking on the part of the owner. Offer to come back in a few days, or call, or provide an address; indicate that the difference will be paid when and if the other parts (or any of them) are found.

You should make your payments in cash, so have it handy. If you pow-wow before making the first offer, get that amount together (plus a little bit more); it's in bad taste to pull out a wad of money to complete the transaction.

Make out the receipt (according to the method described in the Keeping Records section) and list the different items and the quantity of each (such as in the case of more than one motor). If it's possible, load up the stuff then and there; if you must arrange for shipping or transporting, ask if you can leave the stuff (preferable under cover, like in a barn or shed) and indicate for how long, giving both a date and time when you can, or will, return. You might ask when would be a good time to come back; the man may prefer to be there when this is done. Keep thinkin'!

If you have a wind machine to lower, or if you've managed to buy the tower as well, do it then, or suggest when you can. The procedure for both of these jobs is well discussed in the following chapters, but you should be ready (with equipment and know-how) to do this after the transaction if time and weather permit.

We went after a small community's worth of wind-power equipment, so we knew that our Volkswagen bus would not handle all that we hoped to find. After our time, money, and energies were almost exhausted, we got a rental truck and loaded it all up. That which we had purchased, we had transported to depots that we had worked out with a number of farmers, so we only had to drive the truck to these places and load up the stuff. With a rental truck, you'll be on time and mileage, and extra of either (or both) is going to cost you. Check this out beforehand so you don't hurry; it will allow you to weigh the cost/benefit of exceeding these limits if you are running behind. An accident can turn your wind machines into very real junk. If you've been hunting wind machines for a few days (or more), you're going to be very tired; if you have hundreds of miles to go to get home, you might consider getting a good night's sleep before you pick up the truck and load it, or right after. 'Tis the voice of experience speaking!

Afterthoughts

Hopefully this chapter will be a help to you if you need a wind machine and wish to go about getting one of the pre-REA units. They are beautiful machines; in most cases, they are well engineered and constructed, and designed to last many years. If you start talkin' about "the good ole days," you will get sighs and you will get "humbugs." There isn't an awful lot known about what problems these wind machines experienced, but the ones that we are aware of will be discussed in the chapter on restoring them. In the three-quarters of a year since the last expedition, I've grown to like very much the way these things were put together. With the kind of throw-away, short-term use we get from many of today's mass-produced products, it's a real pleasure to see, work with, and use these machines of yesteryear.

Winchanger gearbox
rusted tail
32 v generator
4-prop spoiler
2 long (2-blade) props
32-110 inverter
2 short (single-blade) props
2 Winchanger control boxes
complete 32 v Winchanger

Delco Light Plant
+ control box
Wind King 32 V with props
4-32V motors
1-broken window
box 32 volt light bulbs
32 v drill, saw
32 V razor

I sold these items to Earthmind
for $75.   Richard L. Baker 10-2-74

CHAPTER 2

WIND MACHINE RESTORATION

When Earthmind conducted its second expedition in search of pre-REA wind machines, it had the names of two manufacturers -- Jacobs and Wincharger. When we came home, we had the names of other wind machines: Miller Airlite, Universal Aero-Electric, Paris-Dunn, Zenith, Airline, Wind King, Winpower, etc. I'm sure that's not all of them; just the ones we had happened to stumble upon in those two weeks. As we have worked primarily with Jacobs and Wincharger machines, we can only indicate a restoration procedure for these two units. Even at that, what we have is not representative of all models made under these names, so we may be of little help for what you may find. We do take some consolation in the fact that the models we obtained are by far the most abundant.

Much of the information in this chapter will apply to any type of wind machine that you might find (or have found) becuz, while the various makes of wind machine may appear different, their component parts are often similar. As indicated in the Expeditions chapter, the photos will aid in understanding the parts to the wind machines indicated so that you will know what to look for and how to recognize them in a scrap heap.

Fortunately, the Wincharger and the Jacobs wind machines differ greatly in appearance and design and constitute, when combined, two major types of wind machine made and used in this period. In this chapter, we will discuss them separately, beginning with the Wincharger.

Part A : WINCHARGER IDENTIFICATION

Characteristically, the Wincharger had its model number painted on the tail and sometimes imprinted on the generator; the first things you'll probably want to know is the voltage and power rating. There are four digits to the number. The first two digits will indicate the voltage of the wind machine; if it's a 32-volt machine, the model number will read 3210, 3220, 3238, 3240, and the like. The last digits will indicate how early or late a model it is and this is an indicator for the power rating; the last two illustrated numbers -- the 3238 and the 3240 -- are 1500 watt machines. The two earlier model numbers are 1200 watt or lower; we have not yet determined their precise wattage capability. If you have found a 110 volt wind machine, the numbers will read 1109, 1112, 1119, and the like; we know that the latter one is a 1500 watt unit, but we have no information on the others. In an attempt to find the wattages of these units, we wrote Dyna Technology, Inc., but we did not receive a reply.

Insofar as we found some Wincharger generators which did not have the model number imprinted and either the tail markings were gone or we did not find the tail, there are other clues. The most notable is the number of commutator strips; by pulling off the tail cone and counting them, you can at least determine the voltage of the windplant. The 32 volt units had 40 and the 110 volt units had 80 strips; it is possible that this varies a mite, but if it's close to one of these figures, you will know the windplant's voltage. The length of the armature itself will be an indication of the wattage, so compare with the photos when you've disassembled the generator.

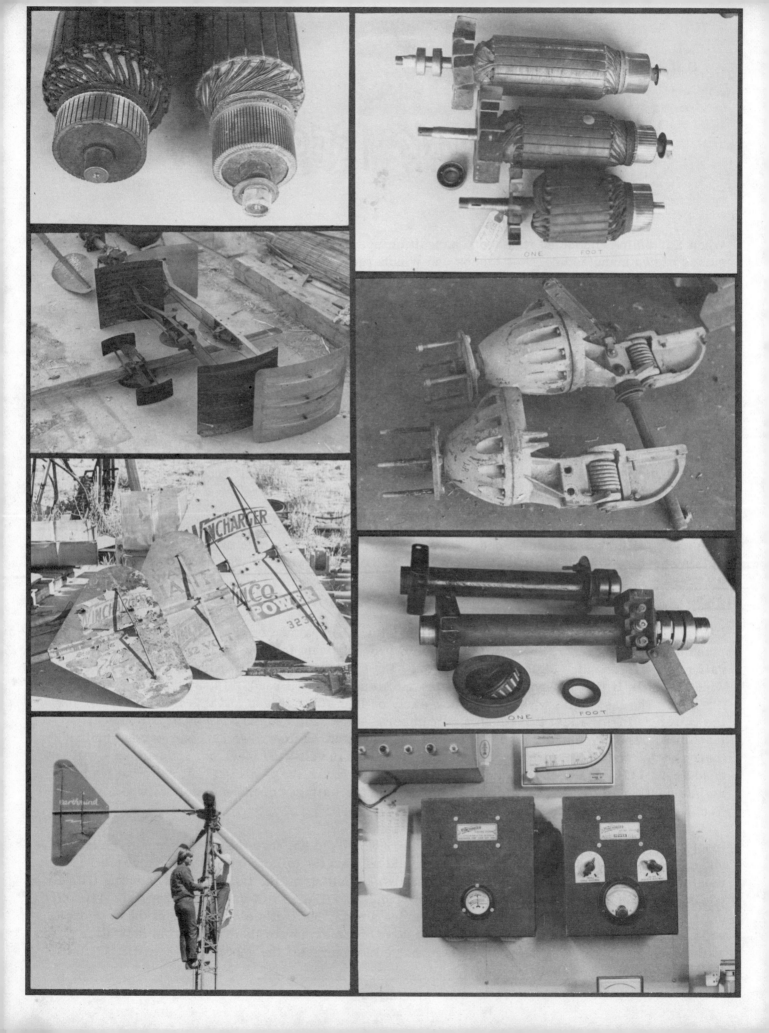

Winchargers were predominantly yellow, but earlier models were painted red; this will be some-what of an indicator for wattage as none of our units painted red exceed the 1200 watt figure. As well, earlier model units had a closed generator housing whereas the later (and higher wattage) units had a ventilator grill in the front (bottom) of the generator housing and a cooling fan on the armature. We did notice that some models had three large holes in the front of the generator housing, but don't mistake this for a grill. These are not the larger machines.

Another solid indicator for wattage was the number of blades on the unit (2 or 4), the length of the props, the material from which they were made (aluminum or wood), the type of spoiler em-ployed, and the type of blade-mounting hub (2 or 4 bolt). Two-bolt mounting-hubs are on lower power wind machines and those using 4-bolts on the blade-mounting hub were either the 1200 or 1500 watt size. Air-brake governors (see photos) were used on all two-blade machines and an enclosed governor (feathering only two of the blades in a four-blade unit) was used for higher power 32 volt units. Most two-blade machines (both blades formed from one piece of wood) are lower power units than the four-blade counterparts; the exception here is the large 110-volt units which used only one propeller assembly and had the air-brake type governor. Some four-blade Winchargers used aluminum blades and others used wooden blades.

The number of slip rings is also an indicator of wattage and, perhaps, voltage; if yours only has two slip rings, then the unit is not 110 volts and it is relatively low power (under 1000 watts). If you have three slip-rings, it could be either voltage and it might be any wattage.

A long-nosed gearbox is an indication of a large, later model Wincharger; probably the result of the blades running into the tower (at high speeds) with the short-nosed models. (See photos for comparison of the short- and long-nosed gearboxes.)

The size of the tail is somewhat of an indicator for the power rating of the windplant (see photo) but realize that it was easy to swap tails on these units; if one became damaged, its replacement might have been larger or smaller than the original. I mention this becuz we ran into this situation on the expedition.

All of the high power 32-volt and 110-volt wind machines we came across had a timken-taper roller (thrust) bearing in the top and the bottom of the turntable support. We found, on the other hand, that smaller wattage, 32-volt Winchargers either used a very small and thin ball bearing or used none at all!

If you are fortunate to find a set of control boxes for the Wincharger you've found, this will be a good indicator of the voltage and wattage of the unit (see photos here and in Control chapter). High power 32-volt and 110-volt wind machines had two boxes -- a "Powermeter" (ammeter) is mounted in one box and the voltmeter in the other. Lower power units used one box with an ex-ternal voltage regulator relay or just a single open chassis and no regulator. If you have two boxes (identical in size), a quick look at the voltmeter will tell you if it's 32 volt or 110 volt; the meters will read 50 volt or 150 volt respectively. All high power control boxes had schematics glued inside the boxes; these may or may not still be there. They will not tell you the wattage of the unit, but you can determine the voltage by noticing the number of cells in the pictured battery bank; if it's 56 cells, you have a 110-volt unit; if it's 16 cells, it's 32 volts.

Photos read L to R, top to bottom--(1) A 32-, and 110-volt commutator, (2) Different sizes of WC armatures with varying wattages, (3) Lo-, and hi-power WC spoilers (air-brake type), (4) long-, and short-nose gearcases, (5) bullet-riddled and rusted WC tails, (6) the 2-, and 3-ring WC turn-tables; note the bearing mounts (top and bottom) for the 3-ring unit, (7) Jim Davis and the author work on a newly-restored, 32 V, 1500-watt Wincharger with (8) its twin control boxes installed.

If you can obtain a manual for the wind machine, the front cover will tell you the model number which will, in turn, indicate the voltage. It will not tell you the wattage unless, of course, you're familiar with the wattage ratings of the different models. There are only two differences between the manuals for the various Winchargers of medium or large size -- the number of cells pictured in the battery bank and the approximate voltage settings for different amp-hour capacity in the batteries. It would seem that the Wincharger Corporation didn't like to indicate the wattage ratings and they didn't like to make up different manuals for each model.

When combined, these indicators should take most of the guesswork out of figuring out the voltage and wattage of the wind machine you've got. There are other, more subtle differences between some of these models, but they are of less consequence.

Wincharger Frame Assembly

The frame assembly is a cast-iron, one piece unit to which everything -- the gearcase, the generator, and the tail -- is attached. Additionally, it bolts to the turntable shaft which, in turn, secures to the tower stub (and tower) and swings through 360° to accomodate changing wind direction.

The photos illustrate the various parts of the frame assembly. A major part here is the attachment of the tail pivot, which allows the tail to be swung around parallel to the propellers for furling the wind machine. This includes the tail pivot pin, the tail spring, the U-bolts which secure the tail to the tail bracket, and the tail adjusting screw (which limits the travel of the tail when furled). Also attached to the frame assembly is the pull-out chain leverage arm and the pulley-bracket associated with the routing of the pull-out chain to the winch located near the base of the tower. A shock spring and bolt are positioned on this unit to absorb the impact if the tail assembly is released too rapidly from the furled position (see Fig. 2-1).

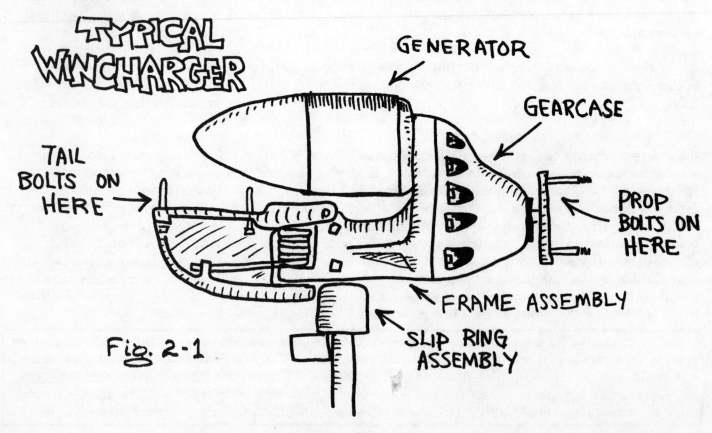

TYPICAL WINCHARGER

GENERATOR

GEARCASE

TAIL BOLTS ON HERE

PROP BOLTS ON HERE

FRAME ASSEMBLY

SLIP RING ASSEMBLY

Fig. 2-1

When restoring the wind machine, carefully inspect this assembly for damage and improperly-functioning parts. If pieces are chipped out of the cast iron, they may be cast-iron welded (by a special process), but it helps here to have picked up the pieces that did break off. The U-bolts should be cleaned or, if rusted or broken, replaced. If you're trying to put the wind machine into "mint" condition, you may want to remove the tail-pivot assembly (pin and spring) but make certain that you have the means to get the spring back onto the thing when you're done cleaning and painting. The tension in it will make this difficult to replace, and for that matter, to remove; watch out when you get it loose. It can pop you a good one or break the casting!

Closely inspect the small pulleys on the frame. There are two of them: one at the opening into the turntable shaft and the other at the end of the leverage-arm; they get very worn from the tension. Also inspect the pins which hold these pulleys in place and the pin, in particular, that holds the leverage arm in position; they are frequently badly worn. Replace them with an equivalent pin if necessary; a bolt will also do the job provided that you find one long enuff to have an unthreaded portion as long as the pin itself. Washers can be used to shim up the difference and permit threading a nut on to secure it tightly. Check it out, though, so the extra length of bolt does not interfere with the movements of these points and lubricate it well.

In some cases, the turntable shaft was frozen in the frame assembly and impossible to remove no matter how much coaxing we could apply (including a 8-lb sledge and lots of rust-penetrant); its removal is not absolutely necessary, so leave it if this represents your situation. Never apply heat or excessive force in trying to do this or anything else where castings are involved, as they will not hold up to it. They can shatter or crack from uneven expansion and it is just this side of impossible to repair them accurately. If it's stuck, leave it. You can, as we did, wire-brush the turntable shaft (they are generally rusty) and paint or coat it with rust inhibitive or a film of oil. Be sure to locate the machine-raising gin pole a little higher to allow the shaft to clear the tower stub turntable when the wind machine is installed on the tower. (See Chapter 4.)

There are two gaskets on the frame assembly -- one for the generator and the other for the gearcase. In most cases, these will require replacing but maybe not, so take care when you pull the generator off as well as the gearcase during the restoration. If you can keep them in one piece, they will serve as templates for making new ones; if not, the machined surfaces of the metal will serve this purpose. The ones we have come across are made from thick paper; you can make these gaskets from manila folders. Saturate them with oil just before you install them or use a non-drying sealer (Form-A-Gasket or the like).

<u>The Wincharger Generator</u>

Once the generator has been removed from the frame assembly, it can be dis-assembled. (See Fig. 2-2) The generator assembly consists of the armature, the main housing, the front plate, the rear plate (with brush assembly), the tail cone, the drive gear and bearings. The drive gear must be removed first; a nut secures this drive gear against the generator and may be held in position by a cotter pin. Get that out first and remove the large washer. Getting the nut off requires a bit of doing becuz you must hold the armature in order to unscrew the nut; I don't know how they did this at the factory, but the only way we could come up with is to secure (very tightly) a pair of vicegrips to the leather or cloth-wrapped gear and then use a large wrench to twist the nut off counter-clockwise. If you have difficulty with this, consider taking it down to a shop and have them remove it; at any rate, give up doing it the vicegrip way if it looks as though you might mess up the gear. It is made of steel and will probably be surface-hardened, but you can chip it.

When the nut is off, the gear can be pulled straight off; it won't twist becuz there's a keyway (and a key) in the shaft as well as the gear to prevent it from doing this during operation. Keep giving the parts a liberal dose of rust penetrant and coax it off with a screwdriver between the gear and the front plate. Again, if you run into difficulty with this, take it down and have it done. We have not yet determined the availability of these gears from manufacturers. There is a number on the

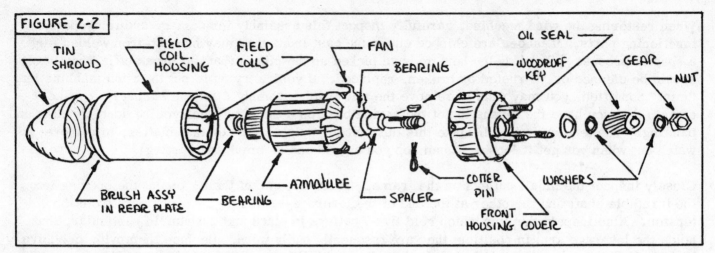

FIGURE Z-Z

TIN SHROUD · FIELD COIL HOUSING · FIELD COILS · FAN · BEARING · OIL SEAL · WOODRUFF KEY · GEAR · NUT · BRUSH ASSY IN REAR PLATE · BEARING · ARMATURE · SPACER · COTTER PIN · FRONT HOUSING COVER · WASHERS

gear but it may not cross-reference to an existing (and available) gear or it may be an exclusive part number for the Wincharger corporation and have no other significance .

Before proceeding further, remove the rear cover cone from the generator (if it's on there) and see that the brushes are not encrusted with dirt. Now give the shaft a spin and watch the brushes or put your finger against a brush and its housing. If the brush is moving up and down even the slightest amount, (like a phonograph arm on a warped record) the commutator is out-of-round. (More on that later.)

After the gear is removed, get the key out of the keyway and pull off the remaining washers. Then loosen and remove the bolts for the front plate of the generator and put them, along with other parts -- the gear, woodruff key, nut, washers, and cotter pin -- in a can or box. Pry between the main housing and the front plate and wiggle it back and forth (tool and plate). The front bearing will stay on the shaft and pull clear of the bearing retainer (in the front plate). Pull the front plate clear and place it aside in the pile for things to be cleaned (with solvent) and painted. The zerks (fittings for a grease gun) should be removed and cleaned and the oil seal (mounted in the front plate) inspected for damage and replaced if necessary.

Pull the armature out of the generator; if it doesn't come, you may have to use a press on the rear of the armature to push it out the front. Don't use a pointed punch in the little hole on the end of the shaft. This hole must remain intact if any lathe work is to be done on the armature. Remove the armature slowly so you don't unnecessarily scrape the field poles and the armature itself. The rear bearing will also remain on the shaft. Inspect the armature carefully, commutator first. If it's got grooves in it or is out-of-round, you're going to have to have the thing turned down and smoothed on a lathe; in the highest probability it can use some turning down to true it up, but if the mica spacers between segments are flush with the commutator surface, it will need to be undercut so that there is a groove between each segment. This can be done in a shop or you can use a hacksaw blade. Grind off the wavy edge of the blade so that it is as narrow as each slot, then break off the end of the blade so that the teeth run all the way to the end. Check the bearings for play or dirt. Check the brushes; are they almost gone? Are they pitted or ridged? Realize that they will be an indication of the commutator's condition when you look them over. Rotate the armature in the bearings -- does the commutator have any flat spots? Work toward getting replacement bearings immediately; you're gonna need them in the future if you don't right now. Let the originals be your spares!

Author's note: In having gone through the restoration on a number of wind machines, my unqualified recommendation is to automatically have the commutator turned down, replace the bearings in the generator (front and back), and install new brushes. Why? Becuz when you put the thing up there, you don't want to have to worry about the thing for years. There are enuff things that will require

(1) Inspection of the commutator reveals deep groove--commutator must be turned down! (2) Gear-pullers separate armature and rear brush plate which (3) needs cleanup, wire replacement, etc.; check the brushes and bearings! (4) pullin' the front generator gear, (5) & (6) removing generator bearings.

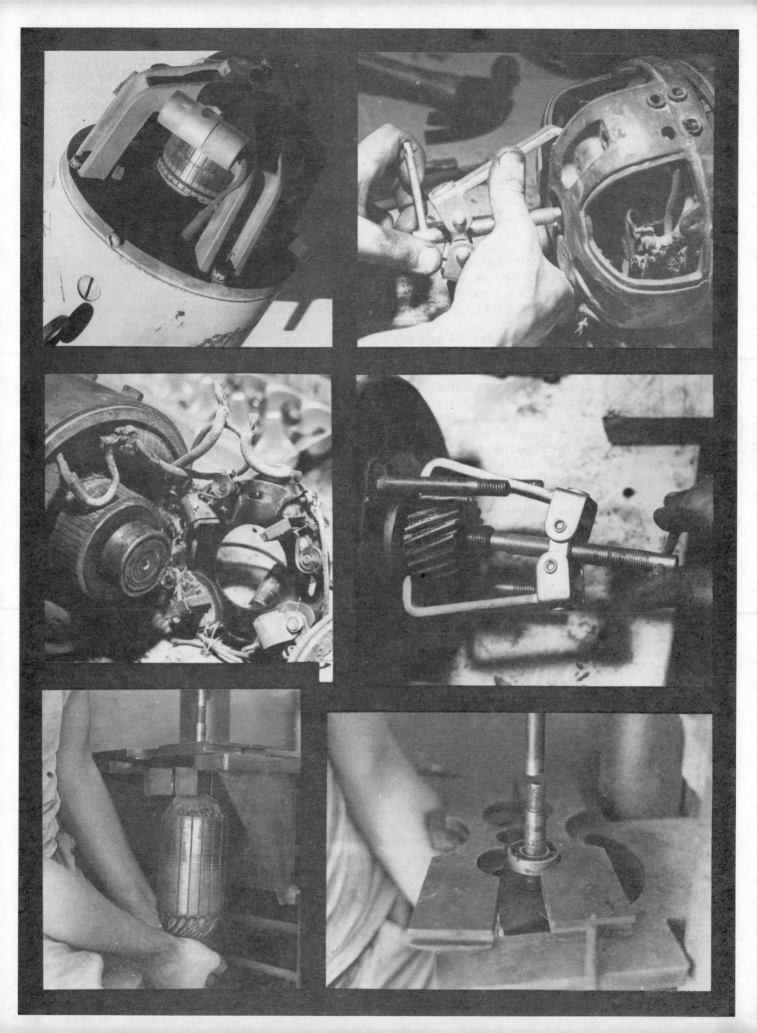

work on the system without having to work on things that you "let be" becuz you didn't want to bother when you had the thing down. If you're in doubt as to whether something should be done, then do it. The replacements are not that expensive; for the generator bearings, brushes, and commutator turn-down -- the parts and work should total to $20 - $25. End of Author's note.

A machine shop can turn down the commutator, but take the armature into a generator shop and subject it to a "growler check"; this will merely indicate if there are shorts in the windings. If shorts are indicated, then see if you can find someone to rewind it. If you can't, I doubt seriously if you could find a replacement. Whether it's rebuilt or checks okay, consult a generator man about the possibility (or need) to have it sprayed with a protective coating of high-resistance resin.

The bearings can only be removed by a bearing puller or suitable press; these tools are expensive to buy (if you don't have one) so have the generator shop or machine shop do it for you becuz it's not expensive and will insure a good job. When you locate and purchase bearings for it, have the same shop press them onto the shaft for you; they're too easily damaged when done at home.

Inspect and replace (or have replaced) any wiring which is frayed or has its insulation cracked. Other than for cleaning purposes or wire replacement, the rear plate of the generator does not have to be removed. If you do this, note all wire interconnections and make a wiring diagram of the connections before you remove them. Some are soldered on and others may be bolted to the terminals. You don't have to be an artist; just draw a picture of the thing so that you will under- stand later how they are connected. Don't trust your memory! Label the wires with a number or letter on some masking tape and secure it to the wires. If you are working on more than one machine, keep the parts separate and labeled so that you don't switch anything; this will not matter with some items, but for others it's critical! The same goes for parts from different sections of the same machine. Beware of Murphy's Law -- if it can be interchanged incorrectly, it will be.

Wires coming from the field coils are particularly fragile and have the nasty habit of breaking at the point just where the wire comes out of the wound-up coils; this is all but impossible to repair. Don't pull on these wires if you remove the rear plate. If you do remove it, and these wires are brittle, you can cut each wire off close to the field coil and strip off the insulation, solder on a new wire, and cover the new solder joint and the original lead with silicone rubber sealant.

Clean, wirebrush, and paint all outside surfaces; use a good enamel and sand and primer all parts before the coat. Allow to dry in the sun for several days (or the oven if you can sneak it in there and don't mind the painty smell in your baked squash). Mask off (with masking tape) all machined surfaces and other paraphenalia that shouldn't be painted. If you bake the enamel on, it'll last alot longer. The newer epoxy paints may be a better alternative. Don't just up and buy just any old colors. Unless you're a hermit, others in your household should have a say in the matter.

When you're ready to install the armature in the housing, first attach the rear plate. Pull all the brushes out of their holders and position the generator so the brushes aren't crushed. Insert the armature carefully; you don't want to ding the commutator! You may want to stand the housing on the rear plate and insert the armature from above. If the rear bearing does not easily slip into its retainer (in the end plate), tap the armature with a wooden block (end on). Don't use a hammer or you will assuredly bolax the bearing or the front gear nut. If it goes most of the way, push the front plate down on the housing and get its bolts started and, with a rotational tightening of the bolts, it should seat properly. Install the washers and spacers as necessary, in the reverse order you removed them (Here's where that drawing comes in handy!). After pushing the key into the key slot, insert the gear, using the nut to push it down to its proper place. Grab the gear with the vicegrips (after you've wrapped some cloth or leather around it to help protect it) and tighten the nut. Install a new cotterpin (if used). Replace the brushes, zerk fittings, and other odds-'n-ends.

If the brushes are new or the commutator has been cut down, you must "lap" in the brushes; this merely means that you want to give the brushes the same arc as the commutator so that they make even contact. This involves getting a strip of emery-type cloth and inserting it between the commutator and brush (each of them in turn) and pulling it out or rocking the armature back and forth so the rough surface of the cloth (which is facing out and against the brush) sands the brush to the contour of the commutator surface. (See Data Sheet 1.)

You should have "packed" the bearings when you installed them (if they were not already this way) but, nevertheless, get some grease into those zerk fittings! Some Wincharger models have a screw opening alongside the zerk fittings in the generator (there's one at bearing locations on some machines) which is opened prior to jamming some grease in there; this prevents some strong-arm from squeezing grease through the seals and onto the armature in a lube-frenzy. When there's enuff grease in the bearing, it starts to come out the hole. Replace this plug when you've done the job.

Three stud-type bolts are used to secure the generator to the gearcase; this means that they're threaded at both ends and, when you remove the generator by loosening the outer nuts, either the nut will come off or the nut and stud will come out. There's an unthreaded portion in the center of the stud and you can get hold of this section with vicegrips if you have to take it out of the generator or get the nut off.

Don't forget the small gasket that goes between the generator and the gearcase; enuff oil is splashed around in the gearcase (by the big gear) to have it leak out at this point if there isn't one there.

The Wincharger Gearcase

The gearcase is comprised of the main propeller shaft, its bearings, the blade-mounting hub, a cast housing, and the large gear. (See Fig. 2-3.) If everything were alright with the main bearings and the gear itself, there would be no need of further disassembly, and good riddance, becuz it's a job that would make most grown men and women cry. But disassemble it anyway. Why? A visual inspection of the gear will quickly reveal if it needs replacement or repair, but for the bearings, there is no way of knowing their condition without disassembly. We've opened these things up to find absolutely mangled bearings and yet beforehand, a spin of the shaft indicated smooth, quiet, and efficient movement. Gotta remember here that in very high winds, there is a backward thrust on the propeller (See Fig. 3-28 and associated calculations in Chapter 3.) which amounts to as much as 500-1000 lbs! Wincharger used ball-bearings for the propeller shaft, but this is a poor excuse for the more applicable thrust bearings (tapered roller-type). We're trying to make the substitution but, irrespective of the outcome, the bearings will need replacing. We have not found a gearcase yet that had a good set of bearings in it!

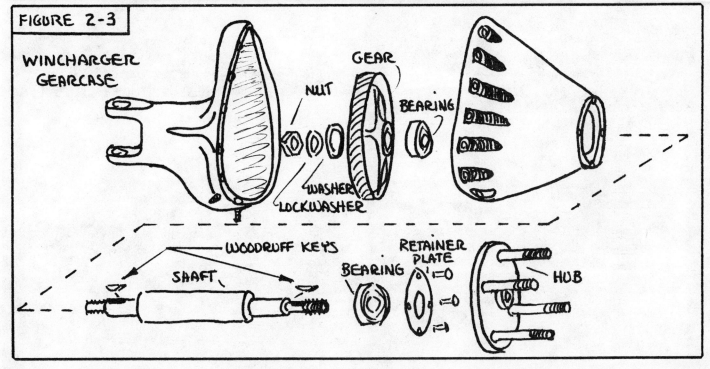

FIGURE 2-3

WINCHARGER GEARCASE

NUT
GEAR
BEARING
WASHER
LOCKWASHER

WOODRUFF KEYS
SHAFT
BEARING
RETAINER PLATE
HUB

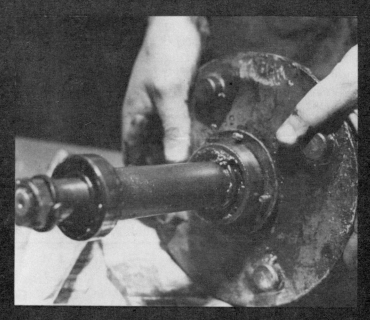
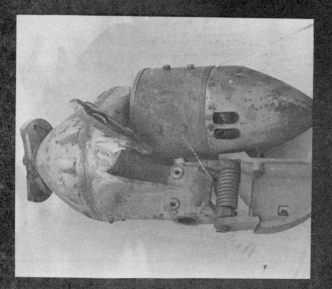

ONE FOOT

The large gear on the propeller shaft is easy enuff to remove with a gear puller; if it has some teeth missing or chipped, it must be removed. We have found both fiber and metal gears here; if it's metal, a welding shop can weld on some new material and you or the machine shop should be able to file it out so it's like new again. If it's fiber, take it with you when you try to find a substitute. Make a lamp out of the old one.

To remove the propeller shaft and bearings necessitates removing the gear. The propeller shaft removes through the front of the gearcase (becuz of the larger sized bearing at the front of the shaft) and that big gear just won't push through there. To get the nut (which secures the gear to the propeller shaft) involves getting a 2 x 4 between the hub bolts (see photo) to hang onto the shaft. A crescent wrench or socket will remove the nut.

Here's the tricky part. It might seem that you could just pull the propeller shaft, hub and bearings through the front end now, but not so. Wincharger stuck a little face-plate in between the hub and the front bearing to keep junk out of there and its got to be removed. The problem? You gotta take the hub off to get a good shot at the four small machine screws that hold this face-plate to the housing, and that hub doesn't like to come off. We cheated a bit and got a small screwdriver in there sideways and managed to undo them. This was tedious; it involved shoving the propeller shaft out a bit when the screws were beginning to hit against the back of the hub, and then loosening some more. With the next Wincharger gearcase, we just took the whole thing down and had a machinist press the shaft out of the hub. Then, we tapped the shaft out of the gearcase itself (from the back). Whatever you do, don't pound the shaft so hard that the threaded end starts to fold over like a mushroom! The machinist's press will do it right if you're not having any luck.

The front bearing is large and the vacated space will easily allow passage of the rear bearing. The bearings are firmly pressed onto the shaft so they'll come with it rather than remain in the housing. Have a shop remove them and press on the new ones you've acquired. If you clean up the shaft at the point where the hub mounts and grease the inside of the hub, you should have no difficulty in replacing it when assembling the thing. Be sure to install the key in the key way.

While you've got the propeller shaft and the large gear out, give the inside of the housing a good cleaning. Short-nosed models have a cast-screen in there which prevents access to the more crudded-up sections of the housing, but do it right and immerse the whole thing in a solvent bath or use strong detergent and a bent scrub brush. If you make it an acid bath, it'll take the paint off as well and leave a clean surface to primer and paint (the outside, I mean).

Hopefully, you've included a drawing in your disassembly procedure; follow this carefully when re-assembling and don't get the front and rear washers interchanged. If you do, the gears may not align correctly or the propeller shaft may run into the rear wall of the frame when the gearcase is bolted up.

There are no zerk fittings in the gearcase; the bearings are lubricated (supposedly) by the splash of oil when the windplant is operating. A very light oil is used here, so the gaskets had better be good ones. The gearbox could hold a couple of quarts of oil, but in reality it only uses less than a pint of oil. Wincharger had a special oil it sold with the windplants, but there's not much hope of finding it. We've found a handsome substitute, however; it's the stuff that's mixed with gasoline for operating chain saws and other 2-stroke engines. A fillspout is located on the top of the gearbox and a drain plug is located at the very bottom. There is an oil-level plug located a couple inches higher up the side of the housing. When you're ready to fill the gearcase, open the oil-level plug and begin pouring the oil through the fill spout; when it runs out the oil-level plug, jam it back in there and stop pouring in oil. Do not overfill! Again, it takes less than a pint of oil. Check this often at first (in case you have a bad gasket and it leaks away); otherwise it won't need attention but once a year, and then all you will need to do is drain it and pour in fresh stuff. If it looks clean when you empty it, you can drain and fill it less often.

(1) in the gearcase, we find a badly chipped gear, (2) gear pullers grab hold while (3) a 2x4 is used to jam the prop hub and keep the prop shaft from rotating when gearnut is removed, (4) the WC prop-shaft, (5) a mangled Wincharger to overhaul, and (6) the complete slip-ring assembly for the WC.

Wincharger Turntable and Slip-Ring Assembly

As previously indicated, the turntable shaft attaches in the frame assembly and mounts into the tower stub. The receptacle for it is the turntable itself and it is simply described as an 18" tube which is secured to the tower near its upper and lower points. When the windplant is mounted in the turn table, the very end of the turntable shaft will project a few inches below the tube (on the large models); this end is threaded. Bearings are mounted on the turntable tube (top and bottom) and for the larger machines, these are Timken tapered roller bearings; for the others, a small and very thin ball bearing was used (at the top only). The thin turntable bearings are inadequate and will most often require replacement. The upper bearing rests against a retainer at the top of the turntable tube and a lower retainer is screwed on to the turntable shaft threads to seat the bearing. (See Fig. 2-4) In this way, the turntable shaft and windplant are allowed free movement (for wind direction orientation).

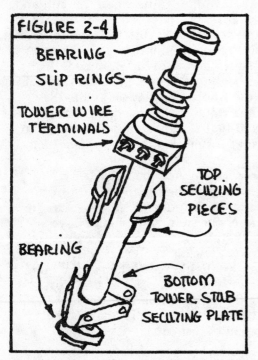

FIGURE 2-4
BEARING
SLIP RINGS
TOWER WIRE TERMINALS
TOP SECURING PIECES
BEARING
BOTTOM TOWER STUB SECURING PLATE

The turntable tube also secures the slip rings, which are used to transfer power from the wind machine to the tower, control box, and batteries. Brass fingers in the brush assembly cup are then positioned alongside the stationary brass rings. These hold the copper brushes as they rotate through 360° (with the windplant) and maintain contact with the brass rings despite the windplant's orientation. (See photos.) The brass rings on the turntable will (unquestionably) require cleaning, but inspect them closely for dents as this will impair their proper operation.

This also goes for the brushes in the brush assembly. You may have to bend them a bit to get a firm contact with the rings or to properly align them so they don't contact more than one brass ring. If they're crudded up, remove them but note the connecting points of the wires and the way each brush assembly is mounted. Use brass cleaner or solvent and polish them with fine sandpaper and steel wool. Do not use a wire wheel on brass or copper sliprings!

The brush assembly half-cylinders have markings on them as to which wire goes where and so does the tower wire connecting-block below the brass rings; take note of these if you want to insure that the wires from the generator will be, finally, connected to the proper wires in the control box. The G+ and G- leads from the generator to the slip ring assembly will need to be larger than the field wire; you'll probably have to replace them becuz they're pretty well shot after constant exposure to the elements. Use solder lugs at each end of the generator to slip ring wires, but install them after you've routed it through the slip-ring cups or they won't fit thru this shroud.

For the Wincharger models using only two slip rings, be advised that these are for the G+ and G- wires. In some instances, if the power of the windplant was low enuff to warrant the absence of a voltage regulator, the field wire (from the generator) was connected to ground (G-) in the generator. Transition models sometimes used the tower as the conductor for field current (conducting thru the bearings!) and a lead was brought off the tower to connect the field to the control box. This is unquestionably the most absurd thing I've ever heard of becuz it means that the tower could not be grounded at its base and guy wires had to be insulated between the tower and ground. The Model 3220 was one of these absurdities; if there are other models with the same characteristic, we did not hear about 'em. For the models that use this system, we are considering replacing the slip ring assembly with the three-ring type. Or we'll just ground it if it's a low power unit. This will be a bear of a job for the former and unsatisfactory for the latter, but that's the way it is.

Wincharger Governor and Props

Winchargers used two or four-blade propellers. The two-blade units used an airbrake-type governor whereas the four-blade units employed a governor which changes the pitch of two of the blades for overspeed control (in high winds). The former method is synonomous with applying brakes in a car with the accelerator still depressed and is truly a "poor-man's governor". The second governor arrangement is a half-way improvement but still leaves two of the blades unfeathered. Obviously, the Wincharger Corporation cut a lot of corners.

If you have a two-blader with air-brake governor, closely inspect the working parts of the brake, particularly the holes in the sheet metal flaps where pins were used to allow movement. (See photos.) Where the original holes have been elongated, thick washers can be welded on to the metal to return the holes to their original size. Or, if only slightly worn, the holes may be rounded out to fit a new pin of the next largest size. Springs were used to keep the governor from activating until the centrifugal forces overcame that tension and caused the flaps to pivot out and "mush" the air; if these are badly rusted, replace them with new ones. Always replace both at a time and get similar specifications on the spring; take one or both with you when you look; chances are you won't precisely duplicate their strength, but you can come close. Adjustments to this tension were available on all of the governors of this type that we've come across. It consists of either a series of holes which allow the spring to be strung between differing distances, or a screw adjustment to adjust at what RPM the governor will activate. We've conducted no tests to determine at what RPM this should occur and have not received answers to any of our inquiries into the matter.

The change-of-pitch governor employed with 4-blade units is a more intricate affair. (See photos.) Again, closely inspect the governor mechanism for anything that looks wrong--broken or chipped parts, worn gears, frozen centrifugal weights, bent propeller attachments, etc. Square steel weights are used in this unit to move some gears and pivot two of the blades when the centrifugal force (or RPM) becomes large enuff to move them in an arc. If a cursory inspection is positive, get one person on one weight and another person on the other and pull 'em apart and see if they move. (See photo.) Is there a lot of slop? If this movement is impaired by rust, remove the pins that hold the weights and get them loosened up by liberal doses of a rust-penetrant and some hefty application of a wirebrush. Unless one of the springs is broken, I would not advise messing around with their attachment or adjustment; if you've no choice, figure out a way to get the springs back on there and don't interchange their position, adjustment bolts, or number of shims (which also serve as balancing weights for the prop-and-governor assembly). If you can't figure out a way to undo the springs without first un-tensioning them, carefully note the number of turns you undo the adjustment bolt on each side. The two gears are linked to prevent one blade from feathering before the other, throwing the rotor out of balance. If one spring is not adjusted precisely to the other, the governor mechanism will activate prematurely or later than it should which affects efficiency or safety.

If the free movement of the pivot arms is not corrected by working with these parts, you may have to pull the bearings located in the governor housing where the pitched-blade arms exit. It takes a special tool to remove the slotted retainer, but it's not difficult to find. Before you tackle this awesome job, I suggest that you remove the zerk fittings alongside them and inspect them and the hole in which they are threaded. Is the grease old? Or dirty? Is there slop in the pivots? We've not had to remove these bearings so we can't provide specific info, but steam ahead if you must.

The governor housing is cast aluminum so if it's got cracks in it, locate a shop to heli-arc weld it. If the blades for the 4-blade unit are made of wood, an aluminum paddle-like thing is attached to the steel extension rods for the two feathering blades; these can also be heli-arced. If aluminum blades are used, all four blades will be of the same length and steel extension rods are then used for all four blades rather than just the two feathering blades.

The four-blade governors have nosecones; these serve the purpose of stream lining the incoming air and protecting the governor mechanism's moving parts from the elements. It's held to the governor with six 10-32 screws. If you haven't got one or it's mangled (most of ours fall into one of these two categories), fabricate one from sheet metal to at least protect the governor mechanism from weather (especially freezing rain, sleet, snow, and hail areas) and sacrifice streamlining if it seems impossible to do both. Not much efficiency that close to the blade center anyway.

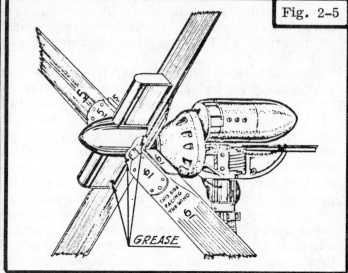

Four-blade props (wood and aluminum) were balanced at the factory (originally); numbers were then stamped on the blades and the governor at their attachment point. (See Figure 2-5). All the windplant-installer had to do was match these up and, with some luck thrown in, no further adjusting was necessary. If you find a wind machine with the props still attached to the governor, check to see that the numbers are legible; if not, use your own coding system. If you obtain more than one 4-blade wind machine, get your coding system sophisticated enuff to prevent interchange of complete sets of blades or individual ones. You'll notice (if you closely inspect the governor parts) some extra holes in the governor castings and some may have bolts through them, holding a number of small, flat hunks of metal of varying sizes. These are the weights; they were added to balance the prop-governor assembly and these things are the reason for all the fuss of checking numbers. More often than not, the bolts are rusted but remove them. Two reasons: you may want to do some cleanup and painting, and you'll want to replace the bolts with new ones so that _any_ balancing you might need to do later will be made a wee bit easier; strugglin' with rusty bolts is no fun at the top of a tower, particularly if you have to remove part of the governor just to get at 'em. Get the right combination of these weights attached to the same spot if you want to get a balanced assembly. You'll probably have to balance it anyway, but you'll have a good headstart if you assemble it the way you took it apart; the most you will have to compensate for is the inbalance that the windplant had after it was installed (if it wasn't correctly done).

If you've got aluminum blades, inspect them for dings and warpage; if they're badly damaged (even one of them), you've got a genuine problem. I'd check some local sheet metal shops for the possibility of some repair work but it might be hopeless to duplicate one. If they're okay, sand them and primer them and then bake on some enamel if you want 'em to look good. Unless you like to send out shards of light for miles around, I suggest a flat finish and a light color for a nice blend with the surroundings. Loud colors quickly become a source of sight-pollution and cause the blades to stand out against the sky too much. Dark colors will heat to very high temperatures when immobile under a hot sun and this can cause unwanted expansion and contraction and possible warpage. A three-fold no-no.

(1) the meshed gears of the 4-blade governor insure that both blades feather together, (2) the 4-blade governor for wood props and (3) aluminum props, (4) the author stands by a rebuilt Wincharger before its installation, (5) and hangs on while installing the props and (6) attaching the generator leads, (7) details of the air-brake governors, like the one installed (8) on a 2-blade, 1000 watt Wincharger.

ONE FOOT

Wood blades must be more closely inspected; cracks in the wood, missing portions of the trailing edge, and a battered leading-edge are the difficult things to correct. A section of tin or copper was generally added to the leading edge (that's the rounded portion of the blade if ya didn't know) to protect it, but this will probably be battered from hail storms and can be easily replaced with a similar material. Here I suggest thin copper sheet or tin-type from printing places. Wincharger props look like they're made from Douglas Fir, but don't quote me on that.

If the blade is okay but needs to be sealed and coated, check with any manufacturer of propellers for recommendations on what to use. (See Bibliography.) Varnishes, sealants, resins, fiberglass, etc. are all possibilities, but I hold absolutely no expertise in this area and can't (and won't) recommend anything. It's a time-consuming affair no matter which road you travel becuz it's patient sanding, application of the coating, sanding, checking the balance, sanding, etc.

Wincharger Tail-Furling Assembly

Wincharger windplants could be manually side-faced or "furled"; this means that cranking a winch at the bottom of the tower would bring the tail around (through 90°) to align itself parallel to the prop. Here, the tail would still align itself with the wind and, in doing so, cause the blades to be edge-on to the wind, incapable of extracting the wind's energy. So, in moving the tail around, the effect of that motion is to "pull" the blades around and out of the wind. Just a matter of reference.

Mechanically, this is accomplished simply; a chain is attached to the tail and threaded through the pullout-chain leverage-arm. It then is looped over another small pulley which is positioned above the hole through the center of the turntable shaft. Below the bottom support of the turntable shaft and tube, the chain is terminated at a swivel. Another chain or wire is attached to the other end of the swivel and attaches to a winch bolted to the tower at its base. The tail-pivot spring wants to hold the tail in the operation position so, to side-face the windplant, the cable is spooled in and the tail is pulled out of its normal, straight-back position.

Anyone that knows anything about wind machines will quickly understand why many Winchargers "ran away" in bad storms; this type of assembly is a very poor design. If the pull-out chain should break, the tail will snap into the operating position; if this shock didn't outright damage the wind machine, it then proceeded to crank up to dangerous speeds. Of course, the governor would help brake the wind machine, but then, we've already indicated how poorly designed those were. So, many an owner watched his wind machine disintegrate, unable to do anything about it. Unless you design a different tail pivot (like the Jacobs system), you're stuck with it. Point is: don't get chincy on the tail-pullout chain and connecting points (See Chapter 4 for installation notes).

Second item: the swivel. This little thing looks like a fishline sinker, but it's a pivot (of sorts) that should keep the pull-out chain from twisting. It's in there to account for the fact that invariably a wind machine will make full turns in one direction more than it will the other. Without it, the pull-out chain will twist and over-tighten. Problem is some of them don't work. Reason? Well, some of them are just cast-metal pieces and you've got a metal-on-metal movement, and a tremendous amount of friction in the swivel when it is under tension. So, it doesn't want to move. The solution? Use a ball-bearing swivel; it will work most of the time if you grease it often. Coat the pull-out chain with grease in the location of the leverage-arm pulley and the pulley bracket (positioned above the turntable shaft hole). Use a strong bolt to connect the chain to the tail position. Inspect the thing often and lubricate it as necessary (if you love your wind machine!)

Wincharger Tail

Your Wincharger tail has one or two stays to support the sheet metal. Where these are bolted to the tail, the metal around the holes cracks and breaks. This is adequately and easily repaired by adding a large washer on each side of each broken hole.

Wincharger Tower Stub

This little beauty is what interfaces the wind machine to the tower you have; if you don't have it, you must fabricate one. We have to do this for most of the Winchargers we've obtained, but haven't done it yet.

If you've got the tower stub, hopefully you've obtained all the other little goodies that need to go with it. (See photos.) The whole assembly consists of a tapered section of tower, the cast-iron inserts (which mold themselves around the turntable for a neat and secure fit to the peak of the tower stub), the stub bracket (which tightens the tower angle-iron around the inserts), and the lower bracket-plate (which secures the turntable tube to the tower stub at its lower point). If you've got a three-leg tower stub (I've never seen a four-leg one) and a four-leg tower, you've got problems I can't help you with. Otherwise, the installation is straightforward and not much to say here. If the thing is rusty, wirebrush it and paint it; it's probably galvanized, but it will rust if this coating is scraped off in spots.

<u>Wincharger Control Box</u> - See Chapter 5

PART B: JACOBS IDENTIFICATION

With the exception of one model, all of the Jacobs units were direct-drive; this simply means that no gears were used. Rather, the shaft of the physically-large generator was also the mounting for the governor unit to which the three-blades (comprising the propeller) were attached, incredibly simplifying the whole system. This and other aspects of the Jacobs windplant make it as distinct as night and day when compared or contrasted with the Wincharger units from the era.

The exception to the direct-drive Jacobs was the Model 15 (See Fig 2-6.) which sported <u>two</u> generators (750 watts each). The Jacobs manufacturing company didn't fool around with their wind machines; 1500 watts for the Model 15 and the direct drive units were 1800, 2500, or 3000 watts. While I have no evidence for the 1800 watt units, the two higher-power units were available in 110 volts in addition to the 32 volts available in all models.

Excepting the Model 15, all the different models of Jacobs windplants were only slight modifications of a central unit which gives credulence to the fact that if you've seen one model, you've seen 'em

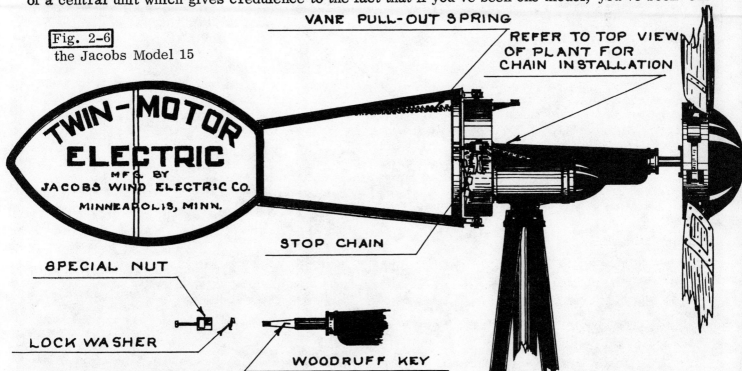

Fig. 2-6
the Jacobs Model 15

VANE PULL-OUT SPRING

REFER TO TOP VIEW OF PLANT FOR CHAIN INSTALLATION

TWIN-MOTOR ELECTRIC
MFG BY
JACOBS WIND ELECTRIC CO.
MINNEAPOLIS, MINN.

STOP CHAIN

SPECIAL NUT

LOCK WASHER

WOODRUFF KEY

all. The generator is the most impressive sight to greet a searching eye, looking for all the world like a huge bomb. A metal plate is pinned to the generator housing and to the Jacobs control box, identifying the voltage, current rating, and model number. If both of these are removed or un-readable, the units can at least be identified as to their power rating by the length of the main housing, the diameter being the same in both models; if the measurement excludes the 1/4 inch thickness of the front and rear mounting plates, the 1800 watt unit has a 9-inch long field casing and the 2500 watt unit, a 14-1/2 inch long field casing. Having never seen a 3000 watt Jacobs (which were special jobs anyway and quite rare), I do not know if it was longer than the 2500 watt unit or not. The control box will indicate the voltage by the full scale reading of the voltmeter-- 150 volts for a 110 volt machine and 50 volts for a 32 volt unit--as will the number of commutator segments (94 segments for the 32 volt units and 188 segments for the 110 volt units). Notable with most Jacobs windplants is that frequently only clean-up and painting are entirely necessary when restoring them; admittedly, there may be adjustments and small repairs, but they don't amount to much unless the thing was dropped, bull-dozed into the junkpile, or overly weathered. The blades, however, were made of wood so they may be pretty far gone.

Jacobs Generator

Two things are immediately impressive about the Jacobs generator: its size and its weight. Or, if you see one in operation, it's remarkably slow speed of 225 RPM for full power output. When the front and rear covers come off, you'll be looking at one of the finest pieces of machinery to be seen. A commutator so thick that it could be turned down every 10 years for a hundred years. A hundred pounds of copper alone. Thick, neatly layed out and spaced coils. And on and on.

Dis-assembling the generator is the surest way to check out everything and clean out the remnants of rat's nest. Gotta get the governor off first so remove the large nut on the main shaft that holds it on; the shaft is tapered and it has a woodruff key (and keyway), so you have to pull it off. I'd advise using a bearing puller type apparatus here; if you just have to do it in your shop, don't use a hammer to get the governor off the shaft becuz it's a casting and is easily cracked by a sharp blow. When you've got it free, put the governor aside for further inspection and dis-assembly.

Get the hemispherical front and rear covers off the generator; they're thin metal and easily bent, so take care you don't mangle them. Later Jacobs machines had a small grounding brush assembly on the shaft forward of the front bearing; this looks like the slip ring brush assembly of a Wincharger and serves to remove static charges from the main shaft which would otherwise discharge through and arc-over the bearings. It secures to the front plate and will cause no interference when you remove the plate, but be careful not to damage it.

Initial inspection before tearing into the beast should include inspecting the commutator for warped or flattened surfaces as outlined in the Wincharger Generator section.

The front and rear plates are held to the generator housing by four long bolts; get a wrench on each end and get these off. If you can, reach inside the generator (alongside the field coils) and get the cloth insulating tubes that the bolts slip through; if you can't get these now, be sure to remove them after you get one of the end plates off. Ours were very fragile with age. The end plates are machined with an inside lip that fits under and against the field housing surface, so they're not going to fall apart when the bolts are removed; if they've got any rust, they may require some not-too-gentle urging but take your time and only light taps with a hammer. Get the front one off first.

Just before or after removing the front plate, you'll want to stand the generator up on its rear plate; insofar as there's a large capacitor (rectangular, metal can) bolted back there, remove it now. Be sure to indicate its hook-up in your drawing. While you're at it, I recommend removing

(1) a disassembled Jacobs, including the governor, (2) close-up of the governor "innards" while (3) the full picture reveals the symmetry of simultaneous feathering of the three blades, (4) one prop-attachment arm has worn gear teeth, easily repaired becuz they're brass, (5) the field coils mounted in the housing, (6) Jim and Charles hold up a Jacobs which has (7) static-arresting brushes

the rear bearing cover; if the armature slides out of the rear bearing retainer, this won't be needed. If it doesn't, however, you're going to have to lay the generator back down to get the plate off, so do it right off and save a few "ergs" of energy (muscular and vocal).

With the generator vertical (prop-end up) and the front plate removed, try to lift the armature out of the housing and rear plate. This is a two-or-three-person job; one to hold the generator and housing (and keep it from falling over) and two to hang onto the shaft and lift hard upward. If it's going to work this way, it's more likely to come with a hard jerk than a steady pull. Realize that whoever is lifting the armature must overcome the 125 lbs (for an 1800 watt unit) or 150 lbs (for a 2500 watt unit) of its weight.

If the spirits are not with you, the thing won't budge. If you've removed the rear bearing plate, just tilt the generator sideway a bit and insert a small block under the end of the shaft and bearing that's exposed through that opening; a 1-1 1/2" diameter nut or socket is ideal to raise if off the ground. Disconnect the field wires and put a cloth down to cushion the rear plate. Get someone to hang onto the shaft (near the governor end) and someone on each side of the housing to lift it clear of the rear plate an inch or two. Say "one, two, and THUREE" and drop the housing! This should push the rear plate downward and clear of the rear bearing retainer; it will land on the towel safely. If it doesn't do it the first time, try again. This is a fairly safe way of getting the armature clear becuz the housing will distribute the force all around the rear plate. If you are not successful, take the thing into a shop and have them press the armature out of the rear plate; in this event, remove the field housing by lifting it over the shaft. This way you only have to heft the rear plate and armature when you take it down to the shop.

Have the commutator turned down if necessary. Send the brushes (or their precise size) to a brush manufacturer to obtain spares or replacements. When the armature is re-installed in the generator, you must shape the brushes to the commutator but here you must be more precise than the Wincharger requires; becuz the generator shaft spins so slowly, the brushes for the Jacobs will never wear-in like those found in the higher speed generator of the Wincharger. (See Data Sheet 1 for notes on brushes.)

Check the generator bearings; again, becuz the generator spins so slowly, these will rarely be bad but, again, it is my recommendation that they be replaced. The original bearing type is still made (See Data Sheet 2) so this is not particularly difficult and you'll find them fairly in-expensive. These are fitted tightly to the shaft so you'll need to have a shop remove the old and install the new.

Check the field coil wires for fraying or broken insulation. Give the field coils a continuity check or see if they draw the rated amount of current when voltage is applied. (Should be 3 amps at windplant voltage.) Clean-out the end cones, and the inside of the generator. If you use some-thing like laquer thinner, you'll have no residue to clean before priming the generator parts; watch out, though, it's pretty evil stuff.

Jacobs Governor

Haven't completely dis-assembled one of these yet, but Jim DeKorne has and he gave the following write-up for the process:

PROP-GOVERNING MECHANISM

Like everything that the Jacobs Company manufactured, the prop governing mechanism is a well-made, well-designed piece of precision machinery. By removing the rear cover plate, the mech-anical principles of the governing mechanism may be observed. What first appears to be a comp-licated "Rube Goldberg" monkey-motion machine, on second glance turns out to be an ingenious and highly efficient means of slowing the plant in high winds. Briefly, it works like this:

The flyweights (A) are held close to the housing under spring tension (B). (See Fig. 2-7) As the plant revolves faster and faster in strong winds, centrifugal force causes the flyweights to overcome this spring tension, and move outward. As this happens, the flyweight levers (C),

which are attached to a geared hub (D), turn that hub to the right. (Viewing mechanism from the rear.) This, in turn, revolves another set of gears (E) which are connected to the propeller shafts (F). In effect, then, what has happened is that the propellers are rotated or "feathered" out of the wind, thus slowing the plant's rotation. Naturally, as the plant slows down, centrifugal force is lessened, and the springs pull the flyweights back into "resting" position. In high, gusty winds, the governing mechanism is continually moving back and forth. This naturally has a wearing effect on the prop-shaft gears, and it is these parts which will wear the most. A set of badly worn prop-shaft gears can cause a plant to "chatter" in strong winds. (I have never actually heard this phenomenon, but have had it described to me.)

Before attempting to install a Jacobs windplant, the prop governing mechanism should be taken apart, inspected for wear, and lubricated. A governing mechanism which, after years of disuse, has "frozen up" or had all its old grease turn into a gummy paste, will not do its job properly, and will almost certainly cause the plant to burn out the first time strong winds are encountered. To dismantle a Jacobs governing mechanism is not difficult, but there are a few tricks to the job which aren't immediately obvious.

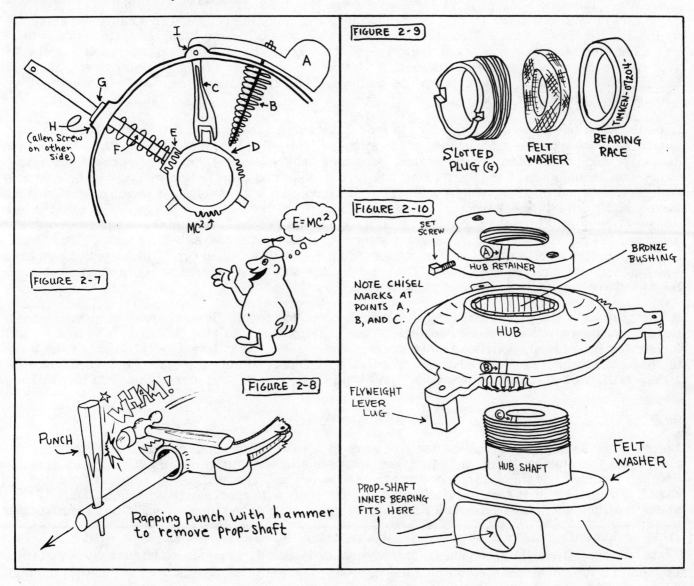

-39-

Removing Prop Shaft (F)

In the governor housing where the prop shaft enters, is a slotted plug-like device (G). Obviously the slot is meant to fit a special wrench, but since few of us will have such a tool, we must make do with something no mechanic should be without--a pipe wrench. First, however, we must remove the allen screw (H) (on front side of governor) which holds the slotted plug in place. After doing this, it is a simple matter to loosen the plug (carefully!) with our pipe wrench. The plug should easily unscrew with your fingers after it has been loosened. You will notice that there is a spring on the prop-shaft--this provides tension so that the props are always responsive when feathering or unfeathering. It is going to be in our way a bit, but there's nothing we can do about it at this point.

Our next step is to pull the prop shaft out far enough so that we can examine the bearings. This is accomplished by putting a steel punch or bar into the hole on the end of the prop shaft, and hitting it sideways with a hammer. (Fig. 2-8) Don't worry--a little bit of hammering should do the trick. I've taken several of these devices apart, and have yet to see one that was too frozen up to dismantle.

As the prop shaft begins to come out, you will first see a felt washer and then the race for the outer bearing coming from the hole where you removed the slotted plug (G) (Fig. 2-9) At the same time, the prop-shaft gear (E) will be disengaging itself from the geared hub (D). Pay close attention to how these two gears mesh, since they must be replaced in exactly the same way you found them. (Once I found one that was "one tooth off"--we finally determined that this was a bonifide factory error, since the prop-shaft itself had been machined incorrectly, and the gear had been repositioned to compensate. This is not typical of Jacobs' usual high standards, and probably reflects some assembly-line worker's Monday morning funk. Ah! - technology! What a price we pay for it!)

Once the shaft has come out far enough to free the bearing race, you will find that there is considerable tension on the unit because of the spring. While this is awkward, it isn't an impossible handicap, and unless there are problems, such as a broken bearing, or severe prop-shaft gear wear, you shouldn't have to take the unit any further than this point. You will now be able to see both the outer and inner bearings--nice tapered Timken roller bearings, in keeping with the Rolls Royce quality you'd expect from a Jacobs machine. (The inner one, by the way, fits into the geared hub (D)--just behind the prop-shaft gear (E). If, as is usual, the unit hasn't been in operation for many years, you will find these bearings gummed tight with 20-year-old grease. It is usually a simple matter to clean them up with a stiff brush and solvent, then repack them with fresh grease. The bearings themselves are tightly fitted on the prop-shaft, and should not be removed unless they need replacement--an unlikely eventuality.

If you are lucky, the prop-shaft gears will not be worn too badly. If you happen to have a set of bad gears, the only thing you can do, aside from leaving them the way they are, is to find a small foundry or machine shop that can make you some new ones. That strange-sized nut, by the way, the one holding the 7/16" set-screw which attaches the gear to the prop-shaft, is a 25/32" nut -- a rare bird, indeed. (I think it was the first time I'd ever used that size wrench in my life!)

Removing Geared Hub (D)

Before disassembling this mechanism, be sure to note the chisel marks which align the hub, shaft and hub-retainer. (Fig. 2-10). When reassembling the unit, these marks must all line up. The hub retainer is removed by loosening the set-screw and unscrewing the retainer from the shaft. The hub itself is then carefully pried off the shaft with a screwdriver blade. You will notice that the hub is sleeved with a bronze bushing--probably gummed up and filthy from years

(1) the author finds a rat's nest in this Jacobs, (2) Mark, Jim Davis, and the author lift a 2500 watt Jacobs on a small stand and attach (3) an Earthmind-designed cutting-tool and turn down (in the assembled unit) the commutator, (4) cleaning between segments finishes the job, (5) and (6) the author straddles DeKorne's Jacobs to turn down its commutator but (7) it needs undercutting in EM's shop.

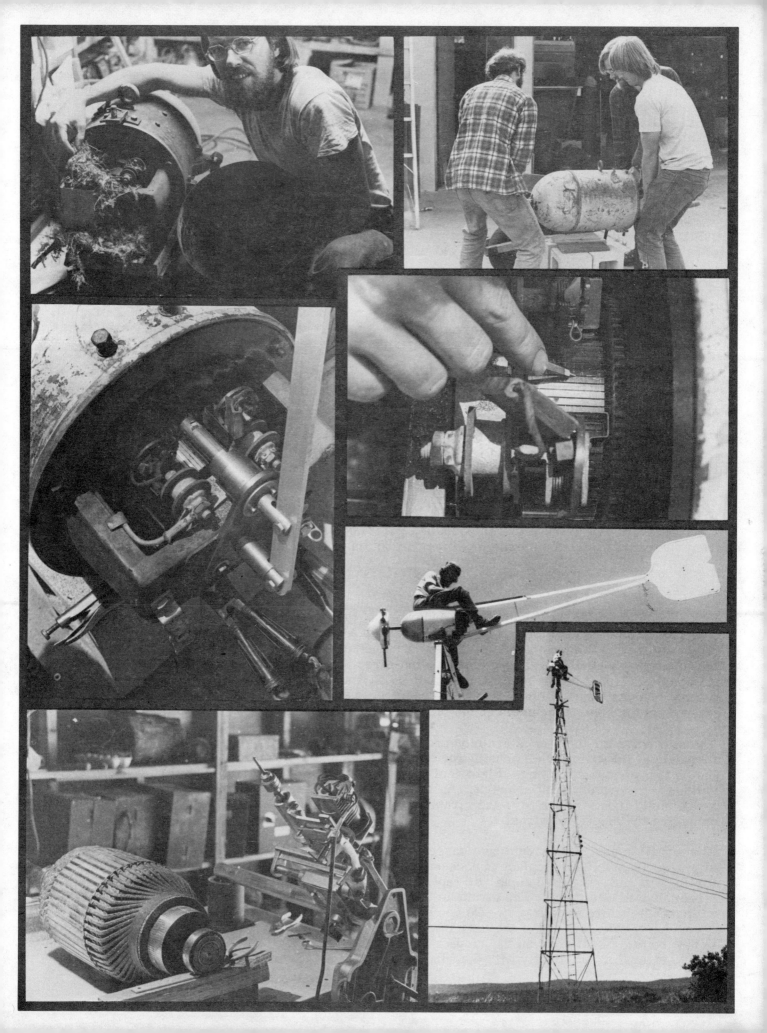

of disuse. Remove the large felt washer, and clean all parts thoroughly with solvent. (Incidently, all of the felt washers you will encounter are placed there to retain lubrication-- "lube sponges", you might call them.) Make sure that the lugs which engage the flyweight lever (C) are free to turn. All parts should be carefully lubricated and reassembled.

Flyweights (A)

Sometimes the flyweights become frozen, so that they are not free to do their thing. Point (I) in Fig. 1 shows where the binding is most likely to occur. I once used a torch to free a flyweight -- heated the weight all around point (I) and gently tapped it with a hammer. Don't do it. The result in my case was a broken flyweight--heating cast iron can be very tricky if you don't know what you're doing. Luckily, I had an old broken-up governing mechanism from which I cannibalized a flyweight to replace the one I broke. Not everyone may be lucky enough to have a few spare parts to cover for dopey mistakes.

The best way to free-up a stuck flyweight is to liberally douse the pivot pin with penetrating oil, and after it's had time to soak in, carefully drive the pin out with a punch. Clean everything up, replace the pin, and the flyweight should work like it was designed to.

After clean-up, lubrication and reassembly, your governor should work like it did when it came out of the factory. It can easily be checked by having two assistants with screwdrivers help you gently pry each flyweight outward an inch or so--the entire mechanism should work freely, though, of course, it will be under considerable spring tension. That's it! End of Jim's write-up.

Something that I'd like to add here. Sometimes, the geared hub (part D) and the prop shaft gears (parts E) were made of brass; this is one reason that many governors have worn teeth on one or more of the gears. This is easily remedied. Take the disassembled parts that need to be repaired to a shop that can braze new brass onto the worn teeth; mention that you would like to get a stronger alloy of brass if that is possible, but it does have to be machinable. You can then file away the excess brazed material or, if you're not up to it, some machine shops can do it for you.

Jacobs Turntable

The Jacobs turntable shaft bolts to the underside of the generator with three bolts. (See photo.) The Jacobs unit, however, does not truly have both a turntable shaft and a turntable tube as in the Wincharger; this is a combined unit here. A monstrous Timken tapered roller bearing is used at the top of the turntable to assure smooth wind-direction orientation despite the 400-600 lbs of Jacobs windplant. Jacobs elected not to use a bearing at the bottom of the turntable but it sports a large bushing which, in the units we've seen, shows no wear whatsoever. Data Sheet 3 illustrates the basic attachment of the turntable to the tower stub.

The slip rings for the Jacobs are mounted on a fiber tube which, in turn, is inserted into the turntable at its lower end; a housing for the slip rings and a mount for the brushes attaches below the bottom turntable bushing. Electrical wires from the slip rings travel up thru the tube to exit below the generator for attachment. As the tail-furling chain passes thru this same space, a small metal tube is inserted in the turntable tube for the winch chain; this prevents the chain from damaging the electrical wires.

The turntable assembly should be disassembled and cleaned thoroughly. Inspect the brushes in the slip-ring assembly and replace if necessary. Clean and polish the slip rings. Inspect the generator-to-slip ring wires and repair or replace them as necessary; use a wire size that's equal to or larger than what's there. The turntable bearing should be cleaned, inspected for wear and packed with grease before installing it. Do you have the bolts which secure the generator to the saddle? If you don't, take this end of the turntable and "fit" it to the generator and, in the same way, "fit" in new bolts. Get it right on the ground; it's no fun to find they just "don't want to go in" when you're struggling frantically with the wind machine installation.

Jacobs Blades

The Jacobs wind machines used three blades. In doing so, they eliminated the problems experienced with two-blade and four-blade propellers (See Props--Chapter 7). Jacobs props were wood, but the finest available--Sitka Spruce. The only attention required was a yearly application of an aluminum paint but, after the years of inactivity, a lot more work may be required. The passage of time seemed to be hard on these blades; some of the sets we have will require the use of wood-filler, resin, or fiber-glass and lots of sanding before the paint can go on. I imagine that some-one who's quite good with wood finishes will be an asset here but avoid the use of heavy fillers becuz of the imbalance they're sure to create for the windplant. It's got to be more than just "looks pretty."

Jacobs Furling Assembly

As indicated in the Wincharger section concerning the furling function, the tail on the Jacobs wind-plant is pulled into operating position. The installation of the winch and determining cable length will be the same, but the threading procedure is different; Data Sheet 4 illustrates the proper connections for the indicated models. Just remember that the Jacobs windplant's tail wants to remain in the furled position (tail parallel to the blades) and you must crank in the wire to get the tail into a perpendicular position for proper operation and crank out wire when furling the wind machine. It's precisely opposite for the Winchargers and most other wind machines, but is a fail-safe precaution.

At least some Jacobs installations used a piece of solid steel wire for the pull-out system (between the two lengths of chain). With less tendency to twist, this wire would undoubtedly make for more positive action in the ball-bearing swivel.

Jacobs Tower Stub

Same situation here as in the case of the Wincharger; if you don't have one you're going to have to fabricate one. We've gotta do this for two of our Jacobs windplants.

Jacobs Control Box - See Chapter 5

Jacobs Balancing

A small balancing tool was provided with the Jacobs windplants in the event that they did not "track"; while this is almost a misnomer, it will suffice if we refer to it as "windplant tracking" to distinguish it from "blade-tracking". Incorrect windplant tracking is due to imbalanced blades; it is distinguishable as a regular rocking motion (side to side) of the windplant during normal wind conditions. Data Sheet 5 illustrates proper procedure for balancing the Jacobs windplant and, for those of you without such a device, the shape and position of the tool itself; it's a rather simple affair and any shop should be able to put one together. If you haven't guessed it, this is more than just a tool; it's the thing that keeps the plant in balance once it's adjusted correctly and is left on the windplant.

Afterthoughts

We have Jacobs and Wincharger manuals which we reprint and sell to those needing 'em; if you have the model of either make that we've described in this chapter, you'd be well advised to obtain the operators manual. This reason is simple; while it is not a shop manual, you get a lot more info in it than you'd find in operator's manuals given with just about anything sold nowadays. Both Jacobs and Wincharger manuals are 18 pages in length and very meaty throughout.

3 TOWERS

If you want to generate electricity from the wind, you must consider using a tower; maybe the reasons are not so obvious, but they are simple -- increased height (above ground level) means more wind (i.e., more usable energy) and less turbulence. Scramblin' up and down (or around the top of) a tower will make things more adventurous, but this has nothing to do with the importance of more wind/ less turbulence. If you're into wind-generators, you'd best get used to the idea of climbing towers.

Turbulence and windspeed vs. Height

You can't see the wind (only its effect on things) but, for a moment, let's pretend that you can. What do you see? Probably the first thing that you'd notice is that it moves more slowly at ground level. Know why? Even if the ground is level and fairly smooth, it will provide friction (or a resisting surface) to the free agent of moving air, and therefore, slow it down. This slow-moving air will, in turn, provide friction for the air above it, and slow it down. This goes on and on; if the wind was constant in both direction and speed, we might be able to see barely distinguishable boundaries between the layers of faster- and slower-moving air. Normal wind will, however, fluctuate in speed and direction, so these boundaries will be constantly changing, and this has a name: Turbulence. If you were standing in the midst of it, you would not fully appreciate its effect; in most instances, it isn't going to be the old "sock you around, throw you to the ground" kind of thing. To an aeroturbine, however, any disruption of a flow of air will steal power it might otherwise use. With some types of aeroturbine, turbulence is more than power-robbing; it can cause some potentially destructive stresses on the machine's components.

Turbulence will be more pronounced with rougher terrain, the more obstructions there are rising above ground, the higher the windspeed, and the more gusty it might be, so it's not something to be ignored or considered insignificant. Rudimentary observations will show detectable differences in windspeed at even ten-foot intervals of height above ground. A formula has been developed (see Fig. 3-1) to aid in figuring out what the windspeed would be, say, at 45 feet above the ground, for a given windspeed at ground level; this applies to a flat, level plain, but it can be somewhat of an indicator in obstruction-ridden or rough ground conditions, too. In the wind-energy field, thirty feet of tower is considered to be the minimum required over a level plain.

If you play with the windspeed vs. height formula, you'll probably want a height that will have the top of the tower snaggin' satellites; a look at the cost for such a venture will quickly bring you out of the heavens (or clouds) and much closer to earth. Knowing that it will be somewhere between the two may not be of much value, so let's look at some relationships between where the tower goes and how high it should be.

Determining Tower Site and Height

The aeroturbine, and its tower, should be located as close to the batteries as possible; this cuts down on the need for a lot of electric wire and the resultant I^2R losses (power that is robbed by the resistance of the electrical wire). For the same reason, the batteries should be located as close as possible to the motors, lights, appliances, etc., that use this power. Sometimes this cannot be avoided, but with long runs of electrical wire the only way to decrease the losses (for any given voltage) is to go to a larger size of wire, and this will cost more.

The tower should be located in an area where it can be raised from a horizontal position to a vertical one. This may seem almost too simple a statement to make, but people do make boats

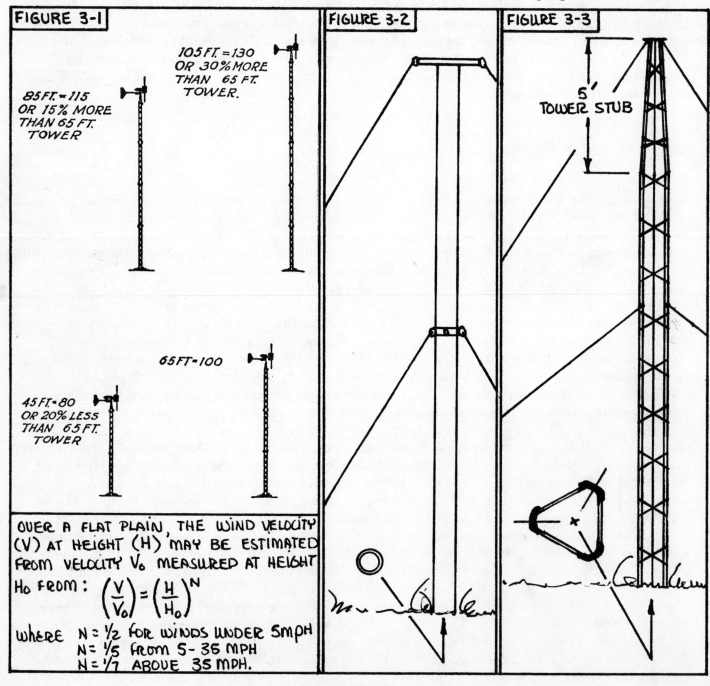

FIGURE 3-1

105 FT. = 130 OR 30% MORE THAN 65 FT. TOWER.

85 FT. = 115 OR 15% MORE THAN 65 FT. TOWER

65 FT = 100

45 FT = 80 OR 20% LESS THAN 65 FT. TOWER

OVER A FLAT PLAIN, THE WIND VELOCITY (V) AT HEIGHT (H) MAY BE ESTIMATED FROM VELOCITY V_0 MEASURED AT HEIGHT H_0 FROM:

$$\left(\frac{V}{V_0}\right) = \left(\frac{H}{H_0}\right)^N$$

WHERE $N = \frac{1}{2}$ FOR WINDS UNDER 5 MPH
$N = \frac{1}{5}$ FROM 5 - 35 MPH
$N = \frac{1}{7}$ ABOVE 35 MPH.

FIGURE 3-2

FIGURE 3-3

5'
TOWER STUB

(or whatever) in houses and find, when removing the finished product, that it won't fit through the door or any windows. If you build the tower from the ground up (this takes a hearty breed of folk), this does not represent much of a problem.

The tower should rise 15 feet above all obstructions within 400 feet. This is a tuff one to get around and if it's just not possible for your situation, then give strong consideration to placing it where the aeroturbine will at least have an unobstructed view (or access) to the prevailing winds in your area. Climatological stations usually keep a record of wind directions; this information is available to the public, so consult it before installing any wind-power system. Be aware, however, that this information results from a few minutes of readings a few times a day (for most stations) and depends on how high the instruments are mounted, what kind of instruments are used, how long it's been since they were calibrated, and where they're located on the property (it's a well-known fact that different readings may be obtained at the same site at points that may only differ by small distances). Data collection for the last 35 years leaves much to be desired where application to wind-electric systems is concerned.

A higher tower is going to cost more money; a lot depends on the type of tower used, but another relationship seems to exist which makes it something other than a direct, proportional increase. My own guestimations seem to indicate that the price goes up with the multiple of the increase factor; i.e., a 40-foot tower will cost four times what a 20-footer will cost (and a 60-footer, six times the cost of the 20-foot tower, etc.). This is not surprising when one considers that a free-standing tower (legs cemented in the earth) must be more spread apart at the base with the increased height, and a guyed tower (such as the Wincharger-type tower -- see Types of Towers section) must use more, and longer lengths of guy wire. This is not intended as a rule of thumb, but it certainly isn't a direct proportion, so check it out.

The importance of these "general rules of thumb" depends very much on the situation. Understanding the intricacy of the relationships will help you make a final decision. As tower height increases, greater windspeeds will be experienced and less turbulence encountered. But longer lengths of expensive electrical wire will be needed, the power losses in the wire will increase, the cost of the tower materials will go up, etc. Therefore, for your situation, threshholds exist, beyond which additional height (in terms of the cost/benefit ratio) will be unproductive.

On the other hand, don't get too bogged down in trying to apply this information to your situation. Some of the factors here weigh more heavily than others, and some apply more to squeezing out a few extra watts than just getting wattage, period. They're not so much determinants of whether you can make use of wind energy as they are factors which will help optimize what you can get. Just don't altogether ignore them!

Types of Towers

Most towers fall (a figure of speech) into one of four groupings -- single-leg, three-leg, four-leg, or octahedron-segment -- and are usually made from one of three materials: wood, angle iron, or pipe. Let's look at them in terms of cost, type and amount of material used, weight, rigidity, ease of construction, tools required, and methods of securing them.

The single-leg tower (see Fig. 3-2) is inexpensive, simple to build, and easy to raise. The most basic material to use here is a telephone pole, but a long section of well-casing pipe is a strong second. A fancier single-leg tower (see Fig. 3-3) was used with Winchargers of the pre-REA (Rural Electrification Administration) days; it consisted of three 20-foot parallel angle-iron sections which formed an equilateral triangle of 12" sides. These sections were bolted together to give the desired height. At least three guy wires (spaced 120° apart) will hold a tower like this, but for wind machines, nothing less than 5 wires (spaced 72° apart) should be used (see Fig. 3-4). In this instance, should one of the guy wires break (they are all too easy to snag), the tower (and whatever is on top) will not be lost; for anything less than 5 wires, it's bye-bye tower and wind machine. More guy wires are required with increased height, but the same anchors can be used if they have been properly distanced from the tower. (A rule of thumb: Anchors for the guy wires should be located at a distance from the tower base of not less than one-half the height of the tower; i.e., a 50-foot tower will have anchors located not less than 25 feet from the base of the tower -- see Fig. 3-5).

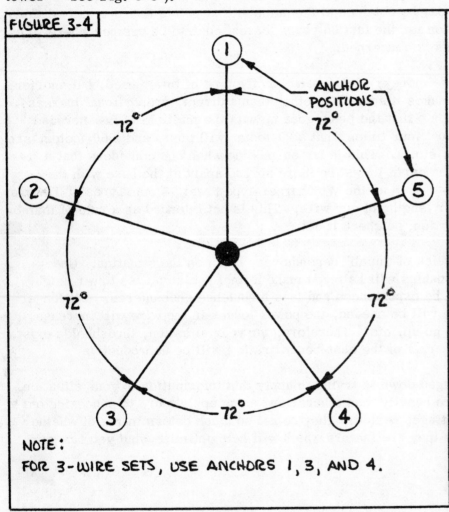

FIGURE 3-4

ANCHOR POSITIONS

72°
72°
72°
72°
72°

NOTE:
FOR 3-WIRE SETS, USE ANCHORS 1, 3, AND 4.

(1) GUYWIRES SHOULD BE SPACED 72° APART. ONE WAY OF INSURING THIS ANGLE IS TO CUT TWO LENGTHS OF STRING — ONE 17-FEET LONG AND THE OTHER 20 FEET LONG — AND GET 5 SMALL STAKES. MEASURE 17 FEET OUT FROM THE TOWER BASE AND DRIVE A STAKE. ATTACH THE 20-FOOT LENGTH OF STRING TO THIS STAKE. IN EITHER DIRECTION, A POINT THAT IS 17 FEET FROM THE TOWER BASE AND 20 FEET FROM THIS STAKE IS ALSO 72° SEPARATED. NEAT, HUH? DRIVE A STAKE IN AT EACH POINT AND REPEAT FOR THE OTHER POINTS, MARKING THEIR POSITIONS WITH STAKES. WHEN INSTALLING THE GUYWIRE ANCHORS, MERELY LINE UP WITH THESE STAKES.

(Author's note: When I say "should not be" or "should be," I am generally referring to the fact that it is physically possible to cheat and I do not wish to be insistent in what I say. I occasionally indulge in cheating (not doing something like it should be even though I know better); but in these cases, I deserve (as will you, if you fudge) whatever happens in consequence. In situations involving wind machines and towers, I have formed what might be called, for lack of a better name or description, Hackleman's Laws. One of them applies here and goes something like this: Should an object of value -- a house, a car, or a favorite rosebush -- be the only thing within a distance to the tower's base of less than the height of that tower, the guy wire that will fail, fray, or be accidentally snagged and broken shall be that one, in the case of less than 5 used, which is

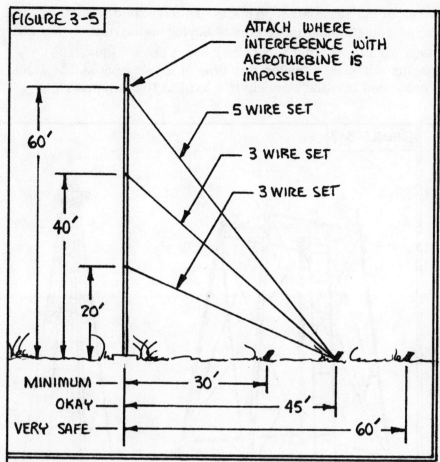

FIGURE 3-5

ATTACH WHERE INTERFERENCE WITH AEROTURBINE IS IMPOSSIBLE

5 WIRE SET

3 WIRE SET

3 WIRE SET

60'

40'

20'

MINIMUM — 30'

OKAY — 45'

VERY SAFE — 60'

(1) THE TOP SET OF WIRES WILL ALWAYS BE A 5-WIRE SET, IRRESPECTIVE OF THE TOWER'S HEIGHT. THREE-WIRE SETS SHOULD BE USED AT 20-FOOT INTERVALS FOR TOWERS HIGHER THAN 20 FEET. THE 3-WIRE SETS MAY USE THE SAME ANCHORS AS THOSE INSTALLED FOR THE 5-WIRE SETS.

(2) IF $\underline{H}$ EQUALS THE HEIGHT AT WHICH A SET OF GUYWIRES IS ATTACHED AND $\underline{Y}$ EQUALS THE DISTANCE FROM THE TOWER BASE TO THE ANCHORS, THEN THE LENGTH OF EACH OF THESE GUYWIRES WILL BE EQUAL TO:

$$\sqrt{h^2 + y^2}$$

(3) THE 5-WIRE SET OF GUYWIRES SHOULD BE A DOUBLE STRAND OF NUMBER 9 WIRE. THE 3-WIRE SETS MAY BE A SINGLE STRAND OF NUMBER 9 WIRE.

(4) ANCHORS FOR GUYWIRES DO NOT HAVE TO BE LOCATED EQUALLY-DISTANT FROM THE TOWER. JUST INSURE THAT THE CLOSEST ANCHOR IS NOT LESS THAN ONE-HALF THE TOWER'S HEIGHT.

(5) UNLESS SOME MEANS IS AVAILABLE WHEREBY ALL OF THE TOWER'S GUYWIRES CAN BE TENSIONED DURING INSTALLATION, TURNBUCKLES OF SUITABLE RATING SHOULD BE USED. LOCATE THEM NEAR THE ANCHORS.

directly opposite in direction (from the tower) of the said object of value. End of valued object. End of tower. End of wind machine. End of Law. End of author's note.)

I have seen single-leg towers that were not guyed, but cemented like free-standing towers generally are. Much deeper holes were made, more cement was used, and in one instance where well-drilling pipe was used, the pipe was filled with cement to increase its rigidity. It was neat lookin', not having unsightly guy wires all over the place. The only problem was that it swayed; in winds of 15 mph, it was discernable. I've yet to see one in high winds, but then, I really wouldn't care to -- I don't like to see wind machines rip apart or fall down. And that's what's going to happen to machines mounted on an unguyed, single-leg tower . . . eventually.

The three- and four-leg towers (see Figs. 3-6 and 3-7) are the most commonly-seen towers; they find frequent use for water-pumping windmills and wind-electric machines. Wooden towers up to 30 feet were common, but this type of tower is most frequently made of angle iron. These towers are, by far, the most expensive; the 4-leg uses more material and will therefore weigh and cost more than a 3-leg of similar height. They are very strong. In some sections of the country (particularly the Midwest) they are found in abundance, and can be purchased for a fraction of the material cost or the cost of a new one of the same size. This is one of those diminishing resources, though, with the price of steel going up and more people buying/using them. You can buy new ones, but a look at the pricetags would gag most folks; they range from $400-$1200 depending on the height. The wide spacing of the legs makes this type of tower very stable when in an upright position; if the legs are cemented into the ground, it's hard to find a more rigid structure.

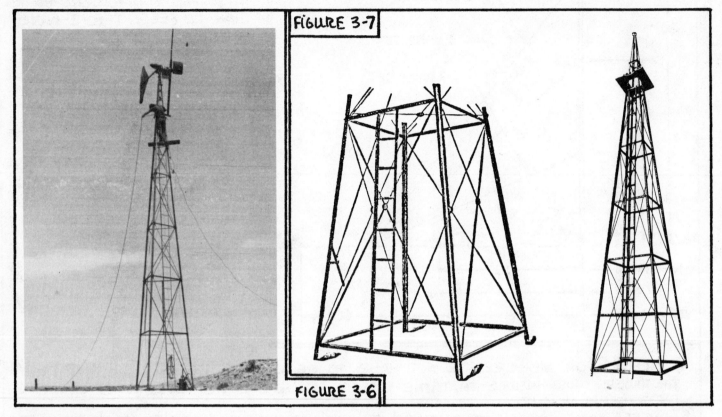

FIGURE 3-7

FIGURE 3-6

The octahedron-module tower is a relative newcomer; it stems from the principles of the geodesic dome and the inherent strength of the triangle (see Fig. 3-8). The first time I saw one of these up close, it was very obvious how neatly this type of tower took the advantages of the 3- or 4-leg towers (rigidity, strength, cemented-leg securing) and the advantages of the single-leg tower (low cost, lightweight, simple, easy to construct, use of less -- and less expensive -- materials, etc.) without their disadvantages. Wasn't too long before I tried building one (without any plans) and, while I did get one together, it was not without having done some real muscle-strainin' and metal-bendin'; that was solely due to my miscalculations. Octahedrons don't draw so well on paper and it's difficult to believe what you're seein' when you're lookin' at one, much less tryin' to see one in your head. (To keep sane, you build them out of straws -- see Fig. 3-9. If the sales clerk at the counter asks you what you're buying all them straws fer, she'll never believe you if you say "an octahedron-module tower"; so just tell her you heard that there was going to be a straw shortage and you thought you'd better stock up on 'em.) I'd advise the purchase of a set of plans from Windworks for building these towers (their address is given in the Bibliography, and other special considerations in the use of this type of tower are given in the Octahedron-Module Tower section of this chapter); we used these plans when we built the next two towers, and the stuff went together like tinker-toys.

EMT (Electrical Metallic Tubing, or electrical conduit) is used in the construction of the octahedron-module tower; if someone figures out a way to build one using wood or angle iron, I'd be fascinated to hear it.

Building vs. Buying a tower

Fig. 3-9

Fig. 3-8

This is a sticky question -- lots of if's and but's and completely situational. Now that I am aware of the octahedron-module tower, I wouldn't look for another type of tower; I'd rather build one becuz it's fun, I can do it right out in the back yard, and build one as high as I'd want. If someone walked up to our door and said, "I have a 60-foot tower a few miles from here that I can bring over, do you want it? for $200?" I'd probably do it. But I wouldn't pay $50 for one if it was 500 miles away. Why? Well, the cost/benefit ratio just wouldn't be that good. I'd have to get myself out there, take it down, disassemble and load it, transport it back here, re-assemble it, and raise it. Even if it cost less than the $150, that would make the two deals "equal (monetarily), the time and energy spent for the latter would shoot it down.

But then we're not talkin' 'bout history, just current events (you!), and maybe you would spend the time and the money. With that bein' the case, here's some things I've learned which may be of some value to your getting a tower:

I'd advise lookin' for one in your immediate area. If you do spot one and find that it's for sale, consider what work is going to be involved in getting it down (if it's up), disassembled (unless you can transport it whole), assembled, and back up. You're only going to be finding three- or four-leg towers so weight is a factor -- they're gonna be heavy! Don't be in such a hurry to get a tower that you commit yourself to money you can't really afford to put out, or energy you don't have to expend. Look over the section on lowering towers (in this chapter). Can you do it?

If you can't find a tower locally, or you can't afford what's being asked for them (in money, time, and energy), then get some information on the octahedron-module tower. If you don't like the way it looks (too progressive, or sumthin') or aren't able to build a tower for yourself, look at the single-leg tower idea. Still no good? Well, then check outlying areas and further and further out from your place. Or check with the utilities; maybe they have some old towers around. (I'm runnin' out of ideas, folks.) Or damaged ones. Or . . .

Tower-Raising Techniques

Whether you've built your own sky scratcher or bought one, in some manner you're going to have to get it from the horizontal to the vertical. Raising a tower is much akin to welding; 90% of the job is in preparation. The actual task is inversely proportional to the amount of ingenuity and knowledge that you have; that is, with foresight and meaningful preparation, raising it is a trifle. I'm oversimplifying it, but -- if you're breaking your back, you're doing sumthin' wrong.

By and large, the simplest way to raise a tower might be to rent a crane or a helicopter and pull it into place. The latter might appeal to the jet set, but not to me! As for the crane . . . well, I might use one if it were real handy and didn't cost much, but having raised towers by the "gin-pole" method, I would not deprive myself (or anyone else) of the fun and excitement of holding a "tower-raisin' bee"!

I've heard of building towers from the ground up, but have never participated in doing it this way. I have thought to do this, but was turned off to this approach primarily for safety reasons; now that I give it some thought, I can see ways of getting around that but I can think of other problems -- fit up, weight handling and support, and minimized rigidity (becuz of the incompleteness) -- and just don't know if it would be easier. I don't feel enterprising enuff to work with it further to see if it would work out well. I'm sure I could do it; I'm just not certain it would be better than constructing horizontally, and lifting it to the vertical.

Tower Physics

There are a few basics to tower raising that ought to be explained at this point just to make it a little easier to talk about other things as we go along. Anytime that someone is trying to tell someone else about sumthin', there are three things that generally come into conflict -- how much to tell 'em, how to tell 'em, and in what order. Assumptions as to what you know are always difficult to deal with becuz of the extremely diversified backgrounds of the recipients of the information. So, while I'll try to optimize these factors, I have no intention of getting sidetracked and writing a physics or math book. Examples will be given as to their application in tower raising (or lowering) but, if you find them to be just so much "greek" to you, be prepared to break out the books on the basics. At any rate, if you do find yourself bogging down, just continue on and see how the stuff is further applied. As much as possible, try to picture in your mind what is happening, why or how it's happening, and when (don't let my casualness on the subject lead you to believe it's not important); this is the cornerstone of tower raising, wind machine raising, and many other things. Take the time to study it. If you don't, then you'll just be playin' Follow the Leader -- knowing <u>what</u>, but not <u>why</u>!

The most essential element of "tower physics" is the lever, or the principle of its use. We use it in everyday life. It allows us to use a small amount of foot pressure to stop several tons of vehicle -- many times over -- whenever we drive a car. It allows us to free a rusty nut on a lawnmower (when our fingers could not do it alone). How? By giving a torque capability. A force exerted at a distance. A mechanical advantage. Different words, but the same meaning. Let's examine this in a few examples to make their meaning clearer.

A board rests between two supports (see Problem 1); it's 10 feet long and there's a 100 pound rock resting on it, two feet from one end. The man in the drawing wants to lift one end of the board.

How much force does he have to exert, and how heavy will it appear to him? We might first draw attention to the fact that a subtle distinction exists between "force" and "weight" in this situation, so I'll define them as I will use them in the text. <u>Weight</u> can be classified as either referring to mass (which is universal and applies to a body outside as well as inside the earth's gravitational field) or as a force (applied within the earth's gravitational field); I will use this latter definition in the examples. <u>Force</u>, on the other hand, will refer (in the examples) to the work or energy expended in picking up objects or equalizing their "effect." Forces will, therefore, be expressed in "ft-lbs" (foot-pounds) and weight in "lbs" (pounds). Don't get confused with this right off; the distinctions will become clearer immediately.

For the situation in the first example, the weight of the stone is 100 lbs. It will produce a rotational force of 200 ft-lbs becuz of its position relative to the lever's pivot (or fulcrum); I arrived at the value of force by multiplying its weight by the distance to the pivot (which is 2 feet), thus giving us 200 ft-lbs. Don't let it bug you that we are multiplying feet by pounds and coming up with ft-lbs; it really isn't the same as oranges multiplied by apples. The man must overcome the 200 ft-lbs of force exerted by the stone if he is to lift the board from his end. He is, however, 10 feet from the pivot so the weight that he feels will be the 200 ft-lbs divided by 10 feet, or 20 pounds. A simple (and equivalent) experiment will confirm to you that this is indeed what he (or you) will feel, so do it if there is doubt in your mind. At any rate, this demonstrates the principle of the lever -- lifting 100 pounds and yet feeling only 20 lbs (this saves the ole back, too).

We left something out of this experiment, though; the board must weigh something! If this was a physics book, they'd probably say sumthin' like "assume the weight of the board to be negligible." In the real, live world, however, there are no such things as "infinitely strong, zero-mass" boards,

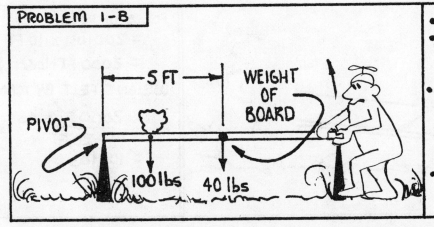

so let's include it and say that it's 40 lbs. How do we figure it in? Well, the board's density can be assumed to be equal throughout its length (this is not an unreasonable assumption -- if we cut the board in half, we would expect each of the 5-foot sections to weigh 20 lbs). With further experimenting we'd find that we can represent all of the board's weight at one point -- in the middle, or five feet from either end (see Problem 1B). With this fact, we can then proceed to calculate the force exerted by its weight. It will be 200 ft-lbs (40 pounds multiplied by 5 feet -- the distance to the pivot). Divide that by the distance the man is from the pivot (still 10 feet), and you have another 20 lbs that he will feel (in addition to the 20 lbs from the stone), making a total of 40 lbs of weight.

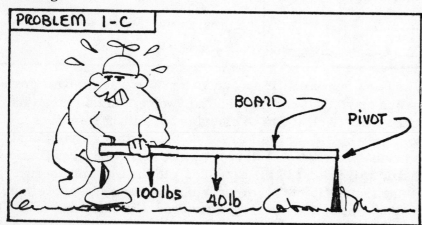

PROBLEM 1-C

- FORCE OF STONE = 100 lbs x 8 FT.
  = 800 FT-lbs
- FORCE OF BOARD = 40 lbs x 5 FT.
  = 200 FT-lbs
- TOTAL FORCE (BOARD & STONE)
  = 1000 FT-lbs !

- POUNDS MAN MUST LIFT
  = 1000 Ft-lbs = 100 lbs
    10 Ft.

If the man went to the other end of the board, would he still only exert 400 ft-lbs of force, or feel just 40 lbs. of weight? Nope -- it's a whole different situation. Look at Problem 1C. The other end of the board is now the pivot (and the fulcrum for the lever), so we'll have to compute the forces relative to that end. The board still weighs the same (40 lbs) and the force that it exerts is the same (200 ft-lbs) becuz it's still 5 feet from the pivot. The stone still weighs 100 lbs but now it's 8 feet from the pivot, not just two; the force that it exerts will, therefore, be 800 ft-lbs (8 ft multiplied by 100 lbs). Stone and board now exert a whoppin' 1000 ft-lbs! How much force does the man have to exert? The same amount -- 1000 ft-lbs! But becuz he's 10 feet from the pivot, he only feels 100 lbs when he expends the energy of lifting it (or holding it just about the support). This example is intended to explain the differences between forces (moving about a pivot) and weights, and how the lever works for you (and where it doesn't). There's a lot of difference between 20 lbs felt on one side of the board and 100 lbs felt on the other. Understanding why there is a difference is the important thing; if you find yourself in a daze, study the diagrams or put on your beeny-copter and try a similar experiment yourself. If you're still with me, let's go on.

PROBLEM 2

FORCE OF POLE =
= 200 lbs x 10 FT
= 2000 FT-lbs

WEIGHT FELT BY MAN
= 2000 FT-lbs
    20 FT
= 100 lbs

Now it just so happens that this man is wanting to put a birdhouse on a pole in his back yard. The pole is 20 ft. long and weighs 200 lbs, and the newly-made birdhouse weighs 40 lbs. Not one for doing a lot of figurin', he decides to just go ahead and do it. He tries to pick up the 200-lb pole. Mercy, but it is heavy! So, he just grabs one end and drags it around the house and into the back yard. Believe it or not, he's makin' good use of the lever again (see Problem 2). We can represent the pole's weight as being located all at the center, so it exerts 2000 ft-lbs of force (200 lbs times 10 feet); he's 20 feet away from the pivot, though (that's the end that's draggin'), so he only feels 100 lbs (2000 ft-lbs divided by 20 feet).

He finds a convenient place for the base of the pole, attaches some wires to the top (to be used to hold it in place once it's vertical), and proceeds to push up on what will be the top (or birdhouse) end of the pole, and begins walking down the pole, lifting as he goes. It starts up all right, but pretty soon it's just too heavy, so he backs off and sets it back down on the grass. What happened? Well . . . he began to lose all that leverage (see Problem 3). When he started, he was feeling only 100 lbs (the same as when he dragged it around the house). But when he moved up the pole one foot, it was more like 106 lbs (2000 ft-lbs divided by 19 feet). At two feet, it was up to 112 lbs (200 ft-lbs divided by 18 feet). At three feet, it was 118 lbs; at four, it was 125 lbs. (By now the strongest of most of us would have quit, but being an ex-weight lifter, he perseveres.) At 5 feet, he's up to 134 lbs. At 6 feet, it's up to 143 lbs. Can he continue? Yep, he makes it to 7 feet, and 154 lbs! That's it. He can't go on. And the tower is only at 27 degrees -- less than one-third of the way up!

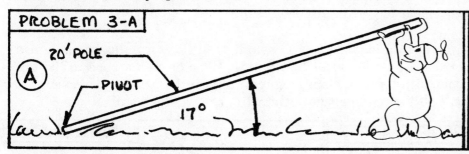

PROBLEM 3-A

(A) 20' POLE — PIVOT — 17°

OUR MAN STARTS PUSHING UP ON THE POLE. HE IS 20' FROM THE PIVOT SO HE ONLY HAS TO LIFT ABOUT 100 lbs. NOTE THE 17° ANGLE.

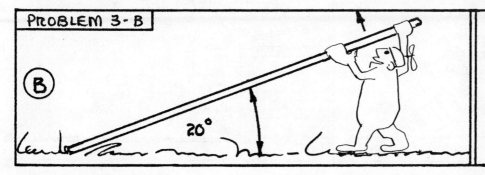

PROBLEM 3-B

(B) 20°

HERE, HE'S MOVED UP 3 FT AND THE ANGLE IS UP TO 20°. BUT HE'S LOSING THE EFFECT OF THE LEVER — NOW HE HAS TO PUSH AGAINST 110 lbs. NOT TO BAD . . . YET!

PROBLEM 3-C

(C) 24°

HERE HE'S MOVED UP ANOTHER 2½' (5½ FT ALTOGETHER) AND THE ANGLE HAS INCREASED TO 24°. BUT THE WEIGHT HAS INCREASED, TOO . . . HE NOW HAS TO PUSH AGAINST 126 lbs!

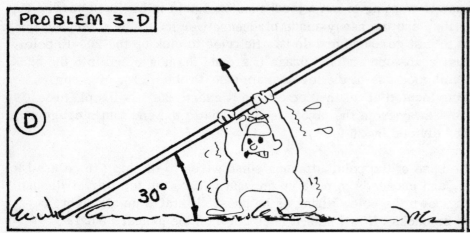

PROBLEM 3-D

D

30°

AT THIS POINT, HE'S MOVED UP THE POLE 8½ FT. AND THE ANGLE IS UP TO 30° — ONE THIRD OF THE WAY UP. HOW MUCH DOES HE FEEL AS THOUGH HE'S LIFTING? WOULD YOU BE- LIEVE 151 lbs? THAT'S RIGHT. ABOUT TIME TO TRY ANOTHER WAY TO DO IT!

Okay, I fudged a bit -- he's not holding 154 lbs at 7 feet, only 137 lbs. What's wrong with the figures? Well, the pole still weighs 200 lbs, but part of that weight starts pushing down on the base of the pole. I mean, when the pole's fully upright, all of its weight is pushing straight down. And that doesn't happen all at once, just sort of gradual-like. So, even at an angle of 27°, some of the weight pushes down (along the pole) and that's less that has to be lifted. So I left out the calculation correction on the portion of the weight that's shifted to push the pole in the ground. That takes knowin' trigonometry (we'll do a bit of that later on). At any rate, I think the point has been made. The man started out with 100 lbs of weight and only made it 7 feet before it was up to 137 lbs and very little gain was made in getting the tower up.

Our man is not defeated, however; he has an idea. (See Problem 4.) He is raising the pole near his house (so that he can get the birdhouse on top after he got it up), so he ties a rope to the top of the pole, and climbs up on the roof with the other end, figurin' to pull the pole up thataway. Not a bad idea, considering that he won't be losing leverage. Or will he? Let's watch.

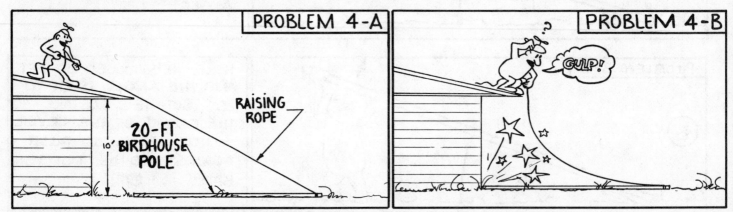

PROBLEM 4-A

RAISING ROPE

20-FT BIRDHOUSE POLE

10'

PROBLEM 4-B

GULP!

He starts pulling on the rope. Hmmm, it doesn't want to move. He pulls harder. Suddenly, the pole slides along the ground and slams into the house. Why'd it do that? Well, he wasn't pulling straight up on the end of the pole, like he'd been pushing -- he's got an angle now. And the effect of that angle is that a portion of the pulling that he was doing was, indeed, lifting, but a portion of it was also pulling the pole toward him. And with nothin' to stop it, it slid (in the direction of the pull) until it hit the house. Well, that's simple enuff to fix. He climbs back down, repositions the pole, and attaches a wire to the bottom of the pole and hooks it onto a water sprinkler back near the top of the pole (he would've used a stake in the ground at the bottom of the pole, but his wife is fussy about tearin' up the lawn). While he's down there he decides to attach two of the wires that are attached at the top of the pole to some other water sprinklers that are to the sides of the pole; in this way, he insures that the pole won't fall to either side as he pulls it up into place.

He's smart about it, too; he chooses some water sprinklers that are in line with the bottom of the pole and perpendicular to the axis of the tower, knowing that this will keep them at a constant tension thru the whole pole raisin'.

Now, it's back up on the roof again. He starts pulling on the rope. The pole doesn't budge. He pulls harder. Still nothing. Wow, that's a lot more than the 100 lbs that lifted it from below! Wanna know how much more?

(Author's Note: Okay, here's where the trig comes in. If you don't know that's short for trigonometry, then we're off to a bad start. If you groan, then you're remembering those drowsy classes that you had to take when you were in high school or college; it really isn't all that bad. You'll find it easy and fun to work with once you have somethin' to apply it to (which may have been sorely lacking when you took the course). There are three functions that we have to work with -- sine, cosine, and tangent. If you can multiply, divide, and are able to look up some figures in the trig tables (found in most math books), you're in. I'm going to go through one example here in the text, but you need the tables if it's going to mean anything to you, so get 'em. The rest of the problems will be worked on the assumption that you know (or can quickly learn) trig; Fig. 3-10 shows the relationship of angles to the three functions aforementioned. Good luck. End of Note.)

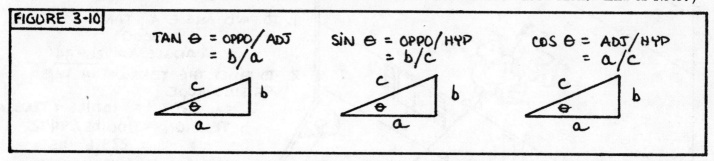

The first thing that we want to do for this situation (see Problem 5) is to find the angle that the rope makes with the tower. We know that the roof is 10 feet high and the pole is 20 feet long; that's all that we need to know to find the angle (other than knowing that one of the angles is 90°!). The appropriate function here is the tangent. So: the tangent of the angle is equal to the roof height (10 feet) divided by the pole length (20 feet), or the tangent of the angle equals .5000, right?

Now, look in the trig tables under the column marked "tangent" until you see .5000 (or sumthin' close to it). Then read across the table until you find the number of "minutes" (there are 60 of these to a degree). Then look up at the top of this column, and you'll see the number of degrees. Together they form the angle we're looking for. That wasn't so bad, was it? We don't have to have this kind of accuracy for what we're doing but you will want to write down the number of minutes just so that you can find that exact place again. Or, write down the value for the sine and the cosine (found under the column heading bearing those names) becuz we will use one of them (if not both) when we continue the problem.

This angle can be otherwise obtained; if the situation were accurately drawn (to scale), a protractor would quickly establish this angle well within the ballpark figures we can use. Determining the actual angle is, however, not the goal of this exercise, but merely the means to finding the force required on the rope to lift the top of the pole. Trig tables would still be required. An individual who knows trig well also knows that it is a matter of ratios; with such knowledge, trig tables are not an absolute necessity to the solution of such problems as I am presenting. Shortcuts are much aliking the situation with food consumption: You can't know what's enuff, until you've had too much. So run it out with trig, okay?

Back to Problem 5: In this case, the angle whose tangent is .5000 is 26°34'. That's our angle. So now what happens? Remember that we are trying to find out how many pounds of pull on the rope will lift the pole. And we know that if the pole was pushed (or pulled) straight up, it would take 100 pounds to do it. So . . . we make another little triangle and we find that we can take the sine function (of the angle 26°34') and it will equal the lift (100 lbs) divided by the unknown pull of the rope. It's not really all that abstract; we can substitute an X for this unknown pull (shades of algebra) and solve for the X. This means that X equals the lift (100 lbs) divided by the sine of the angle. If you didn't write this down when you found the angle in the first place, find 26°34' and look across, reading the figure in the column marked "sine." This is .44724, but if you're running a pencil calculator, round it off to .45 and divide it into 100. My Heathkit calculator got 223.6 lbs for the 5-digit number and 222.2 for the 2-digit one. Close enuff for wind energy work.

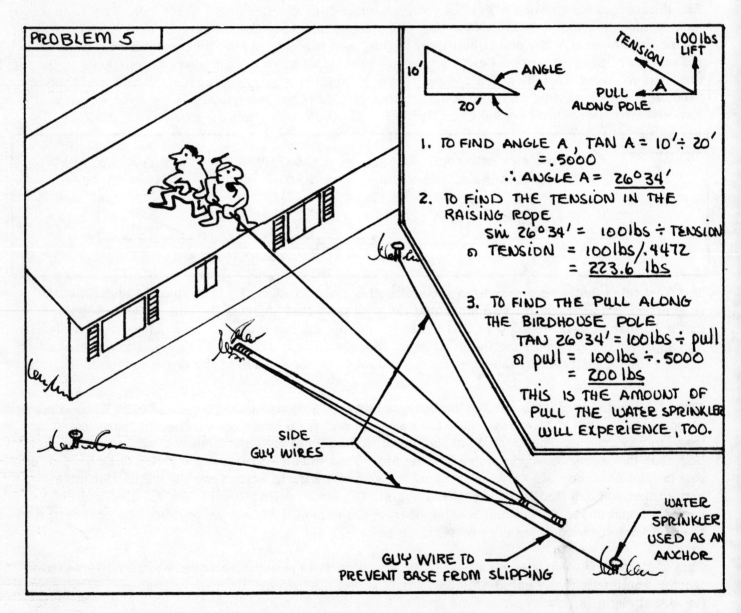

PROBLEM 5

1. TO FIND ANGLE A, TAN A = 10' ÷ 20'
= .5000
∴ ANGLE A = 26°34'

2. TO FIND THE TENSION IN THE RAISING ROPE
SIN 26°34' = 100 lbs ÷ TENSION
∴ TENSION = 100 lbs/.4472
= 223.6 lbs

3. TO FIND THE PULL ALONG THE BIRDHOUSE POLE
TAN 26°34' = 100 lbs ÷ PULL
∴ PULL = 100 lbs ÷ .5000
= 200 lbs
THIS IS THE AMOUNT OF PULL THE WATER SPRINKLER WILL EXPERIENCE, TOO.

SIDE GUY WIRES

GUY WIRE TO PREVENT BASE FROM SLIPPING

WATER SPRINKLER USED AS AN ANCHOR

Well, how do you like that? To lift the pole, our man is going to have to pull with a mighty 220 lbs (plus) on that rope! No wonder he couldn't get it to budge! And if you're wondering where all those pounds of pull are going, figure out how much pull the pole gets in the direction of the house (along the ground). It isn't that hard; it turns out to be the 100 lbs divided by the tangent of the angle (which we found to be .5000, right?). That comes to 200 lbs! Sure hope the sprinkler that's keepin' the pole from sliding into the house is well secured! If you're wondering how you can get 100 lbs of lift and 200 lbs of pull (along the pole) from only 220 lbs of pull on the rope, chalk it up to the craziness of the math; it's the only kind where 220 can be equivalent to 300!

(Author's Note: If I am giving you the impression that knowing trig, algebra, or angles is necessary to raising poles (or towers), then I am losing you somewhere. Nothing could be further from the truth. There are people who've raised towers that might not be able to explain why they do it the way they do (as I have) but they certainly have raised towers! The reason is simple -- they've got the principle of the thing. I really don't care to convince you to do the math -- you will or you won't. I do want you to be able to picture in your mind why certain things will work and other's will not. The man who's raisin' the pole for his birdhouse is comin' up against a mess of problems -- like those you might encounter if you were trying to raise sumthin' similar -- and I'm tryin' to think of every wrong way it can be done. While I'd know better, maybe you wouldn't. I'm really not into sayin', "this is the right way -- do it!" Becuz that's not liberating knowledge. End of note.)

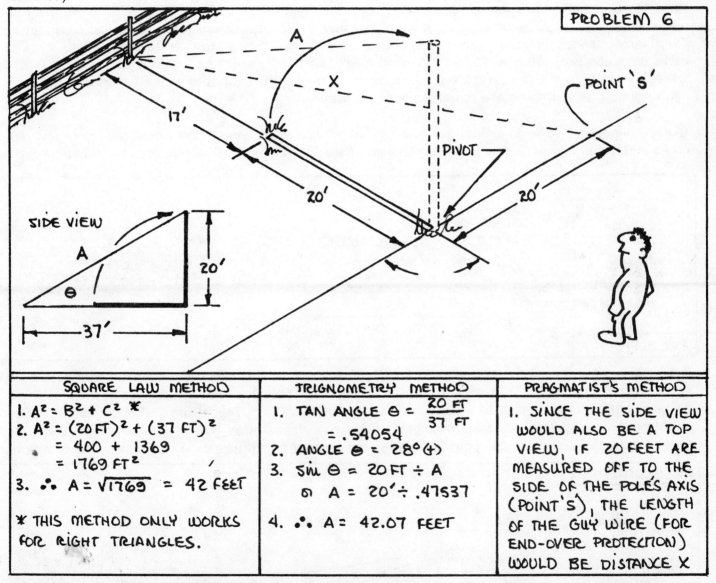

SQUARE LAW METHOD	TRIGNOMETRY METHOD	PRAGMATIST'S METHOD
1. $A^2 = B^2 + C^2$ ✱ 2. $A^2 = (20 \text{ FT})^2 + (37 \text{ FT})^2$ $= 400 + 1369$ $= 1769 \text{ FT}^2$ 3. ∴ $A = \sqrt{1769} = 42 \text{ FEET}$ ✱ THIS METHOD ONLY WORKS FOR RIGHT TRIANGLES.	1. TAN ANGLE $\theta = \dfrac{20 \text{ FT}}{37 \text{ FT}}$ $= .54054$ 2. ANGLE $\theta = 28°(+)$ 3. SIN $\theta = 20 \text{ FT} \div A$ or $A = 20' \div .47537$ 4. ∴ $A = 42.07 \text{ FEET}$	1. SINCE THE SIDE VIEW WOULD ALSO BE A TOP VIEW, IF 20 FEET ARE MEASURED OFF TO THE SIDE OF THE POLE'S AXIS (POINT 'S'), THE LENGTH OF THE GUY WIRE (FOR END-OVER PROTECTION) WOULD BE DISTANCE X

Well, our man is a bit chagrined; with the largest amount of energy he exerts, it will not budge. Finally, he calls over a neighbor friend, and together they try it. Well, it moves a little bit but then, it falls right back. His neighbor suggests that they attach the rope to a car and pull it up that way. Now, there's an idea. A car can exert a lot of force, right? Well, maybe. Let's see how they do it.

His neighbor has a light, imported pickup with a stick shift, so he brings it over, driving onto the lawn. The man's wife is watching the whole thing by now (she wasn't too happy about the roof shakin' that was going on when the two of them were trying to lift it that way), so the neighbor takes care not to rip up the lawn as he drives over to the pole. Our man has been busy re-arranging the guy wires for a pull from another direction, and he attaches the wire hooked onto the bottom of the pole to another anchor -- a nearby fencepost. But again, he's using his head. He knows from before (with the roof-top effort) that once the pole was upright, it wouldn't fall over in the direction of the pull becuz the edge of the roof would be there to keep it from doing this. The situation is different now, so he attaches a wire to the top of the pole and ties the other end to the fencepost. How long does the wire have to be?

Well, there are three ways of determining this (see Problem 6). The first two involve trig and the third simulates the condition on the ground. Our man that doesn't like to work with the figures just marches off 20 feet to the side of the base of the pole (this represents its height) and then measures the distance from this point to the place where the wire will be secured -- the fence post. Yep, it turns out to be real close to 42 feet (give or take six inches) which is found by the "square law of triangles" and normal 3-function trig. The man measures off 42 feet of guy wire, attaching one end to the top of the tower and the other to the fencepost.

Everything seems to be in order, so the neighbor attaches the rope to the top of the tower and the other end to the bumper, starts the engine and eases forward until the rope is taut. Then he gives

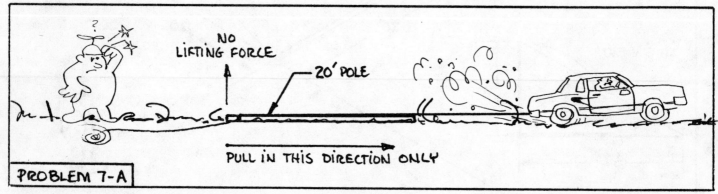

it a little more gas. Nothing happens! A little more gas -- still nothing happens. The wife is screaming at him to stop. What's that? The wheels are spinning! What's wrong? Well, it's a scheme that looks as though it might work, but it won't. Why? Becuz there's no lift angle! (See Problem 7.) All of the pull is directed along the axis of the tower. If there was a few tons of tower instead of a meager 200 pounds of pole, only one of five things could happen (none of which

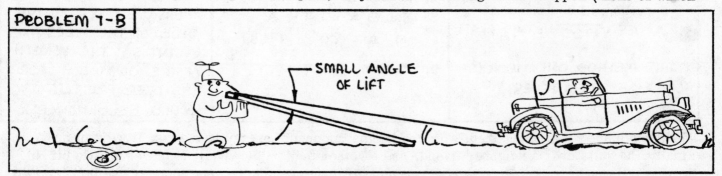

will raise the tower or the pole!). The line will break. Or the tower (or pole) will go sliding along the ground in the direction of the pull (if the base is not secured, or if the wire securing it breaks). Or the clutch will burn out in the truck. Or the tower will collapse like an accordian (in which case, it wasn't worth raising anyway!). Or the scene will be one of active immobility and the rear wheels of the vehicle will slowly dig into the terrain.

PROBLEM 7-C

END-OVER PREVENTION GUY WIRE

0249876

CAUTION
US ARMY

The neighbor, meanwhile, has been calming down our man's wife while he's over looking at the situation, sees the problems, and yells at the neighbor to try again. He picks up the top of the pole as his neighbor gives the vehicle power and, sure enuff, it starts to go up. Up and up it moves until, finally, it's straight up and down. Even the wife is quiet as the three admire the finally-raised pole. Then the wife drops the bomb. "How are you going to get the birdhouse up there?" The husband is looking a wee bit red. Whoops! When they were raising the pole near the house, he'd planned to use their 10-foot ladder to reach the top (by putting it on the roof and laying it against the pole). But he's not by the roof any more. He suddenly has an idea, though; they can bring the pole back down, bolt on the birdhouse, and raise pole and birdhouse together. The neighbor backs off the truck and the pole swings back until it touches the ground again, while hubby goes and gets his pride-and-joy -- a cast-iron birdhouse weighing 40 pounds. He bolts it onto the pole. When he tries to lift the end of the pole, though, he finds that he can't. Why? Well, remember that it takes 100 pounds worth of lifting to move just the pole; with the birdhouse attached right at the end, he feels the full 40 pounds of that, too. With two of them trying it, they can hold it up, but then there's nobody to drive the truck (the wife can only drive an automatic) and she's not hearin' the idea that she help lift it while the neighbor drives, so it's thinkin' time again.

What's the next best thing to raising the pole to provide a lift angle? Why, givin' the raising rope an angle (just like on the roof, remember?). The only problem here is that the roof ain't handy any more. But, thinks our man, we can "simulate" the roof being there by standing the ladder up between the pole and the truck and draping the raising rope over that. And if a pulley is attached to the ladder near the top end, the rope would freely travel over it during the raisin'. He explains the idea to the neighbor and wife and they set about doin' it.

The pulley and guy wires (not shown) are attached to the ladder (see Problem 8) and the raisin' rope is strung thru the ladder and over the pulley. The ladder is raised to a vertical position and its guy wires are secured (thereby holding the ladder in this position) to water sprinklers in the immediate vicinity (the yard is well plumbed). Back into the truck goes the neighbor, firing the engine up and easin' out the clutch to take up the slack in the rope. He then gives it a little more oil-juice and . . . up she goes! What a pretty sight!

Okay, let's examine a few of the incidentals to this most recent try. With the birdhouse attached, what's the tension in the rope at the beginning of the pull (no tower angle) and what's the lift angle? Introduced a few terms, didn't I? Let's see what they mean before we work out the problems.

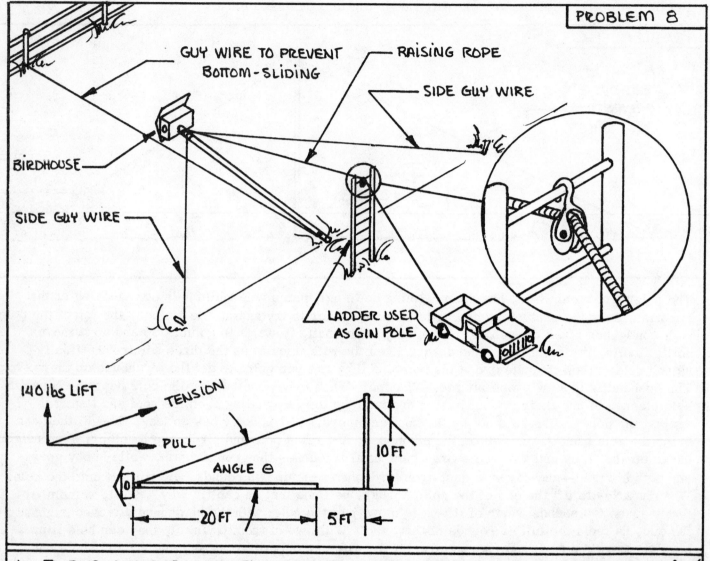

1. TO FIND <u>ANGLE Θ</u>, LET TAN ANGLE Θ = 10FT $\div$ 25 FT = .4000 $\therefore$ ANGLE Θ = 20° 19′
2. TO FIND <u>TENSION</u> IN THE RAISING ROPE, LET SIN 20° 19′ = 140 lbs $\div$ TENSION OR TENSION = 140 lbs $\div$ SIN Θ = 140 lbs $\div$ .34721 = <u>403.2 lbs</u>
3. TO FIND THE <u>PULL</u> ALONG THE POLE (TENDING TO PULL IT TOWARD THE TRUCK) LET TAN 20° 19′ = 140 lbs $\div$ pull OR the pull = 140 lbs $\div$ TAN 20° 19′ which = 140 lbs $\div$ .4000 = <u>350 lbs</u> OF PULL ALONG THE POLE.

Tension in the raising rope is the same as the number of pounds that it feels like it's lifting. The tower angle is defined as that angle which the tower (or pole) makes with the ground; when it's lyin' there, it has no angle (or it's zero). When it's raised, it will increase its angle with the ground until it's fully upright, at which time the tower angle will be 90°. The lift angle is defined as that angle which the raising rope (or cable) makes with the tower that it's attached to. When the man was pushing straight up on the end of the pole (or if he'd been pulling straight up on it), the lift angle was 90°. Remember that this was the only situation where the tension on the rope would have been equal to the required pounds of lift. When he tried it from the roof, the tension in the raising rope was much larger becuz the lift angle was less than 90° (in fact, it was 26°34'). And when they tried to raise the pole (with the truck) while it was lyin' flat on the ground, there was a zero lift angle, and the wheels just spun. By these examples, it should be clear that a large lift angle is desirable; it simply reduces the amount of force that must be exerted to do the job, and it considerably lessens the amount of tension in the raising rope (or cable). If the lift angle cannot be large initially (and in many cases, it cannot), the next most desirable thing is to have the lift angle increase as quickly as possible during the raise.

In our example, the ladder serves as a "gin pole" -- a device that is frequently used in home-style tower raisings; more information on its use will be discussed in the next section. I have in this example, however, placed it 5 feet from the base of the pole and this is not altogether necessary; for the pole (or any single-leg tower), the gin pole may be located right at the base of the tower. For the more commonly-raised 3-leg, 4-leg, or octahedron towers, the width of the base must be taken into consideration for the placement of the gin-pole (to prevent interference) and I only did it for the example so that I'd have an opportunity of making you aware of that circumstance at this point. On with it!

Problem 8 details the computation of the lift angle and the tension in the rope. I hope that you have been doing the problems all along; if you have, that you'll have the gist of the thing by now and my workin' them out will serve as a check for yours. If you keep gettin' an answer that's different from

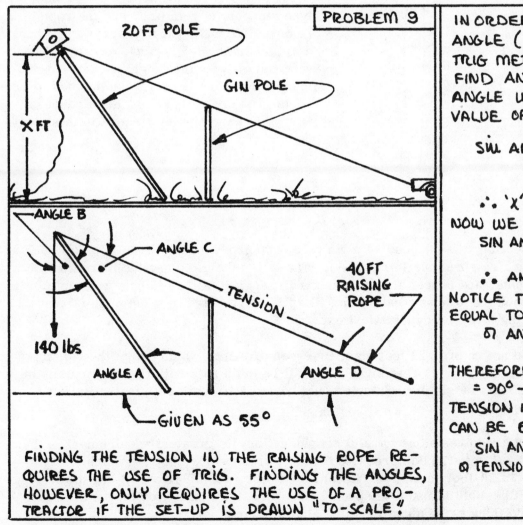

PROBLEM 9

20 FT POLE

GIN POLE

X FT

ANGLE B

ANGLE C

TENSION

40 FT RAISING ROPE

140 lbs

ANGLE A

ANGLE D

GIVEN AS 55°

FINDING THE TENSION IN THE RAISING ROPE RE-QUIRES THE USE OF TRIG. FINDING THE ANGLES, HOWEVER, ONLY REQUIRES THE USE OF A PRO-TRACTOR IF THE SET-UP IS DRAWN "TO-SCALE"!

IN ORDER TO FIND THE LIFT ANGLE (ANGLE 'C') BY THE TRIG METHOD, WE MUST FIRST FIND ANGLE 'D'. TO FIND THIS ANGLE WE MUST FIND THE VALUE OF 'X'.

SIN ANGLE 'A' = X ÷ 20 FT
then 'X' = (SIN 45°)(20')
= (.707)(20)
∴ 'X' = 14.14 FT

NOW WE CAN FIND ANGLE 'D'
SIN ANGLE 'D' = 14.14 FT ÷ 40'
= .3535
∴ ANGLE 'D' = 19°28'

NOTICE THAT ANGLE 'B' IS EQUAL TO 90° MINUS ANGLE A
or ANGLE B = 90° - 55°
= 35°

THEREFORE, ANGLE C
= 90° - 35° - 19°28' = 35°32'

TENSION IN THE RAISING ROPE CAN BE EASILY FOUND. LET:
SIN ANGLE D = 140 lb ÷ TENSION
or TENSION = 140 lbs ÷ SIN 19°28'
= 140 lbs ÷ .3535
= 396 lbs

-63-

mine, check over what I did; maybe I've made a mistake! Be sure to let me know if you do find an error on my part, or just can't get yours to agree!

We've just gotta throw in one more problem, so let's say that the tank runs out of gas just when the tower reaches an angle of 45°. The The neighbor leaves the tank in gear and puts on the emergency brake (these prevent the forces exerted by the pole from pulling the vehicle backward) and runs off to get some gas. So, while he's doin' that, let's look at what the lift angle is, and how much tension is on the rope at this angle (see Problem 9).

Once the truck is gassed (you'd be gassed, too, if someone filled you up with high octane), the raising commences again and continues until the tower is upright. Guy wires are secured all around, the ladder-type type gin pole is removed, and the vehicle is removed from the yard. Everything's hunky-dory, right? Well, sorta, anyway. The wife ran off with the neighbor man and our man watches the big bird that decided to take roots in (or, rather, on) his birdhouse. Sorry, I can't think of a moral to this story!

The Gin Pole

As indicated in the last section, the purpose of a gin pole is to give a lifting force to a pull such as that exerted by a truck on a raising rope (or cable). The taller the gin pole, the more angle it will give to the raising cable, and hence, the greater the lift angle. If the gin pole were infinitely high, the raising cable would be almost straight up (like it's being lifted by a helicopter) and all of the pull would be a lifting force (a hypothetical extreme).

In reality, a gin pole need not be over 20 feet high; I've seen drawings which depict the raising of a 130-foot tower with a gin pole only 20-feet high, so you'll be quite safe with that as a maximum. I don't know what the minimum height of a gin pole could be and still work satisfactorily, but I wouldn't use anything less than 15 feet.

What you use for a gin pole requires some careful consideration; its greatest requirement is that it not bend or break when subjected to compressive forces (which work mostly through its axis -- see Fig. 3-11). I've used a 20-foot section of Wincharger tower (for a 54-foot, 3-leg tower) and it worked fine. I wouldn't hesitate to use a telephone pole, or a 4 x 4 beam, or maybe even a 3-inch diameter pipe, but I'd think twice about anything else that comes to mind.

When you've found a likely candidate for the gin pole, you must make one of those decisions that I'll be throwing at you occasionally: To secure the tower-raising cable to the gin pole (Fig. 3-12), or to run the cable through a pulley that's secured to the gin pole (Fig. 3-13). I have worked with the second method only, so I cannot personally vouch for the other, but I have seen it in drawings and see no reason why it wouldn't work.

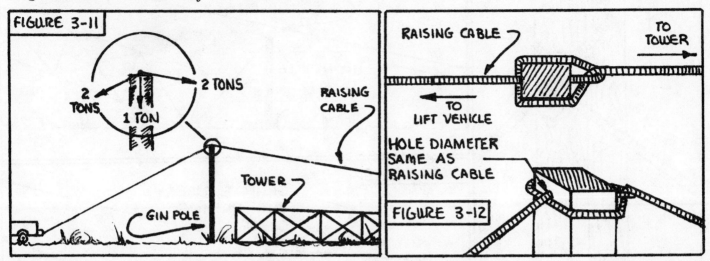

It's important to understand the implications of doing it one way or the other, however, and to understand what will happen to the gin pole once the tower has been raised to the point where the raising cable will "clear" the gin pole (see Fig. 3-14), beyond which it is no longer required. The tower angle that must be achieved to reach this point depends on many factors -- the tower length, the gin pole height, the distance between the tower base and the base of the gin pole, etc. -- but the effect is still the same. Use of the tethered method or pulleyed method depends on a number of factors, some of which we have not yet discussed, so the decision cannot be made at this point. Keep the following relationships in mind, though, as you are provided with that information.

1. With the tethered method, the gin pole will be "raised" with the tower (lifted into the air by the raising line -- see Fig. 3-15); you won't want to use this method if you have selected a heavy gin pole, unless you like the idea of a few hundred pounds of gin pole dangling from the raising line twenty feet up in the air at the end of the tower raising. If you're using the pulleyed method, the gin pole will just slide along the raising cable, but here again, you will have to take some precautions, (like securing a line to it) or it may come whizzing down the line and collide with the truck. This is a real no-no if you're raising a light tower and you're using people to raise it instead of a truck.

2. Either method will require the use of guy wires to keep the gin pole from toppling over to either side during the raise. The placement of these guy wires is not significant in the case of the pulleyed method; the gin pole will not need to move (and, in fact, should be secured to prevent it from doing so), so the wires can be hooked as shown in Fig. 3-16 (at least three will be required just to keep it from falling over before the actual tower-raising begins). The tethered method, however, requires that the top of gin pole be permitted free movement (in the direction of the pull) during the raise; the wires used to prevent side-fall must be located directly to the sides of the gin pole (somewhere along a line which is drawn through the base and perpendicular to the tower axis -- see Fig. 3-17) if they are to remain snug (and not loosen or tighten further) during the raise. Obviously, the

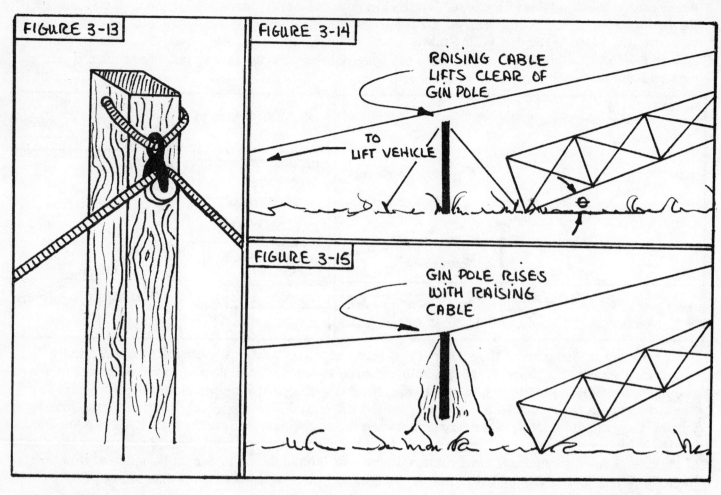

FIGURE 3-13

FIGURE 3-14

RAISING CABLE LIFTS CLEAR OF GIN POLE

TO LIFT VEHICLE

FIGURE 3-15

GIN POLE RISES WITH RAISING CABLE

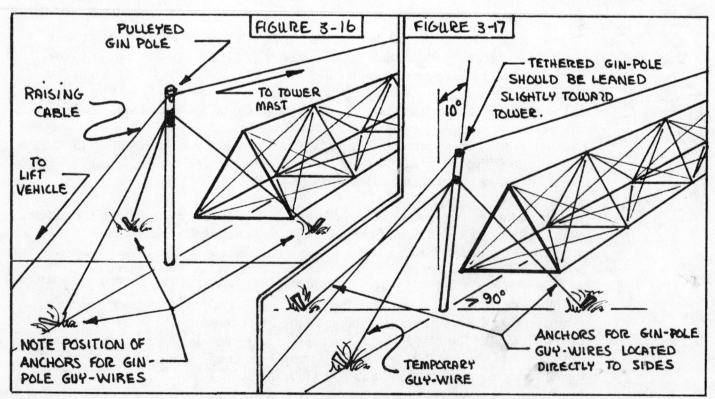

FIGURE 3-16

PULLEYED GIN POLE

RAISING CABLE

TO LIFT VEHICLE

TO TOWER MAST

NOTE POSITION OF ANCHORS FOR GIN-POLE GUY-WIRES

FIGURE 3-17

TETHERED GIN-POLE SHOULD BE LEANED SLIGHTLY TOWARD TOWER.

10°

90°

TEMPORARY GUY-WIRE

ANCHORS FOR GIN-POLE GUY-WIRES LOCATED DIRECTLY TO SIDES

gin pole will not stay upright with just two wires, so a third, temporary guy wire can be used to keep it upright (if it's leaned as shown) until the raising commences.

3. If a pulley is used, care should be exercised in securing it to the gin pole to insure that it is not going to slip or break under the compressive forces previously mentioned. As indicated in Fig. 3-11, the compressive forces are very large so don't get too casual when you make this tie-up.

The base of the gin pole should be placed on a hard and level surface so that it does not dig in or canter to the side during its use in the tower-raising. If you've got soft ground, you might place a piece of 2 x 6 under it to help the situation. Insure that all tie-ups are tight before the raise; the gin pole may only be used for the first one-third of the raise, but its proper performance is a critical factor. Negligence here will unquestionably snap the raising cable or create enuff slack that a crashed tower is the very least that can happen!

The Raising Cable

One of the more important components of the tower-raising equipment is the raising cable itself; it must be strong enuff to do the job and then some (if you want any kind of safety factor). How strong it needs to be depends on the height of the tower and its weight. If you're buying cable for the job, it won't be too difficult to get that info (unless you're getting it surplus), but if you've got a piece of sumthin' lyin' around the place that turns out to be long enuff to be used, you may not know what it is rated to pull or lift. Whatever the situation, it might be helpful to understand that the maximum tension the cable will experience (during the lift) will occur at the beginning, or start, of lift. This is a very neat safety item (unless you are lowering a tower), becuz you can assume that whatever cable is used will do the job. Then, before the raise starts (or just as it starts) you give it the "acid test." If it's going to break, it should break immediately and you will drop the tower a few feet at the most. Mind you, I am not recommending this method. If it does break, you're going to have some highly dangerous cable whipping around for a few seconds. I mention it here primarily to indicate that you shouldn't get into a frame of mind of trusting even brand new cable; it only takes one small kink, or nick, to create the possibility of breakage, and under the stress conditions of raisin' a tower, it must be considered a certainty. A closer look at some of the drawings in this chapter should tell you one thing -- tension in the raising cable will be decreasing very rapidly as you lift a tower (becuz, if you remember, the lift angle is increasing) so, if it doesn't break within the first few feet, the possibility of its breaking will be decreasing very rapidly thereafter.

Cable is rated in two ways: what it will lift (in lbs or tons) with a steady pull and what it will lift rapidly (like if it were snapped). This means that a specific cable may be able to lift several tons normally (if done slowly) but will break, if snapped, while it is lifting only one-fourth of a ton. This has other meanings when a cable is used for tower raising, so let's deviate a moment, and discuss them.

If you have a tower that weighs 2 tons, do not assume that you need only find a cable that will lift two tons. With the kind of lift angle most of us will have initially, the tension on the raisin' cable initially will be many times the weight of the tower. It is a rule of thumb that a lifting force of one-half the tower's weight is required at the top, but this is the situation if it's pushed from beneath or pulled from above. Becuz this can't be done when using a gin pole, a minimum of 4 times this force is rule of thumb for the cable at the low lift angle. That means, therefore, that the cable should have a minimum rating of twice the weight of the tower. A safety factor of two is considered rule of thumb, so it should be rated in pull 4 times the weight of the tower. For the lift angle that will result with a 20-foot gin pole and 60-foot tower, this is probably sufficient; for a tower twice that length (120-footer) this will be doubled again.

I've already indicated that the normal situation will be that the maximum tension exerted on the raising cable will occur at the start of raise; if you check out some of the drawings, you'll see that it will only be toward the end of the raise that the tension will be small enuff in the cable for it to be able to sustain (that means survive) a sudden snap, or jerk, on the cable. This can easily occur if something slips a little, or if the person operating the truck pops the clutch. It can help ease a troubled mind to say the probability of breakage decreases as the tower angle increases, but bear in mind that "probability" is a description of a finite number of things doing something a certain percentage of the time of a whole bunch of times that it's done. This is very much of a mind thing, and has little to do with real events (as losers at casino tables will vividly attest) so don't let it fool ya!

With this in mind (especially if you have a cable of unknown ratings), you can perform a little experiment. When you're ready to lift the tower, take the slack out of the cable and then pop the clutch on the truck. This will probably kill the engine on the vehicle, but the tower should jump up a little and hold (or just fall back into place). If it doesn't break, chances are real good that the cable will be able to take a steady pull. Now run a second test. Pull on the raising cable until the tower has lifted a foot and then block the wheels on the lift vehicle so that the tower can't go back all the way down. Then pop the clutch. This will cause the tower to raise up a smidgen and then bounce up and down a bit. If it can do this, it will probably survive a snap during the raise. If it does break, it still might be useful for a raise (becuz the steady pull didn't break it and you know the snap rating is of a lower value) but I'd have to be desperate before I would use it. At any rate, now is the time to be thinkin' 'bout who you're gonna get to operate the lift vehicle -- they should be a real smoothie on the clutch and not someone likely to get rough on it when excited or pressured.

Steel cable is not the only thing that can be used for the raising cable; I'm certain that a sturdy hemp, nylon, or whatever would do nicely. These are generally rated in steady pull; they may indeed have a snap rating but I've never seen one so indicated, so watch out! Without any tensile strength specifications, I'd use one-half inch (maybe) or larger, but I'd sure inspect it well for rot or fraying, and would assuredly give it the "snap" test previously described. I admit my ignorance about rope, and hesitate to provide tables of "ratings" for various kinds and sizes. It doesn't make sense to provide someone (who is also ignorant on the subject) with a false sense of security about such things; it does make sense for you to find it out for yourself or to protect yourself (by allowing for it) if you can't find out. Enuff said.

If the info is of any use, we used a 5/16-inch steel cable (with a hemp center) on Jim's 54-foot tower (a three-leg monstrosity which must have weighed 2 tons). We got the cable at a nearby surplus place (450 feet for, I think, $80) and we experienced no difficulty with it and had no indication that it was under any severe stress.

Securing the Cable to the Tower

There are two methods of securing the raising cable to the tower: Direct (see Fig. 3-18) and using a pulleyed sling (see Fig. 3-19). The pulleyed-sling method seems to be intended for use with towers over 60 feet in height; the only time that I've used this method was to raise a 40-foot Wincharger-type tower which had a Wincharger attached to it at the time, and the sling did not "come into effect" (a pulleyed sling is a physics trick which is supposed to fool the raising cable, making it appear as though a shorter tower is being raised). If you use the pulleyed sling for your very tall tower, connect the top of the sling within ten feet of the top of the tower and the bottom of the sling within 30 feet of the top; the raising cable attaches to a pulley which is allowed free travel along the sling. If you are making a direct connection to the tower, the raising cable should be secured at a point about one-sixth of the height of the tower down from the top of the tower (i.e., for a 60-foot tower, that would be 10 feet from the top). For steel cable, use cable clamps to connect the wire to the tower; for rope, tie a decent knot (or get someone to do it that can especially if you are using nylon rope), or you'll risk it coming undone during the raise or not being able to get it undone after the raise!

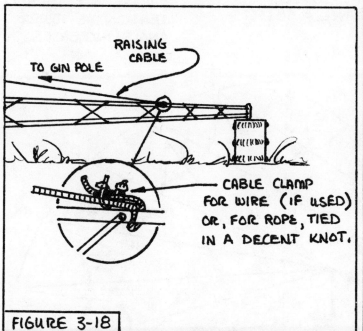

FIGURE 3-18

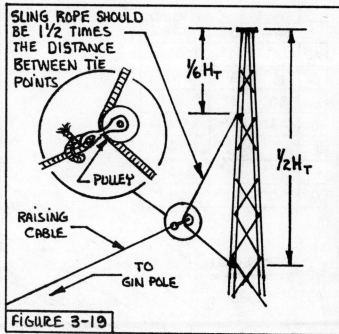

FIGURE 3-19

Raising Cable Length

Next question for the raising cable is: How long? Well . . . that depends (wouldn't ya know it!) on the tower's height, the amount of room you have for the vehicle to move around in, what obstacles might interfere with the raising cable's movements, and whether or not you are going to use a pulley-type mechanical advantage during the lift. Okay, that's a lot of "depends" so let's go thru some basic relationships.

1. The lift vehicle should be as far away from the tower (initially) as possible. While this will have no relative importance at the beginning of the raise, it will allow for a rapid increase in the lift angle as the tower goes up (see Fig. 3-20) and you should by now know the importance of a large lift angle. A compromise is in order here; increased distance between tower and lift vehicle (which defines any vehicle being used to exert the pull on the raising cable) will make for a direct increase in the length (and expense) of the raising cable.

2. The raising cable must be allowed free movement during the raise. Here's another one of those mental images that you're going to have to conjure up; if your vehicle goes between a few trees, it might clear but will the raising cable (as it rises) also clear? Are there power lines or telephone wires in the way? The best way

to check for these possibilities (if they exist at all) is to determine the total distance that the truck will travel during the raise (from start to finish), put yourself at the point where the truck will begin initially, and walk along the route for that distance, looking back and up (to where the top of an imaginary tower will be at the end of the raise). It's no fun to get a tower up most of the way to find that something will interfere with the cable; by the same token, it's lousy to go thru some of the extra effort to compensate for an obstacle which looks as though it will interfere when it really wouldn't. Either way, it is worth the effort to check it out.

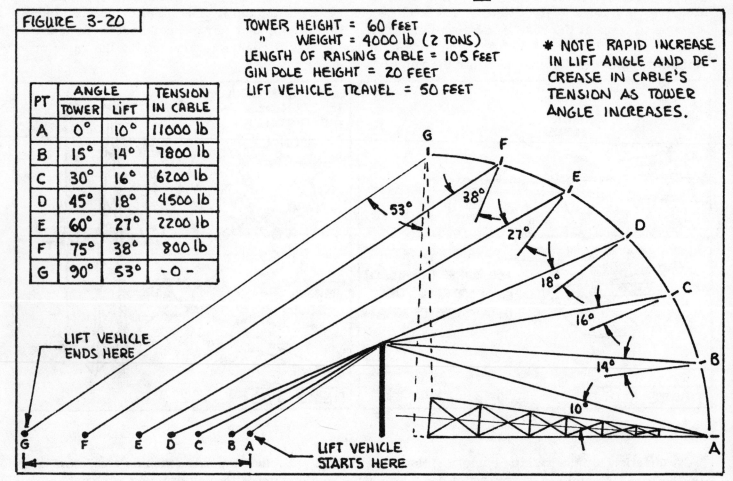

FIGURE 3-20

TOWER HEIGHT = 60 FEET
  " WEIGHT = 4000 lb (2 TONS)
LENGTH OF RAISING CABLE = 105 FEET
GIN POLE HEIGHT = 20 FEET
LIFT VEHICLE TRAVEL = 50 FEET

* NOTE RAPID INCREASE IN LIFT ANGLE AND DECREASE IN CABLE'S TENSION AS TOWER ANGLE INCREASES.

PT	ANGLE		TENSION IN CABLE
	TOWER	LIFT	
A	0°	10°	11000 lb
B	15°	14°	7800 lb
C	30°	16°	6200 lb
D	45°	18°	4500 lb
E	60°	27°	2200 lb
F	75°	38°	800 lb
G	90°	53°	- 0 -

LIFT VEHICLE ENDS HERE

LIFT VEHICLE STARTS HERE

3. The lift vehicle must be able to move through a distance sufficient to allow the tower to come full upright. A seemingly obvious point, but how do you determine this? Fig. 3-21 shows one way (with only a few small guestimations) whereby you can come close enuff to determining what distance your vehicle will travel in your situation.

4. There are several ways in which a lift vehicle can be relieved of having to exert the full force (or raising-cable tension) required to raise the tower; one that should come to mind is to use two vehicles. If each vehicle is separately tied to the tower (by a raising cable) this unnecessarily complicates the situation; as well, the actual raising will probably be quite jerky (and the strain on the cable more severe) because the vehicles would have a hard time of pulling exactly equal with one another through the entire lift. A simpler arrangement that accounts for this problem is shown in Fig. 3-22; any momentary slackening of the pull from either vehicle will be instantly taken up by the other.

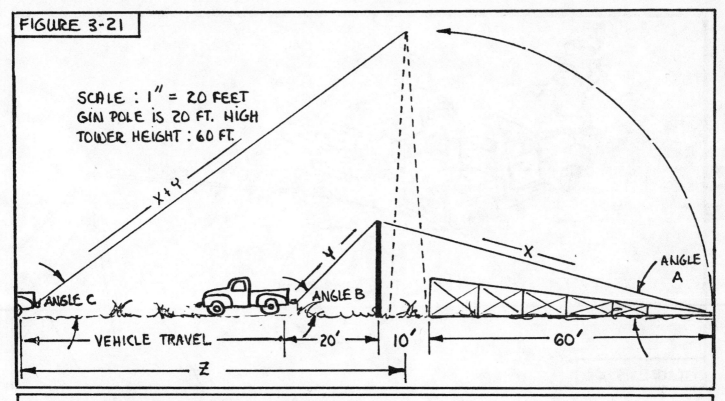

FIGURE 3-21

SCALE : 1" = 20 FEET
GIN POLE IS 20 FT. HIGH
TOWER HEIGHT : 60 FT.

X+Y

Y

X

ANGLE A

ANGLE C

ANGLE B

VEHICLE TRAVEL

20'   10'   60'

Z

▷ RULER METHOD OF FINDING VEHICLE TRAVEL
1. DRAW THE SET-UP TO SCALE.
2. MEASURE X AND Y AND ADD; THIS IS THE RAISING CABLE LENGTH.
3. PLACE ONE END OF THE RULER AT THE TOWER MAST (WHERE IT WILL BE WHEN UPRIGHT) AND SWING THE OTHER END UNTIL THIS MEASURED DISTANCE INTERSECTS A POINT ON THE GROUND LINE. THEN MEASURE THE DISTANCE FROM THIS POINT TO THE POINT WHERE THE VEHICLE STARTED. MULTIPLY THIS NUMBER OF INCHES TIMES THE SCALE USED; THIS IS THE DISTANCE THE LIFT VEHICLE WILL TRAVEL DURING THE RAISE.

▷ TRIG. METHOD OF FINDING VEHICLE TRAVEL
1. TAN. ANGLE A = 20'/70' = .2857
2. ANGLE A ≈ 16°
3. SIN 16° = 20'/X or X = 20/SIN 16°
4. X = 20/.2756 = 72.5' ←
5. TAN ANGLE B = 20'/20' = 1 or
6. ANGLE B = 45°
7. SIN 45° = 20'/Y or Y = 20/SIN 45°
8. Y = 20'/.707 = 28.3' ←
9. X + Y = 72.5' + 28.3' = 101 FEET *
10. SIN ANGLE C = 60'/101' = .5940
11. ANGLE C ≈ 36.5°
12. TAN 36.5° = 60'/Z or Z = 60'/TAN 36.5°
13. Z = 60'/.7400 = 81.1 FEET
14. VEHICLE TRAVEL = Z - 20' - 5' **
15. VEHICLE TRAVEL = 81.1' - 25' = <u>56.1 FEET</u>

35°
√.002
?
A
X ÷
(.707)
.3535
SIN 19°

* LENGTH OF RAISING CABLE
** DISTANCE FROM GIN POLE TO CENTER OF TOWER BASE (WHEN TOWER IN RAISED POSITION)

-71-

FIGURE 3-22

If you have only one vehicle available for use as a lift vehicle and it's not a truck or tractor but rather a VW bus, small car, horse, or a buncha friends, then consider using some kind of "mechanical advantage" along the lines of a block-and-tackle. Fig. 3-23 illustrates the use of the simplest mechanical advantage (of two times); this cuts the pulling force required by the lift vehicle in half (provided the two lines are parallel). You won't be getting something for nothing, though; you have to have a very strong anchor at hand such as a large tree or tree stump or a stationary vehicle able to take at least one-half the required lifting force. As well, for each factor of mechanical advantage used, the distance the lift vehicle will travel is increased -- by that same factor. So . . . for a mechanical advantage of two (times), the vehicle must travel twice as far as it would travel if no mechanical advantage was used; for an advantage of three, three times as far, etc. This means the raising cable will also have to be longer -- that's right, you guessed it -- by the same factor.

If you use a mechanical advantage, be sure to hook it up the right way. In raising Jim's 54-footer, we tried to use a mechanical advantage of two but we got in too much of a hurry and hooked it up backwards (this gave us a mechanical-disadvantage of two) and almost burned the clutch in his truck trying to lift the tower. It just wouldn't lift. We figured it out, re-arranged the lines, and proceeded uneventfully.

5. If lift vehicle travel is severely restricted, or obstacles abound in the intended direction of pull, consider using a pivot anchor (see Fig. 3-24). It will have to be very secure as it will generally experience forces that could be (depending on the angle) as much as twice the raising-cable tension. We used this method in raising Jim's 54-footer (in addition to using a mechanical advantage of two) and it worked admirably. A truck was used as the pivot anchor; it was braked, blocked, and staked to the ground so thoroughly that I thought it would probably be left anchored as a monument to the tower's raising. There is one disadvantage, though, in using

a pivot anchor; it does not allow the lift angle to increase as quickly as a non-pivoted pull would. This is, however, of little concern if it's a situation where the tower can't otherwise be raised, so it's just an observational note.

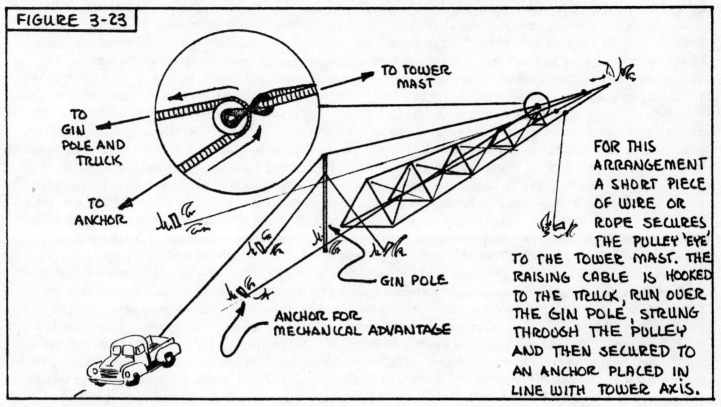

FIGURE 3-23

TO TOWER MAST

TO GIN POLE AND TRUCK

TO ANCHOR

GIN POLE

ANCHOR FOR MECHANICAL ADVANTAGE

FOR THIS ARRANGEMENT A SHORT PIECE OF WIRE OR ROPE SECURES THE PULLEY 'EYE' TO THE TOWER MAST. THE RAISING CABLE IS HOOKED TO THE TRUCK, RUN OVER THE GIN POLE, STRUNG THROUGH THE PULLEY AND THEN SECURED TO AN ANCHOR PLACED IN LINE WITH TOWER AXIS.

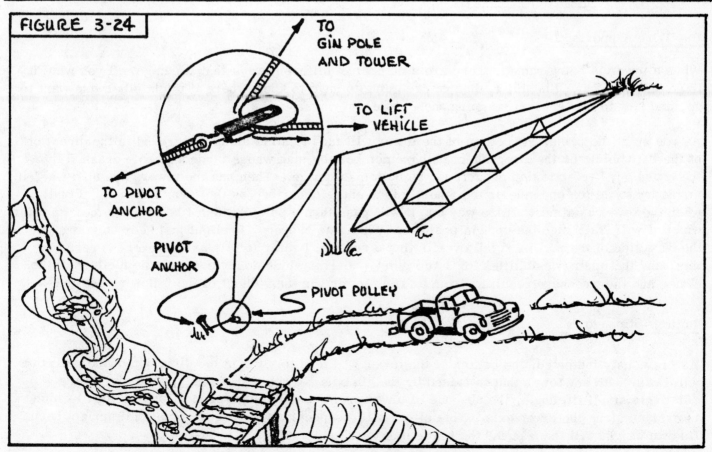

FIGURE 3-24

TO GIN POLE AND TOWER

TO LIFT VEHICLE

TO PIVOT ANCHOR

PIVOT ANCHOR

PIVOT PULLEY

This is a lot of "if's" to figure out, so get out some paper; there's no sense in strugglin' with it in your head. Get a ruler, protractor, and graph paper and make a series of drawings; this will help make the situation clearer and the decisions more sound. One of the drawings should be a m ap which shows the tower site, the position of the tower, and the surrounding area; note all trees, houses, garden plots, ditches, fences, or anything that would represent an obstacle to a vehicle, or the raising cable. All of the drawings should be "to scale"; for an accurate representation of these items in the map, use a long tape measure (or a consistent stride in walking off distances) to find the distance to each of these objects from some reference, say the tower base. (Sighting along a properly-used protractor will give bearings which will make the maps even more accurate.) Do a good job on this map; it will be used for plotting out the varied possibilities for raising the tower, among other things. Then make a drawing for: configurations for using the mechanical advantage, ways to route the raising cable, places to plant the various anchors, placement of the pivot anchor (where applicable), etc. Make more than one drawing if it's starting to get cluttered. So far, you've made top views; now you'll want to make some side-view drawings of the way it will look before the raise and after. If you draw them to scale (like letting one inch equal ten feet), then you'll get a very close approximation of the lengths of certain guy wires or the raising cable, and can avoid having to brush up on trigonometry to mathematically arrive at the lengths. Tricky, huh? This will quickly let you know if a certain power line is going to represent a problem if it's done this way or that, and it will let you know the best way to use what you've got. All of these drawings are extremely helpful, so don't underrate the idea of making them. When it comes time to start making decisions, it's always helpful to have other people informed of what's going on becuz the suggestions, comments, questions, answers, etc., will be most welcome. Unless one person is going to do all the setup, it will be a master plan that all can work from when the time comes. And finally, when all is readied and the magic day arrives, it can be used in the pre-lift pow-wow (for all of those folks involved in the tower-raising), letting everyone know who will be where!

Guy Wire Supports

When a tower is being raised, there are a number of different ways that it can go. If you want it to go only one way (like up!), then you're going to have to know where it might otherwise want to go, and how to prevent it from going these different ways.

As you start the raise, the bottom of the tower will tend to slide along the ground in the direction of the lift vehicle or the direction of pull (remember the man whose birdhouse pole crashed into the house?); I refer to this occurrence as bottom-slippage. Then, as the tower goes up a way, it might try to fall on one side or the other; this event is described by the term side-fall. Finally, when the tower is almost all the way up, it will pass thru a point (which I refer to as teeter) after which it will "fall" into the upright position. When this happens, it might just keep on going (in the direction of the pull) and fall over in that direction; I refer to this as end-over. Preventing this, and the other possibilities for a "downer" (a term which describes both the feelings of the owner and the wreckage resulting from a fallen tower) is the subject of the following sections.

Bottom-Slippage

As previously indicated, the bottom of the tower will tend to slide in the direction of the pull; this will occur with any tower that is raised by the gin pole method and is due, primarily, to the relatively small lift angle, the absence of tower angle, and the high proportion of the pull which is exerted along the tower axis. This effect will disappear as the tower comes full upright becuz its own weight will then "push" the tower into the ground.

The simplest means of preventing this occurrence is to anchor the bottom of the tower. While this can be simply done at the base by driving stakes into the ground, this does not afford much protection. Why? As the tower is raised, it will pivot about one or two legs and it is easy for the pivoting action to cause the bottom of the tower to ride up and over the stakes. A far more effective means of anchoring the bottom is to attach wires to the two legs which will provide the pivot (see Fig. 3-25); for a single-leg tower, only one leg is available and, therefore, only one wire is attached. The other end of these wires may then be secured to an anchor located along the tower axis and in the direction of the top of the tower (as it lies horizontally). These anchors and wires must be very strong, as together they must be able to withstand the brunt of the tension on the raising cable at lift-off, so use the same size and kind of cable used for the raising cable itself.

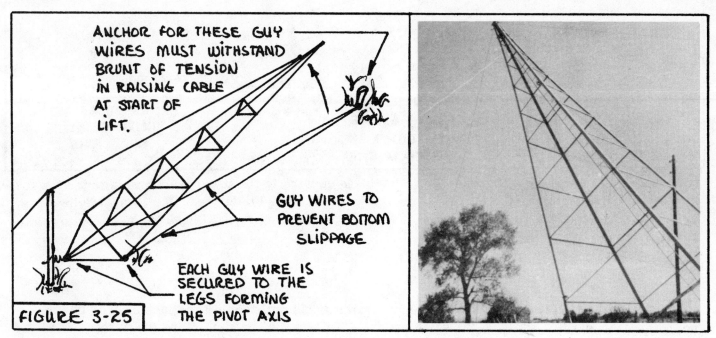

FIGURE 3-25

ANCHOR FOR THESE GUY WIRES MUST WITHSTAND BRUNT OF TENSION IN RAISING CABLE AT START OF LIFT.

GUY WIRES TO PREVENT BOTTOM SLIPPAGE

EACH GUY WIRE IS SECURED TO THE LEGS FORMING THE PIVOT AXIS

Side-Fall

During the raise, a tower can fall to either side (perpendicular to the pull). While it is more likely to occur with a narrow-base tower (one that has no base width -- like a single-leg tower), it can occur with any tower. This is due to soft ground under the base , a change in the direction of the pull (or a pull that isn't perfectly aligned to begin with), and the effect of wind. It is prevented from happening by attaching guy wires to each side of the tower and securing them to anchors in the ground (also located to the sides of the tower); in this manner, a guy wire on one side prevents it from falling to the opposite side and vice versa.

If you don't want to be changing tension on them during the raise, you must locate them along a line drawn through the pivot axis of the tower and perpendicular to the tower axis (and direction of pull). This sounds a lot more complicated than it really is (see Fig. 3-26). They should be located at a distance from the base of the tower of not less than one-half of the tower height, but they may be located at a much greater distance if you happen to have sumthin' out there that will do the job (like a fencepost or a dead tractor) and it is along that line drawn through the pivot axis of the tower. Don't fudge! If it isn't in line, don't use it!

The guy wires used to prevent side-fall must be able to withstand at least two hundred pounds of pull (such as that exerted by two men) but a safety factor of 500 lbs is recommended. These wires should be attached to the tower at a point about one-fourth of its height from the top. As the wires will be "following" the tower as it is raised, they should be positioned so that they are not interfered with during this movement. When we raised Jim's 40-footer, we could not position one of the side guy wires to clear an anchor line for a nearby utility pole; consequently, we had to pause during the raise to secure a temporary guy wire, remove the existing guy wire (see photo), get it around the utility line that was causing the interference, re-tie the guy wire, and remove the

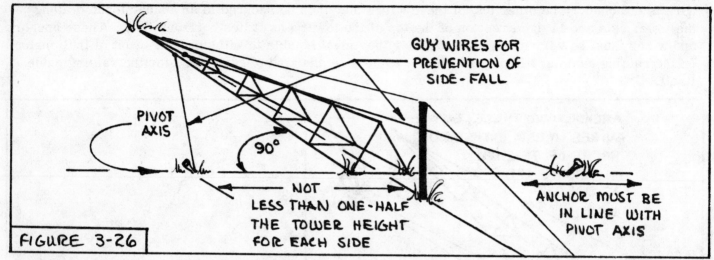

FIGURE 3-26

GUY WIRES FOR PREVENTION OF SIDE-FALL

PIVOT AXIS

90°

NOT LESS THAN ONE-HALF THE TOWER HEIGHT FOR EACH SIDE

ANCHOR MUST BE IN LINE WITH PIVOT AXIS

back-up wire. Becuz we'd forgotten to tie the back-up wire to the tower before we started the raise, I ended up having to climb the tower. This didn't bother me (I didn't feel like I was defying death or anything), but I think it might bother others, so plan ahead or you'll have to lower the tower to do it!

End-Over

When a tower is nearly upright, it will reach a point that I call teeter (for lack of ever having heard another word to describe the same event). This is the position where the center of gravity of the tower is directly above the pivot axis of the tower; at this precise point, it   "balances". If it's a single-leg tower, it will occur when the tower is fully upright (like you'd balance a pencil). If you have a 3-leg, 4-leg, or octahedron tower (which can be thought of as having 3 legs), it will occur before the tower reaches vertical position. After it has reached this point, it will (if completely freed) just "fall" into the upright position. If you need some proof of this, try this little experiment:

Get a drinking glass (preferably one made of plastic, or sumthin' unbreakable) and put it on a level surface. Use one finger and slowly begin pulling it to one side until it's just balanced, and let go. Only three things can happen. The thing will stay balanced, or it will fall over on its side, or it will "fall" into an upright position, rocking back and forth until it comes to a vertical rest. When you balanced the glass, it was at teeter. And if you let it go and it fell into an upright position, it rocked over to the opposite side just a bit (but not enuff to fall, probably). Well, a tower will do the same thing as the drinking glass did but when it rocks over to the opposite side, there is a very high probability that it is going to keep on going, falling over on its side in the direction of the pull. Unlike the drinking glass, which will rarely fall to the other side, the tower has the weight of the raisin' cable on that side, and that and gravity are all that it needs to get past the teeter point on that side.

Well, it's easily prevented. Just add in another guy wire, attaching one end near the top of the tower and the other end to an anchor (which can be the same one that's used to prevent bottom-slippage). Like the guy wires used to prevent side-fall, it needs to be able to hold onto a few hundred pounds, but figure 500 lbs and play it safe. Its length is determined by one of the three methods described in Problem 6.

In raising both of Jim's towers, we used a truck as an anchor for the guy wires used to prevent bottom-slippage and end-over (see photos). In addition, we used a "Power-Pull" (a small, hand-cranked, portable winch) to ease the towers into their final, upright positions as they approached "teeter." (We were sure that we couldn't stand to see them fall into place and hear the end-over prevention wire twang as it went taut.) Consider doing this to ease the tower into vertical position.

Additional Notes

Guy wires will be running hither-and-yon by the time you're ready to lift the tower into place, so learn well what they do and where they go or your mind will be tripping over them like your feet probably will. It may take a bit of mental gymnastics to see what will be happening, but its worth should not be underestimated; working with a few tons of tower can be hair-raising. Knowing that you've taken care of 99% of the "things that can go wrong" is immensely helpful in preventing ulcers and cardiac arrest during the actual lift. In raising the first of the two towers at Jim's place, we had one of those 1% things occur -- the legs buckled (the tower was missing a few vital pieces at the base and their absence went unnoticed). We had gotten it up to a tower angle of about 45° when this happened, but we merely stopped the raise, looked over the situation, and then lowered it back down to repair the damage. Panic or "do something!" reactions to these little mishaps can have grave results.

Guy wires and anchors are used to prevent any (or all) of these events from happenin' to you during the raise. I've seen drawings where people were used instead of the anchors, but I don't hold to the idea of this alternative to the affixed-in-ground anchor. First off, it's askin' for trouble; even a simple, small anchor will have more restraining capability than a person, and will hold while a person goes skittering across the ground. If everything goes right, most of these guy wires will have only a small amount of tension on them (so it's possible to use a person), but that's why you want to use the fixed anchors -- for that going-wrong situation. The fixed anchor will keep the tower precisely where it should be (and thus preventing an unwanted tension in the guy wire), whereas a person will find it difficult to know how much force to exert (without a reference) and, once the tower is out of position, the forces required to get it back grow much greater very quickly. And the person on the other side is holding tight so you'd have to fight that. Geesus, that's a nightmare! No thanks!

As far as I'm concerned, you only start the raise when everything that can be accounted for, is. So that leaves only the freakish kinds of thing that can happen. If what you have provisioned for won't take care of those, there's nothin' you can do . . . so don't try. That's what kills, folks. And if you've got guy wires and people all over the place, the odds are real good that somebody's going to be under that tower when it comes down. Towers are expendable -- people aren't!

Pre-Raise Preparation

It might seem like it's time to start talking about actually raising the tower, but there's still a lot to do. Some of this you may have already done, but it's included here as a checklist of sorts for those that haven't even gotten a tower yet. I've probably forgotten a few things, so don't substitute it for your own head. The Pre-Raise is divided into three sections -- anchors, final tower preparation, and the raising equipment itself.

Anchors

Once the tower has been procured and the site for it selected, extensive thought should be given to the manner in which it will be secured for the years to come. If it's a single-leg tower that you will be using, you have little option; the tower should be secured with guy wires in the manner described for single-leg towers (as shown in Fig. 3-4). The type of anchor to use will vary depending on various aspects of your situation and the soil condition, so I have included drawings of the types that I am familiar with (see Fig. 3-27). The single-stake type is recommended for use in the raising process only; it is sufficient for the guy wires used to prevent side-fall or end-over. It may be used successfully, as well, for temporarily securing a tower which is awaiting final cementing of its legs (after which these guy wires would be removed); it is not recommended for permanent guy-wire anchoring. The multi-stake type can be used for a permanent guy-wire anchor but only if the soil conditions are such that the ground is very hard as they will eventually loosen if not. If you don't want to worry or constantly recheck guy wires using this anchor, don't install it. The Wincharger manual recommends the spiral-type anchor when making permanent guy-wire installations, but I would refrain from using it if soft ground represents your situation. The flat-plate type is suitable for most permanent guy-wire anchoring, but insured that a proper depth is reached if installing this type. The auto-tire type is included becuz of its possibility for use in this situation; but I would recommend its use only where the soil is aliking desert sand conditions (this is derived from an old trick for winching a vehicle out of sand in the desert).

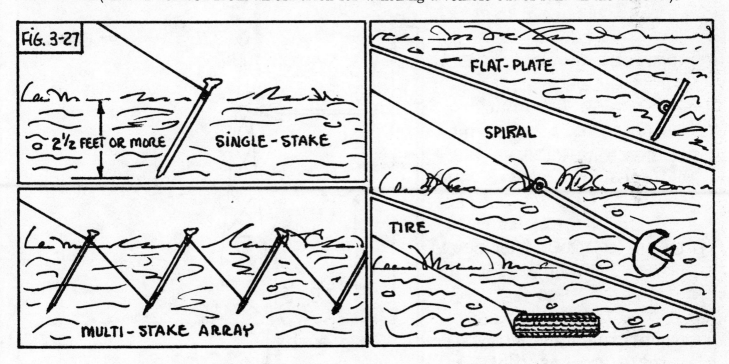

For the 3-leg, 4-leg, and octahedron towers, the legs may be cemented and guy wires altogether not used (I'll include some information here on how to do this), but for the most part you're going to have to do some research in this area. Cement is neat stuff, but in the hands of amateurs it comes out just like that -- amateurish! Know what you're doing! If you don't, study up on it extensively, or get someone that does know (or has done it before) to do it. Check 'em out thoroughly; you may be enlisting the aid of another amateur. A few poured patios is not a good indication that they know what they're doing. I've never cemented tower legs before (although I will be doing three towers in the near future) so I can't give you any specific advice beyond what's included here; I just don't hold any expertise in the area at present.

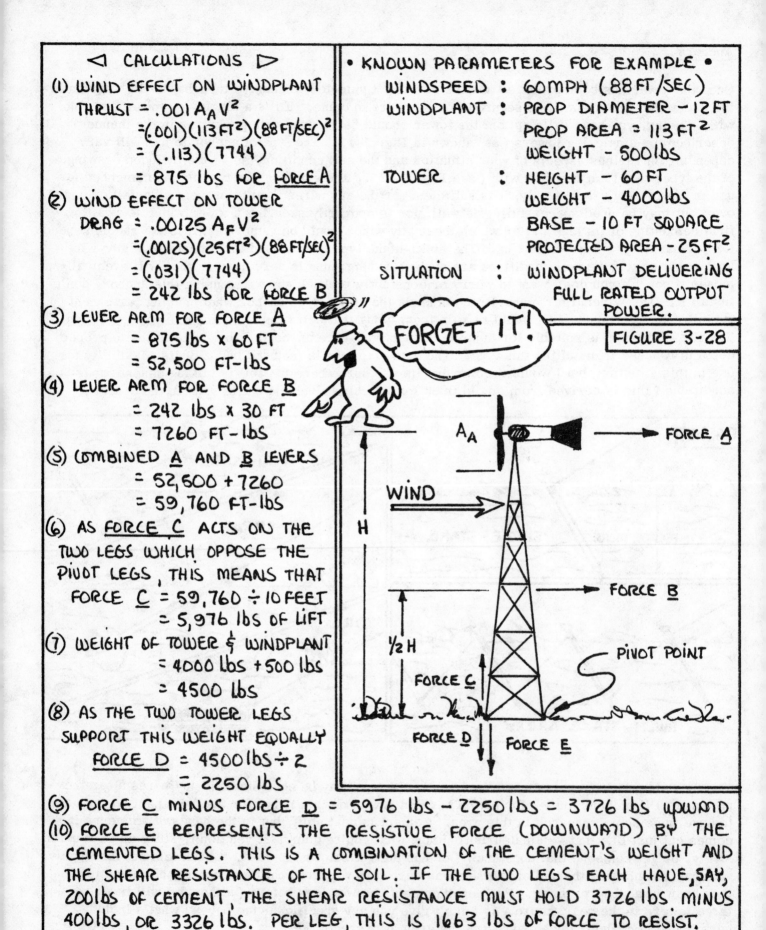

◁ CALCULATIONS ▷

(1) WIND EFFECT ON WINDPLANT

THRUST $= .001 A_A V^2$

$= (.001)(113 FT^2)(88 FT/SEC)^2$

$= (.113)(7744)$

$= 875$ lbs FOR FORCE A

(2) WIND EFFECT ON TOWER

DRAG $= .00125 A_F V^2$

$= (.00125)(25 FT^2)(88 FT/SEC)^2$

$= (.031)(7744)$

$= 242$ lbs FOR FORCE B

(3) LEVER ARM FOR FORCE A

$= 875$ lbs × 60 FT

$= 52,500$ FT-lbs

(4) LEVER ARM FOR FORCE B

$= 242$ lbs × 30 FT

$= 7260$ FT-lbs

(5) COMBINED A AND B LEVERS

$= 52,500 + 7260$

$= 59,760$ FT-lbs

(6) AS FORCE C ACTS ON THE TWO LEGS WHICH OPPOSE THE PIVOT LEGS, THIS MEANS THAT FORCE C $= 59,760 ÷ 10$ FEET

$= 5,976$ lbs OF LIFT

(7) WEIGHT OF TOWER & WINDPLANT

$= 4000$ lbs + 500 lbs

$= 4500$ lbs

(8) AS THE TWO TOWER LEGS SUPPORT THIS WEIGHT EQUALLY FORCE D $= 4500$ lbs ÷ 2

$= 2250$ lbs

• KNOWN PARAMETERS FOR EXAMPLE •

WINDSPEED : 60 MPH (88 FT/SEC)

WINDPLANT : PROP DIAMETER – 12 FT

PROP AREA = 113 FT²

WEIGHT – 500 lbs

TOWER : HEIGHT – 60 FT

WEIGHT – 4000 lbs

BASE – 10 FT SQUARE

PROJECTED AREA – 25 FT²

SITUATION : WINDPLANT DELIVERING FULL RATED OUTPUT POWER.

FIGURE 3-28

FORGET IT!

WIND

A_A

FORCE A

H

FORCE B

½H

FORCE C

PIVOT POINT

FORCE D

FORCE E

(9) FORCE C MINUS FORCE D = 5976 lbs – 2250 lbs = 3726 lbs UPWARD

(10) FORCE E REPRESENTS THE RESISTIVE FORCE (DOWNWARD) BY THE CEMENTED LEGS. THIS IS A COMBINATION OF THE CEMENT'S WEIGHT AND THE SHEAR RESISTANCE OF THE SOIL. IF THE TWO LEGS EACH HAVE, SAY, 200 lbs OF CEMENT, THE SHEAR RESISTANCE MUST HOLD 3726 lbs MINUS 400 lbs, OR 3326 lbs. PER LEG, THIS IS 1663 lbs OF FORCE TO RESIST.

For a 60-foot tower, cemented legs should be at least 5 feet in the ground; a 30-footer might be able to get away with 4 feet. For higher than 60-feet, check with tower manufacturers and find out what they recommend. Lighter towers will need more rigid (or deeper) anchors becuz their weight does not tend to help keep the tower from blowing over. Narrower-based towers will require stronger securing becuz they have more of a tendency to topple than the wide-base ones. (Make sense?) Wind machines provide so much surface area to the wind in normal operation that the wind will try to push the top of the tower back. And, in turn, becuz the tower is secured to the earth, this is further translated into trying to topple the tower (about the pivot of the base). Fig. 3-28 illustrates these forces and one way they can be calculated (for worst conditions). Remember that the tower is just one big lever (and remember how effective levers are) and you're on the right track. These forces are not constant, so they'll "work" on a poor cement job until there's enuff "give" to break it up.

I recommend a fluted-type hole for tower-leg anchoring (see Fig. 3-29), but it's a hand-shaping job becuz mechanical or post-hole-type diggers can't make it for you. It not only makes the mold for the cement, but it will provide a wedge that is difficult to get out of the ground once it's buried.

FIGURE 3-29

TOWER LEG

LEG EXTENSIONS

D

2D

FIGURE 3-30

16"

3"

3"

16"

SLAB THICKNESS 4"
LEG SOCKET DEPTH 1"

Throwing rocks (or, in general, adding weights) on top of the anchor is no good; weight alone will not hold the anchor in place. What you do want is a high shear-type resistance, and that's mostly going to be a soil condition. Adding the cement does give a weight factor (which helps), but the idea behind it is to provide a large, underground form or shape to the anchor. Building codes deal with this type of anchoring for houses and the like, or the industrial installation of street-lamps, traffic signals, and large display signs, so there are many sources for this specific installation. Check 'em out if you find the information I'm providing still doesn't give you a clear picture of what to do, but keep in mind that the type of anchor depends on the application so it may not be a clear-cut straight-across-the-board way of doing it for a tower.

Once you've decided on the way to secure the tower (for a free-standing anchorage -- this means no guy wires used), the next question is: When do you do it? You could cement some leg stubs in position, raise the tower, bolt its legs to these stubs. Or you can just dig the holes and then raise the tower so that it's positioned above the holes, and attach the leg stubs, cementing them in place. Having raised towers that used both methods, I find myself in favor of the latter method. It does take some extra preparation; you have to do something to prevent the tower from falling into the holes during or after the raise (see photos). Pre-cemented leg stubs, though, are one helluva mate-up problem, especially for a large tower; you have to use some kind of large jack to move the tower around until you can throw the bolts through the holes (see photos). So both require preparation, but with the noncemented way there's no real problem with getting the precise alignment required of the other (the tower base can have shifted slightly from the intended or attempted positioning without the need to get it back).

The single-leg tower, by the way, should have some kind of base support; this can be a cemented block (as called out in the Wincharger manual -- see Fig. 3-30) but, as the weight of the tower and wind machine, and guy-wire pressure will prevent the bottom from scooting out from under the tower, the socket holes are not necessary in firm soil conditions. To prevent the tower from sinking into the earth, however, a cement slab or some kind of flat, hard surface should be used. We inserted a few 2 x 6's under ours and it's working admirably.

Tower Paraphernalia

To get power from the wind machine down to the batteries requires the usage of electrical wires (unless you've got an inside line on Tesla's work) and the time to install them on the tower is before you raise it. It can be done afterward, but it's difficult and time-consuming. Fig. 3-31 illustrates some of the ways the wires might be secured to the tower as well as ways to hang the wires when hooking up to a nearby structure (housing the batteries).

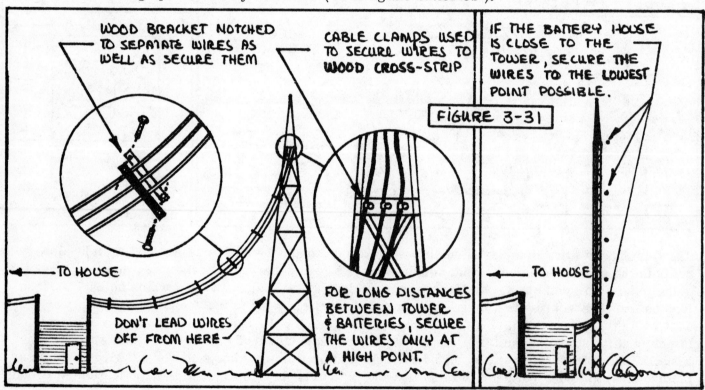

Lightning protection is a necessity for towered wind machines; these will protect the machine, the control box, and the fire hazard that comes from a direct or close hit by a bolt or static buildup during an electrical storm. You can buy lightning arresters (check with surplus places that deal with electronics stuff or ham equipment or contact the local utility office for more info on where they may be obtained) or you can use an old trick that was developed to reroute the lightning; this takes advantage of the fact that lightning doesn't take corners so well (understandable, since it's traveling so fast) and involves zig-zagging the power wires a bit (see Fig. 3-32). Better check with the codes in your area, though, as I'm certain an inspector of your system wouldn't be too thrilled by this old-timey substitute. The other standard procedure here is to ground both the tower and control box; the tower may be well grounded as is, but the control box should be grounded to a

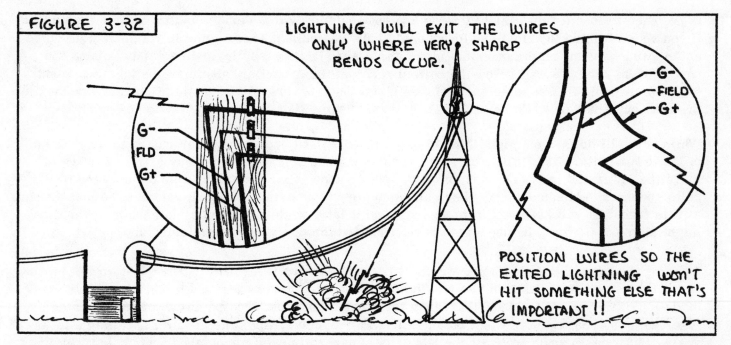

FIGURE 3-32

LIGHTNING WILL EXIT THE WIRES ONLY WHERE VERY SHARP BENDS OCCUR.

G-
FLD
G+

G-
FIELD
G+

POSITION WIRES SO THE EXITED LIGHTNING WON'T HIT SOMETHING ELSE THAT'S IMPORTANT!!

water pipe or a copper grounding rod driven about 8 feet into the ground. The whole idea in lightning protection is to provide an easy, non-resistive path for the lightning to ground. If it doesn't have it, it'll take what path it can find, and it ain't particular about it. It's super-high-voltage stuff, so it can go through just about anything, and the hotter that item is gonna get if it cannot dissipate the heat caused by the flow of current. Melting guy wires and blown fuses are not funny in this situation becuz high winds generally accompany such storms. Don't shrug off doing something about it!

In some areas you may have to install a red warning light on the tower, especially with very high towers. This is a bummer for wind-electric system installations becuz of the power this light consumes, but at least consider it (if the codes don't outright demand it). Neither you nor some low-flyin' pilot is going to like his flyin' into your unlighted tower. If you need, or decide, to use this warning light, install it before you raise the tower becuz it's a hazard as soon as it gets up there and will be difficult to install afterwards. You should probably arrange to have it sense light conditions (or their absence) and switch on and off automatically. It's a bummer to have a crash becuz you forgot to turn it on, or in having drained batteries becuz you ran it during the day, too.

While the tower is still on the ground, get the tower stub ready to receive the wind machine you're going to install. This means installing the slip-ring assembly, lubricating the lolly-shaft bearings, and attaching all components necessary to lock the wind machine in place. While you're at it, install the wind machine-raising gin pole or (if it will get in the way of the tower raising) as much of its support assembly as you can at the moment. Being on top of a tower is fun for mountain-climbing people like myself, but this may not represent your attitude and, if not, you're going to have to think ahead on such things. It's real easy to get carried away with puttin' up your first tower, so write it down and do it before the beast goes up.

Most 3-leg and 4-leg towers have ladders on them so the top is easy to get to, but if yours doesn't (or it's a home-brew job or an octahedron tower), better think about installing one beforehand. A commercially-made ladder might be adaptable, or you can build one yourself; for our octahedron towers, I have built one using EM T (electrical metallic tubing, or conduit). While ours is welded together, bolting one together is not out of the question. Make it well, though; 40 feet up in the air is no place to lose a rung! Most towers are not equipped with a service platform near the top, but if you've got a mind to, most any tower could have one built. These come in real handy if you're anticipating working on the machine alot and it sure beats grappling with a safety belt all the time. Make sure it's well below the bottom reach of the propeller! Some of the folks we talked to on our expedition lost some good friends up on those towers during installations and removal of the wind machines or while servicing the things. Seems like a real silly way to go!

While it's still down, you might think to use a little WD-40 (or some other rust inhibitive) on all of the tower bolts. This'll help 20 years from now when you're movin' away or just wanting to move the tower and have to disassemble it. Never know when you might have to get some of the bolts undone to add something. There are some pretty amazing rust penetrants on the market, but a little foresight will keep you from having to do it later while the monster is upright. Vaseline might also work (you'll be needing to have it around for the battery terminals, anyway).

Painting the tower is another thing worth considering before it's raised. The question is: Is it rustic or just rusty? Rust isn't some kind of disease that covers ferrous materials; it's the rapid oxidation of the metal itself and that fancy terminology means "eroding away" or "being eaten up." After so many years, there won't be any left. For massive, thick metal towers, this is a lot of years, but for thin angle iron, or the EMT that's generally used for octahedrons, it is a reality not wisely ignored. If you do paint it, think about the sight pollution a psychedelic tower is going to produce and try to merge it into the background. If it's galvanized, you must use a paint that's exclusively made for galvanized metal, or it'll weather off in a few years' time. Of course, if it's galvanized, that's a rush inhibitive, so it's not necessary to paint it except wherever the galvanizing has been damaged (where the tubing was crushed) or burned off (by welding).

There may be some other things that you'll want to do to (or with) your tower before it's raised; if you think of any, write them down somewhere or you'll surely forget them until after it's up. Once you start thinking about raising a tower, it'd be a good idea to carry around a small notepad for such tidbits, or a loose-leaf binder which can also hold the drawings you made, and the like.

Setting Up for the Raise

Setting up for the raise should probably be done the day before you intend to actually raise the tower; what you want to avoid is doing the setting up and raising on the same day. If you're doing a good job of setup, you're going to take more time than you might allow (you know, little problems here and there, a cable clamp you need to get from the store, etc.) so give yourself all the time that's necessary. If you've got some pressure (like a whole bunch of people show up), then you'll get hurried, you'll get mad becuz you're hurried, and get mad becuz you're mad. Tower raising is exciting stuff for the local inhabitants, so they'll come even if you didn't advertise or send out "invites" (somehow the word just gets around). But it's not a show and they didn't pay for tickets, so don't feel like you owe them anything, or can't say "No, I'm not going to raise it -- it just isn't ready," becuz you can and should.

Fig. 3-33 illustrates one way whereby a single, long guy wire can be used to prevent side-fall (both sides) and end-over. If you have purchased a very long length of wire for the raising cable, cut alength for the raising line that you will need and use the remainder for the guy wires needed to prevent bottom-slippage. If you still have a lot left over, then use this same wire for side-fall and end-over prevention (there is, after all, nothing wrong with using wire that's rated heavier than required) and a way to use one long, continuous wire for bottom-slippage, end-over, and side-fall prevention is illustrated in Fig. 3-34. If you make the overlap (between the cable clamps

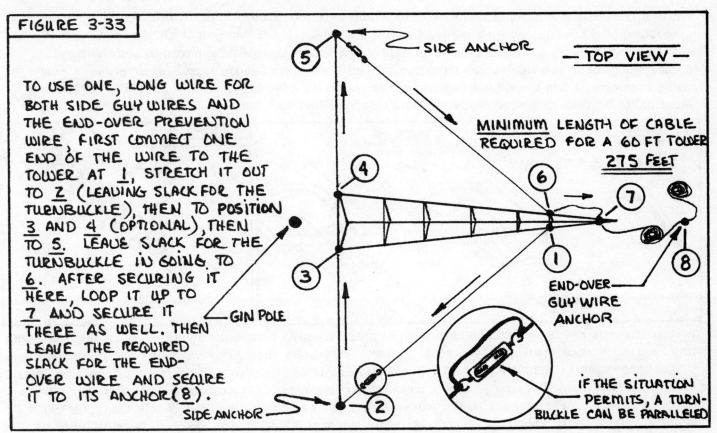

FIGURE 3-33

— TOP VIEW —

SIDE ANCHOR

MINIMUM LENGTH OF CABLE REQUIRED FOR A 60 FT TOWER
275 FEET

TO USE ONE, LONG WIRE FOR BOTH SIDE GUY WIRES AND THE END-OVER PREVENTION WIRE, FIRST CONNECT ONE END OF THE WIRE TO THE TOWER AT 1, STRETCH IT OUT TO 2 (LEAVING SLACK FOR THE TURNBUCKLE), THEN TO POSITION 3 AND 4 (OPTIONAL), THEN TO 5. LEAVE SLACK FOR THE TURNBUCKLE IN GOING TO 6. AFTER SECURING IT HERE, LOOP IT UP TO 7 AND SECURE IT THERE AS WELL. THEN LEAVE THE REQUIRED SLACK FOR THE END-OVER WIRE AND SECURE IT TO ITS ANCHOR(8).

GIN POLE

SIDE ANCHOR

END-OVER GUY WIRE ANCHOR

IF THE SITUATION PERMITS, A TURN-BUCKLE CAN BE PARALLELED

at each junction) a couple of feet in length, then you'll be able to tighten or loosen these cable clamps to adjust tension for the specific situation. It requires more cable clamps (for this option) becuz you can just install one cable clamp at each of the junctions, but I recommend it; the versatility of the situation makes it just the same as using individual wires for each situation (which involves cutting up the wire just for the tower raising) without having to cut up the wire (which means you have a handy piece of wire which can be used for all kinds of things around the place).

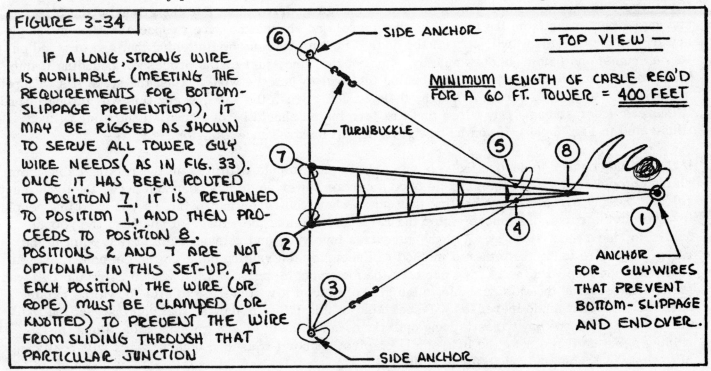

FIGURE 3-34

SIDE ANCHOR

— TOP VIEW —

MINIMUM LENGTH OF CABLE REQ'D FOR A 60 FT. TOWER = **400 FEET**

TURNBUCKLE

IF A LONG, STRONG WIRE IS AVAILABLE (MEETING THE REQUIREMENTS FOR BOTTOM-SLIPPAGE PREVENTION), IT MAY BE RIGGED AS SHOWN TO SERVE ALL TOWER GUY WIRE NEEDS(AS IN FIG. 33). ONCE IT HAS BEEN ROUTED TO POSITION 7, IT IS RETURNED TO POSITION 1, AND THEN PROCEEDS TO POSITION 8. POSITIONS 2 AND 7 ARE NOT OPTIONAL IN THIS SET-UP. AT EACH POSITION, THE WIRE (OR ROPE) MUST BE CLAMPED (OR KNOTTED) TO PREVENT THE WIRE FROM SLIDING THROUGH THAT PARTICULAR JUNCTION

ANCHOR FOR GUY WIRES THAT PREVENT BOTTOM-SLIPPAGE AND ENDOVER.

SIDE ANCHOR

While you're at it, you might install a wire which will substitute for the raising cable once the tower is upright. You can just secure the raising cable, but if you pull it off the truck that it was secured to for the lift, then the tower is unprotected until you get it secured to something else. Either way, then, use the backup wire and, if you wish, just secure it and remove the raising cable entirely. I don't mind leaving guy wires out in the elements, but I sure don't like leaving steel cable or real nice rope out; it doesn't last long that way.

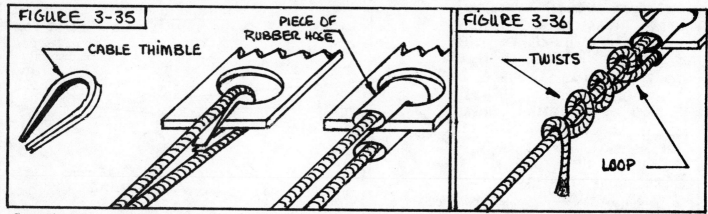

FIGURE 3-35   CABLE THIMBLE   PIECE OF RUBBER HOSE

FIGURE 3-36   TWISTS   LOOP

Securing guy wires or the raise cable to the tower, truck, or anchors should be done in such a way as to insure that they will not fray while in use. Fig. 3-35 shows two ways this can be done to protect the cable (for future usage). The idea here is to keep from having to bend the wire sharply or have it rest against a sharp edge of metal which can nick, fray, or cut it when it's subjected to some tension or other stress. Cloth works nicely for most situations but "cable thimbles" will work best especially when you are routing wires through holes where the cloth is unlikely to fit. You can bend them open a bit with pliers, but be sure to close them after you've hooked them through a hole and inserted the wire. If you're terminating a wire at that point (tying it in a knot and twisting it), insure that once you're done, the wire can't slip off the thimble. If you don't have thimbles, file or sand any rough edges and insert a piece of rubber or nylon rubber hose to keep the wire from touching any sharp, or sharply countoured, edges of metal.

If you are using metal or heavy wood stakes as anchors, drive them into the ground about 3 feet and angle them away from the tower, so that there's no chance the wire (especially if it will angle upward during the raise) will slip off the end. This can be done by flattening the pipe or wood on its outermost end (which occurs anyway, most of the time, just by the process of pounding it into the ground) or driving another stake behind the first to jam the wire against the stake it's wrapped around, or tied to. Be careful, though, that you don't crush the wire, becuz this will fatigue it and it'll break under stress. Guy wires that are terminated should be tied first, then twisted (as illustrated in Fig. 3-36); if you just twist it, it will unravel under tension.

If the method chosen to secure the raising cable to the gin pole will prevent the raising cable from rising completely clear of the gin pole once a certain tower angle has been achieved, then you must release the guy wires that are holding it in place when you reach that point. If you have few people involved in the raise, then merely stop the raise and release the wires. If you have the people available, have them stand by all of the guy wires involved, and release them at that point in the raise. If you're using the tethered method (of securing the raising cable to the gin pole), the gin pole will then rise with the raising cable as the tower angle increases. If you're using the pulleyed method of securing the raising cable to the gin pole, then it will be free to slide down the raising cable as the tower angle increases. Be certain, in this latter instance, that you instruct the individuals releasing the guy wires to hang onto them, and slowly let the gin pole slide along the raising cable until it's near the lift vehicle or pivot anchor (if used); otherwise, it will really zing along the cable and crash for certain.

Only in the instance where the raising cable is pulleyed to the gin pole must you concern yourself with insuring that the gin pole is placed where it will not interfere with the base of the tower when it is raised. I've never raised a tower where this was not the case, but I have always placed the gin pole far enuff away to prevent this from happening under any circumstance. To get the maximum benefit from the gin pole, you should place it as close to the tower as possible, but in no case should it be closer than 5 feet. For a pulleyed gin pole, it should be the width of the base <u>away from the pivot legs.</u>

When you position the gin pole, make certain that it is perfectly in line (or as perfectly as you can get it) with the tower axis. Place the base of it on a board (or some other hard surface if soft ground is present). Secure the guy wires attached to it only after someone has confirmed that it is perfectly vertical (a bubble-type level can be used here). If it is out of alignment with the tower axis or is less than vertical, this will cause some severe side pressure on the gin pole during the raise, and one of its side guy wires might break.

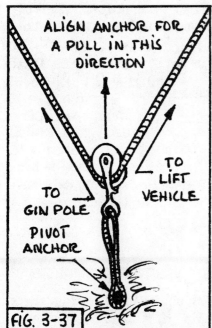

ALIGN ANCHOR FOR A PULL IN THIS DIRECTION

TO GIN POLE PIVOT ANCHOR

TO LIFT VEHICLE

FIG. 3-37

If you're using a pivot (like that described in Fig. 3-24), be sure that the anchor you choose and install is also directly in line with the tower axis (for the same reasons indicated above for the gin pole). Make sure that the pulley to be used is well-lubricated and large enuff to take the tons of force exerted on the raising cable and tower. Secure it with the same strength of cable used for the raising cable, and don't hesitate to take many turns around the pulley's "eye" to "beef-up" the connection. If you're using a vehicle for the pivot anchor, be certain to orient the vehicle so that it "splits the angle" between the tower-axis line and the actual direction of pull (see Fig. 3-37). If you're driving an anchor into the ground (or installing one of the anchors depicted in Fig. 3-27), this will mean slanting the anchor in such a way to account for the apparent, bisected-angle direction of pull.

If you're installing a pulleyed-mechanical advantage, be certain to draw it out first and work from the drawings; an advantage of two is complicated enuff whereas three or above are outright confusing, even if you are working with a drawing. Use pulleys that will stand the strain, and connect them to the tower, anchor, and vehicle with raising cable-strength wire. Lay them out neatly so they will not become tangled, twisted, or snagged when you're ready to tension them. Fig. 3-38 describes the combination of mechanical advantage and pivot anchor that we used to raise Jim' 54-footer.

The Lift Vehicle

I have made casual mention of the lift vehicle requirements elsewhere, but there are a number of points I haven't covered; hence, it gets its own section. Whatever type of vehicle it might be -- tractor, truck, sedan, space-hippy van, or motorcycle -- it should have a manual transmission. I have no doubt that an automatic might make for a very smooth raising, but there's good reason for having a stick shift. If you know anything about the automatic transmission, then you should know that, should the engine die if it's in drive, low, or reverse, it will still move freely. If an engine dies in any gear of a stick shift (and if the clutch is out), the vehicle is prevented from moving becuz the engine is still directly (mechanically) connected to the wheels. You can simulate an automatic transmission effect in a stick-shift vehicle by simply pushing in on the clutch (whether it's in gear or not), and then the vehicle is free to move. Unfortunately, you can't simulate a

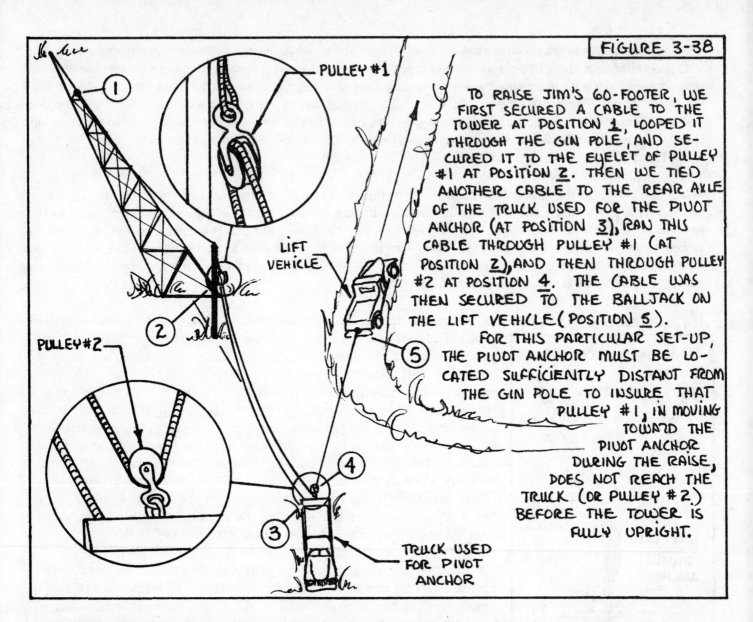

FIGURE 3-38

PULLEY #1

PULLEY #2

LIFT VEHICLE

TRUCK USED FOR PIVOT ANCHOR

TO RAISE JIM'S 60-FOOTER, WE FIRST SECURED A CABLE TO THE TOWER AT POSITION 1, LOOPED IT THROUGH THE GIN POLE, AND SECURED IT TO THE EYELET OF PULLEY #1 AT POSITION 2. THEN WE TIED ANOTHER CABLE TO THE REAR AXLE OF THE TRUCK USED FOR THE PIVOT ANCHOR (AT POSITION 3), RAN THIS CABLE THROUGH PULLEY #1 (AT POSITION 2), AND THEN THROUGH PULLEY #2 AT POSITION 4. THE CABLE WAS THEN SECURED TO THE BALLJACK ON THE LIFT VEHICLE (POSITION 5).

FOR THIS PARTICULAR SET-UP, THE PIVOT ANCHOR MUST BE LOCATED SUFFICIENTLY DISTANT FROM THE GIN POLE TO INSURE THAT PULLEY #1, IN MOVING TOWARD THE PIVOT ANCHOR DURING THE RAISE, DOES NOT REACH THE TRUCK (OR PULLEY #2) BEFORE THE TOWER IS FULLY UPRIGHT.

stick shift with an automatic transmission becuz the transmission gear shafts must be rotating a certain number of rpm before the automatic clutch engages. If the engine dies in an automatic-transmission'd vehicle that's lifting the tower, all hell's going to break loose becuz the vehicle is free to roll back. Becuz most automatic transmission-equipped vehicles are also using power brakes, they are most ineffective unless the engine is running -- jamming on those dead brakes is no fun. Dig?

Even if you are using a stick shift, give serious thought to having someone follow the lift vehicle during the raise, blocking the wheels to prevent rollback should the raising have to be stopped suddenly. Jim's son and a neighbor friend did this when we raised the 54-footer, becuz the brakes in the vehicle were not all that good and the engine wasn't much better. A couple of big logs were used, and the boys just slid them along the ground behind the rear wheels as the vehicle advanced. With this procedure, if the engine died or Jim (who was driving the vehicle) was given the word to stop momentarily, the logs would have prevented a rollback of more than a few feet. Other blocks were laid on the running boards, so that the boys could block the front wheels as well if the pause was longer than momentary (like if a situation had to be carefully looked over, a guy wire adjusted). This might sound a little bit dangerous for anyone handling the blocks, but we carefully instructed the boys to keep their hands and feet away from the wheels of the vehicle. We had them move alongside the vehicle (instead of behind it), and used long-enuff logs so they were nowhere near the wheels. If you have no option but to use an automatic-transmission'd vehicle, this is an absolute must.

When securing the raising line to the lift vehicle, get it tied up to the frame or the axle. Some vehicles are equipped with a ball-jack on the back, for pulling trailers, boats, etc. This might do, but inspect it well to see that the bumper has been reinforced and secured with additional support members which attach to the frame. If in doubt, tie up to the axle. Anything but reinforced bumpers will be no good for this job.

As it is essential that the driver know what is going on, you might consider setting up the lift vehicle so that it raises the tower by driving in reverse. This is a no-no for an obstruction-riddled path the lift vehicle might have to travel or maneuver through, but if it's fairly clear, it can be a very positive way to do it. As most vehicles have a lower gear in reverse (compared to the lowest gear forward), this also means that more torque can be applied to the situation. I do know that it will also create a situation where the drive wheels are less likely to spin, but I'm not sure how much difference results from driving it this way, or if it is really of any consequence. But these are all fringe benefits to the advantage afforded to having the driver clearly see the tower and what's happenin' around it. If a good winch exists on the front bumper, this will be a good place to hook up the raising cable. Of course, if you've got a winch, you might just use that, right? Just remember that if you use a winch, it doesn't really matter that it might be rated to handle 8000 lbs; you're still going to have to secure the vehicle.

Pre-Raising Pow-Wow

Either the day before, or the day you're planning to raise the tower, you'll want to hold a little get-together, and go over the whole thing. I call it the pre-lift pow-wow. You should call together anybody that will be involved in the raising -- and I do mean everybody! If everyone knows what everybody else is supposed to be doing, then things are going to run a lot smoother, especially if some little thing goes wrong. At the very least, you should pass this book around or offer it to all involved, becuz maybe they may be doing it next. Go over the drawings. Explain what can happen, and when. Explain the jobs that need to be done, and (if you haven't already filled these positions) determine who will do what. And where. And when. If you've built a little tower that's a model of the one to be raised, go through all the motions with it. Talk about what everyone should do if this wire breaks, or that anchor pulls out, or the raising cable snaps when the tower is partway up. (If you tell them anything else but "Get the hell outta there," then you've just flunked the course.) Walk around the tower site. Point out the various guy wires. Show 'em which way the truck is going to go, and how far it will move. Show which wires are going to raise which way. Show 'em where to stand and what to look at and what to watch out for. If you can't do this, you've got some rereading and studying to do. Or find somebody that can do this. It's helpful, but not absolutely essential, that everybody knows what's happenin'. The next best thing is to have most of them know what's happenin'. But at the very least, one person should know what's happenin'!!

Pow-wow is a good process to go through -- you'd be amazed at how much feedback it will give you, how well you'll learn it yourself, and how many potential problems might be suddenly "in the light." What you don't or can't understand brings fear; maybe everybody will still be this way after they've been told, but they'll operate much more automatically when sumthin' happens that "wasn't on the menu."

Work out hand signals for the raise; shouts can go unheard or be misunderstood when you've got the noise from a revved-up engine. It is essential that the driver of the lift vehicle be able to see the tower or someone who can. Whatever hand signals are worked up, make them simple and universal (see Fig. 3-39 for some examples) and practice them so they become natural; otherwise, someone is going to be yelling STOP when their hand is raised and signalling GO. Walkie-talkies are handy little things for events like this, and quite good for the small distances between the folks involved.

OFFICIAL TOWER-RAISING HAND SIGNALS and BODY ENGLISH

UP

DOWN

FIG. 3-39

LEFT
(OR RIGHT, AS THE CASE MAY BE)

FULL LOTUS
(USE ONLY IN EMERGENCIES)

Where the people go depends on the situation. I don't think that I would risk a large tower-raising without at least 4 people. I'd put one near the top of the tower to remove the barrel (or whatever) that I had the top of the tower restin' on; I'd want that out of there once the tower had lifted from it just in case the tower came back down (so the tower would have a flat landing). I'd put someone by the gin pole; it's one of the more dangerous spots to be, but one of the more important, too. From here, the base of the tower and gin pole can be watched for slippage, the top of the gin pole can be watched for anything that might come loose, and the movements of both gin pole and tower keenly observed. Another person would be in the lift vehicle. And I'd have at least one person manning the block for the wheels on the lift vehicle. If this was all of the folks available, I'd get the person near the top of the tower to help with wheel-blocking once the tower was goin' up.

If I had gathered more people, though, or a few of those that showed up to watch were game for the idea, I'd put them to work, too. I'd get someone on each of the guy wires that presented side-fall, to just stand there and feel the tension in those wires as the tower went up. They're going to tension and slacken a bit, anyway, but they could let us know if some kind of stress was buildin' up, before it'd pop them, or pull the anchors. I'd have two people standin' clear of anything until the tower angle was such that the gin pole guy wires had to be released. They could run in and cut or loosen them at a signal, or shout, and get the gin pole safely down and along the raising cable -- and then get back outta there. I'd put someone else on blockin' the wheels and keep whoever is up near the top of the tower there, so he'd be able to say when the end-over prevention wire was startin' to get tight.   And maybe, I'd stick another person over there by the driver, just to help relay any chitchat that was goin' on to and from him.   And I'd be darned sure to get somebody to take movies or pictures of the whole thing . . . just for posterity and all that.

Of course, you can double up some of the jobs, but the idea of people running over, under and around the tower doesn't appeal to me; it's sumthin' like people roulette.   Besides, it's too distracting.   You'll want to be puttin' all of your attention to what's happenin' with the tower.   So plan it to be quiet . . . and let the tower do all the moving.

While you're doing the sightseeing tour with the folks that are involved, clean up any debris in the immediate vicinity of the tower that might interfere with people movin' around.   You don't need an obstacle course when you're trying to move quickly (like when it's rainin' towers and wires!)   If you're going to have a lot of people participating in the event, or just if they're watchin', you might try marking out the perimeter of the tower's reach.   Grab a sack full of flour (make it white flour -- it's not much good for human consumption anyway) and make a trail of it around the tower. If you get a string or rope that's equal in length to the tower's height and attach it to the base of the tower, then you can use this to mark off a very concise boundary.   This'll let folks know what's safe and what ain't.   You can also instruct the curious and watchful members of the audience that this is as close as they can get -- period!

(Author's Note: I don't mean to sound negative, telling you to mark off a danger zone; it'll sound funny when you've done the thing and are wondering what all the extra precautions were for.   If I were raising a tower tomorrow, I wouldn't do half the stuff I'm telling you to do.   But then I try to be responsible for my actions.   And I want to be responsible here, too.   When all the writing is done, and the book's published, and folks are buying it and raising towers from the information I've supplied, I'll know that it wasn't for a lack of something I didn't emphasize enuff that somebody got hurt, or that a tower came down when it was supposed to be going up.   I was sorely tempted at points to say, "You don't really need to do this" or "You can get away with doing it so-and-so," but I didn't.   I haven't lost a tower yet, but I'm still afraid I'm going to.   That, friends, keeps me in touch with the situation; it's when you start thinkin' you've really got it "wired" that you begin to make mistakes -- it only takes one to make it go bad.

Doing It

So now you're ready to do it.   You've already checked and rechecked the wires, the cables, the anchors, the people involved, and still you walk around and keep lookin' for things that might not be just right.   Everyone's in their position, the lift vehicle's engine is idling, and everything that needs to be said has been said.

So do it!

Take a breath or two, and move into it slowly.   Give the GO signal.   The lift vehicle should first take up the slack.   When it's done that, check the angles.   Is the raising line right down the center of the tower?   Not quite?   Back up the lift vehicle and re-orient.   Okay now?   Yep!   Take up the slack again.   Do you have to give the cable the "acid test"?   All right, give it a little power.   The top of the tower should lift about a foot.   You can pop the clutch here, or just run over and grab onto the top of the tower and pull it down.   Give it a strong jerk.   Bounce it up and down a little -- it should be able to take this easily.   Everything all right.   Get everybody positioned.

Let the clutch out on the vehicle. Slowly. Rev the engine a little until she starts to take the load. Don't let it rev up too much; you don't want to be riding the clutch. You want to let it all the way out and just give it enuff gas to keep from killing the engine. And she'll start movin': the vehicle, forward; the tower, up. And up, and up, and up. The base of the tower will move a bit, taking up the slack, tensioning the wires. The gin pole is creaking and groaning under the compressive forces. The pulley is catchin' and then lettin' the wire slide through it. Lots of tension every-where: vehicle, tower, wires, and people. The tower will seem to float up, like in a dream. Can this really be happenin'? Yep, it's going up. Watch it, though, you've got a raisin' cable that's just about to clear that gin pole. A little more. That's it. Now . . . HOLD IT! Logs sliding under the rear wheels. The tower's swaying a bit with the change in motion. Wipe a brow and let it die down. Call in the folks that are going to free the gin pole's guy wires. Check with the folks checkin' on the strain in the side guy wires. One a wee bit tight? How's the other one doin'? Okay? The one that's tight isn't all that bad, but maybe you'd better let the turnbuckle out a bit, anyway. Okay, things look good. A glance at the audience -- they're just standin' there in complete awe. Maybe a quick chat with the driver of the vehicle or, if that's you, a quick chat with the gin pole watcher. A little slower with the vehicle? Okay. Back to the station. Ease out on the clutch, a little gas, get the clutch all the way out, and she's movin' again. Up and up and up. Reachin' for the sky. A bird flyin' overhead gives you the eye -- what's all this insanity? Keep your mind tuned to it. She's nearly up now. And you get the signal from the person standin' to the side -- the end-over prevention wire is straightening out. Watch 'em both. Give the SLOW signal. Steady. Suddenly, it's tight. Give the STOP signal. The tower sways now in the wind. Back up the lift vehicle a bit. Nope, the tower isn't comin' back down. Sure enuff, she's past teeter. Okay, let out the end-over guy wire a bit. Or let the Power-Pull out until she's on all legs (unless it's a single leg). Now . . . ain't that a beautiful sight? Give somebody a hug and chug some carrot juice. That's it. You've done it! You! And some friends!

Post-Raise

Don't wait too long before you finish the job! You've only got 4 guy wires on that tower, and it takes only one wire snagged and pulled to bring down a lot of work. If you've got a single-leg tower, get that fifth wire on NOW! You can shift the wires that you used for the raise, but you must substi-tute a wire for each wire that you remove from an anchor, and reposition according to Fig. 3-4 and Fig. 3-5. Don't have people climbin' on the tower when you're doing this, becuz you can goof and disconnect a vital wire -- there's no sense in compounding mistakes.

If you're going to cement the tower legs, either start working on it, or prepare everything for a wait until you do; in this latter instance, this only involves placing the guy wires so they are in no danger of being snagged or pulled out. Insofar as they're "temporary" wires, they often get treated like that, and the care and attention rendered them is not nearly what permanent ones receive. To keep people from falling over or running into the wires, tie tassles of cloth on each wire around eye-level.

Cementing Legs

When you're ready to cement in the legs, the first thing that you'll want to do is to level the tower. This can be done several ways, but blocking up the base will prove more work than using the guy wires as "adjusters." Tensioning and loosening guy wires is going to allow for a finer adjustment to the readings afforded by the bubble-type level than blocks inserted under crosspieces. Turn-buckles will really help here. If the tower is really out of kilter, you may have to loosen the guy wire from its anchor and readjust it. If you need more slack, remember to turn the turnbuckle all the way in before you re-tie the wire; this will allow for further slackening. If you want it tensioned more, untie it, turn the turnbuckle all the way out, and re-tie; this will allow further tightening. Whenever you release a guy wire, know what you're doing. If there is any possibility of the tower being in danger of falling for lack of that guy wire, install another wire and secure it before you do any untying of the guy wire needing coarse adjustment. You should keep checking the bubble on the level, checking it in two directions each time (like north-south, and east-west); this will let you know which wires need tensioning or loosening. If your guy wires are fairly tight to begin with, you will probably have to tighten one wire and loosen another for each adjustment you make. Be certain that you loosen one before you tighten the other, though! Turnbuckles allow for some pretty good torque, and guy wires can pop.

Assume that you have dug the appropriate holes, leveled the tower, and attached some extensions to the tower legs (the ones which will be then encapsulated in the cement). You are now ready to cement the legs. By some rough approximation, you should be able to figure out how much you'll need; if not, get someone that can look at it. If you have a truck bring in the cement, they'll need to know how much -- be ready to tell 'em how many "yards" you need (this is cubic yards, which is cubic feet divided by 9). If you live near a cement company that does a lot of business, you might check with them at the end of the day. They may have cement in their trucks that they want to get rid of, and you can get it free just for the asking! Make sure you have everything ready so they make a fast dropoff, and you'll have established yourself as a good dump for any stuff they have left over. There will be a limit to the amount of cement you need unless you're into monoliths, so be thinkin' about other folks you can turn on to the deal. If you are remote enuff to make trucking in the cement unfeasible, or if you can't afford the cost and want to mix it yourself, know what you're doing.

I would postpone any work on cementing legs if you've got damp weather or high winds; the former will keep the cement too wet to cure; and the latter will shake the tower enuff to keep the cement from firmly grasping the legs. Guy wires can be tensioned hard to keep the tower more secure during the few days' curing time for the cement, but they cannot be tensioned enuff to take out all the movement. So check the precipitation and wind forecast!

When the cement has dried, bury the remainder of the leg extensions until the ground is level or slightly bulged upward at the legs of the tower. For lightning protection, this might be a good time to drive in a ground stake. Even if you have the leg extension buried in cement that goes down five or six feet, that part of the leg which is encapsulated will not be grounded, just in the ground. Drive some pipe or rod in and connect it with some heavy wire (#4 or larger) to one of the tower base bolts. All done? Get up on the tower and shake it good (throw your weight around a little bit) and have someone look at what's happenin' there at the base while you're doin' it. If the legs move up and down a bit, you've goofed it. If the top of the tower shakes a bit, but there's no vertical motion at the base legs, that's normal. Go ahead and remove the guy wires. If it did move down there, you must add more cement, dig deeper, or keep the guy wires attached. Don't remove them and call it okay -- it won't take long for the action of the wind (once a machine is installed) to work the legs loose even more. Then you're going to shake a wind machine to pieces or bring it all down in a real "blow."

If you have previously installed the leg extensions and cemented them, you now get to go through the fun of trying to bolt all of the legs to their respective extension stubs. If this is your situation, hopefully you watched the bottom-slippage wires as the tower started to go up. You made certain that you allowed for enuff stretch in these wires, and the legs did not move past the stubs too far. The stubs aren't broken off, crushed, or otherwise mangled and no longer capable of mating up to the legs. In our case, we backed the tower off about a foot to allow for stretch in the wires, and

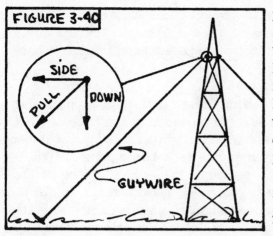

FIGURE 3-40

placed a log under the legs right near the end, securing it solidly to the legs. This formed the pivot for the base of the tower during the raise. Additionally, this helped to keep the legs from burying themselves with the tower's weight and the raising motion; it further insured that the ends of the tower legs were not likewise mangled. While we had a jack that would easily lift the tower -- a component of the force they exert not only keeps the tower from going sidewise, but also pushes it into the ground. (See Fig. 3-40.) If something slips during the raise and the legs do bury themselves, you may have to loosen all the guy wires a bit before you try to jack it up to where the legs will bolt to the extension stubs. Watch out for the ole fingers when you're trying to push a bolt through each; one of them might become a permanent part of the tower. Ugh!

If you have installed a single-leg tower, install good anchors if you have not already done so. If the ones that you have installed don't seem adequate after you've tried them, make up some others. Just make sure that you have the 5 wires close to 72° apart. Install large, strong turnbuckles so that you have the capacity to tighten them after a while, as the tower will settle a bit despite the basecap. The wire attachments will work out any slack in time. You may have to untie the wires, open up the turnbuckle, and re-tie them if they have more slack than the turnbuckle can adjust out. If the wires have been properly spaced, you will not necessarily need to install a temporary wire when you untie the main wire. Just don't have the machine running when you do, or pick a non-windy day for the adjustments.

If you have temporary wires to be cemented, or have installed a guyed tower, make up a schedule to check the guy wires frequently (especially at first). Keep to it! It only takes a few moments, and will relieve any worry in the middle of the night when a full-fledged gale comes up.

Tower Safety

For whatever reason you climb a tower, don't be without a safety belt. And when you stop to observe, adjust, or whatever, attach it. It can be a simple thing -- just some rope, and a ring, and a snap hook. Or it can be a webbed belt, with a pouch or loops for tools. Don't just wrap it around you. Put it through three or four of the belt loops on your jeans, so it can't slip up and off. A lot of things could happen to render someone unconscious and the strongest arms or legs are of no help at all. I could truly bore anyone with all of the strange little things that have happened to me, with and without a safety belt attached. Most of them were pretty stupid -- and you don't get any kind of credit for the things you can't foresee (or even the things you can). Once gravity takes hold, your time is measured in split-seconds.

Static electricity can build up on top of a tower, especially where there are parts of it that are insulated from the rest; if you grab hold of it, you can get a small shock. It's not much -- no more than what you'd get by touching a doorknob after walking across a rug. But the effect of the shock is to make you let go; that's a purely automatic reaction. And that's what'll get ya! So beware.

If you wear a helmet, you'll prevent a few bumps you might otherwise acquire in running into the blade tips. They have a sneaky habit of turning around and pointing straight down <u>after</u> you've looked to see if they're oriented safely. Sometimes the bottom of the wind machine will swing around on ya, too. I don't like helmets so I have the bumps to prove I don't wear one. I do wear a cap or a bandanna (tied like a scarf) whenever I'm working on a tower, though; it keeps my long hair from catching in things and covering my eyes. Can't always spare the hand to push it back and out of the way!

Other than falling bodies, the next most dangerous thing is falling tools or parts of wind machines; that is truly uncalled for, but it happens. It's really handy to have someone at the base of the tower to talk with when you're workin' on the machine, but you don't need to reward them with a 3-pound crescent wrench traveling 35 MPH! If your pockets are bulging, you're settin' up for droppin' sumthing! Figure out another way to secure them, or make two trips. One thing you can do is hook a piece of line to your belt. When you get topside, let it go, and just haul things up and down as necessary. If you make it twice as tall as the tower (or the height at which you are working), then you can drape it over sumthin', and have the person at the base of the tower haul things up or lower them down. Or tie little pieces of string to the tools so if they're dropped, they only drop a foot or two, and you can retrieve them. Or attach a pouch or box to the tower at the place you're workin', and store 'em in there. If you have parts of the wind machine to remove in order to get at other parts underneath, take along a few extra lengths of line, and tie them to the tail of the machine or the tower. Then tie them to the thing you're removing before you take it off. That way if you slip, you don't end up mangling the nosecone, the governor, a blade, or a tail cover and your friend, to boot. Get line that is appropriate for the thing that's supposed to dangle from it; hawsers aren't necessary for nosecones, and kite string is absurd for props.

If you do drop something, yell "HEADS UP." I've always thought of this as something really absurd to say, but for some reason it's easier to remember -- and it's understood. Of course a person below is not supposed to look up, just cover the ole head and tuck away to make the least target for whatever's comin' down. Helmets are a must for those standing at the base of the tower while someone is workin' on top, but they won't be of much use for anything over 5 pounds. So instruct such a helper to stand clear of the tower base until you need something attached, and then have 'em get back out of there. There is nothing which requires that person to be right at the base, anyway.

You may find it helpful to wear gloves in climbing up and down towers, especially if it snowed the night before and you've got sub-zero weather; if ya don't wear 'em, you'll leave a lot of skin on the metal. This will also protect you from any residual static charges that build up on the tower or some of its components. When you take them off up there, be sure to secure them well somewhere. They really like to fly off, and it can make for a painful or uncomfortable trip back down. If it's cold on the ground and there's wind aloft, get a jacket on; that wind will be working along with the cold to produce a chill factor which will freeze you all too fast. If you haven't got anybody to come and get you, they might just leave you for the spring thaw!

One final note: I've seen folks carryin' things up towers with only one hand used to climb the tower. There is no mistaking it when someone is doing this. It isn't easy, and it looks jumpy and awkward from the ground. The trick is to shift the body weight in until it's close to the ladder, then let go of the one rung and grab the next before the body falls out to the point where the next rung is no longer reachable. Yep, it does work, and you can do it, but you deserve whatever happens. Tower rung roulette, they call it, and there are no missers in the club -- only fools! If you see someone doin' that, just back away from the tower a bit to give the body plenty of landing room.

Tower Lowering

Unless you build your own tower, or someone just drives up and delivers one to you, chances are real good that you're going to have to lower a tower before you get a chance to raise one. And that is unfortunate. Why? Well, becuz it's harder to lower one than it is to raise one. Okay, maybe you do have gravity in your favor. But, consider the situation with the bottom-slippage guy wires and the raising-cable tension. These will both be minimum when you start to lower a tower, but they will rapidly approach maximum toward the end. You don't get to subject anything to the acid test until it's too late. As well, the vehicle can only provide a braking force to the raising-cable tension, and it's hard for it to keep from sliding along. If ya jam blocks under the wheels, it makes it a wee bit difficult to get them out (you'd have to back up). And you don't know if the gin pole is strong enuff, etc. Once that tower has started down, you're committed to it. And that's not a fun place to be.

If you haven't got the experience, then you haven't got it, so you might as well just do it. Make sure you study the material on raising towers well -- most of it will apply, only in reverse. You'll need the same guy wires, and they must be located identically. Allow for plenty of cable length when you lower the tower; this is no place to come up short. You must use a gin pole! Otherwise, you'll lose control in the last 10 or 20 feet and you'll surely damage the tower somewhat, if not completely. Make certain that the area you're lowering the tower into is clear of obstructions; if it does fall, you'll want it to impact on as level a surface as possible. This will distribute the impact and lessen the likelihood of extensive damage. If it hits a tractor or something solid like that, about midsection, it'll bend it in half just as pretty as can be. If there is a wind machine on the tower you want to lower, and you've never lowered either before, don't try them both at this point unless you're in the junk salvage business. Take the wind machine off first, and then lower the tower.

I have never lowered a large tower, like the ones we raised with Jim on his homestead. I imagine that the most difficult part is to get the raising cable onto the gin pole, once the tower is down to where it's necessary. One thing is for sure, though -- count on it not lining up to one that you've rigged up. You will have to stop the lowering at that point, so be ready for it. You'll want to rig up the gin pole so you can tell when you've reached that point. You'll either have to climb the gin pole and get the raising cable secured to it (tethered or pulleyed method), or you'll have to relocate the gin pole so that it is directly under the raising cable at that point. The raising cable must unquestionably come to rest on it and not slip off. The only thing you're going to have to do is get a pulley on the raising line before you begin the lowering (unless you have one that opens up). Think it out.

The safest way to transport a tower any distance is to dissemble it and transport it in pieces. This will seem a lot more work than required if it's only a short distance from where it's at to where you want it to be, but I think that transporting it whole might not really be any savings at all, energy-wise. If it's a long tower and you insist on transporting it whole, you might rig some wheels out there at one end; this might, however, not be very legal and it'd be too much like the ole, long-ladder type fire engines they used to have (the ones with the driver in the back as well) and tiz a bit more than I would tackle. Nope, I'd stick to the ole WD-40 and a couple of good wrenches and take the thing apart; if you do this, draw out the sections and cross-pieces and use some kind of coding to identify the pieces. Mark the actual tower pieces, too. Save dem bolts and nuts and lockwashers and washers!

Notes on the Octahedron-module Tower

If you want to build an octahedron-module tower or, at least, check out the possibility of using this type of tower, get the Windworks plans. They are extremely well done and easy to understand. I take issue in this section with the limitations imposed by the plans but you will need those plans to understand fully what I'm talkin' about here.

Windworks says that structural strength and esthetics were the criteria in the final design for the tower. Their plans do not tell you precisely how to build a tower higher than 30 feet but the necessary info is there if you can understand a few basic relationships. I totalled up the material waste and came up with a figure close to 10%; that's not too bad, but I tend to optimize materials use and let esthetics slip a bit. And I wanted a taller tower, so I changed some things. If you study their plans and look at my recommendations, you can design and construct a tower which is at the approximate height you want it to be, and it'll be easy on your pocketbook.

Windworks wanted their octahedron-module tower to look like the Eiffel Tower. This makes a very sound structural design, but it cost them convenience and some material waste. One of the first things that you will notice (when you look at the plans) is that they specify some rather unusual lengths for the vertical and horizontal struts; some of 'em are called out to the nearest 1/32nd of an inch! Okay, you gotta get each set of vertical or horizontal struts the same length but you don't really need to get a weird length. Second thing you'll notice is that the lengths of both horizontal and vertical struts decreases as you get closer to the top of the tower. These pieces get smaller at a progressively slower rate as they approach the top of the tower -- this gives the Eiffel Tower effect and you'll want to follow this pattern to preserve structural strength.

When I modified their design to optimize material use and shoot for a taller tower, I forgot about tower height and esthetics. If you design the tower my way, you may end up with a height of 53 feet, but you'll probably use the same amount of material as someone who tries to design the tower to a nice round 50 feet. EMT comes in 10 foot lengths; if you want to optimize material use, you must remain painfully aware of the fact that you're gonna have lots of material left over if you don't plan it out. You'll need six of any specified length for vertical struts and three for horizontal. Let's look at an example. You need six 8-foot lengths. Six times eight is 48. Can you get these sections out of five 10-foot sections (50 feet). No, of course not! You'll use six 10-foot sections and you'll have six 2-foot sections left over. Okay, maybe you can use them elsewhere. But nowhere do you have a need for six vertical struts of this length. And you'd need only three at a time for the horizontal. Sure, you can cut a bit off three of them, then use them for a horizontal triangle at a higher point on the tower. But you've just introduced waste. Comprende? Well, maybe you can use them for the bottom support struts (not shown).

Designing your own tower is fun. Get out a piece of paper. Lay out some columns as I've done. Start with the vertical struts and select a length. Specify the number of pieces of tubing required (how many 10-foot sections used). Describe what is left over. Identify it with a letter so that you can easily show the transfer of this remainder (or a portion thereof) to another position as you proceed. Decrease the length of vertical and horizontal struts at approximately the same rate as the Windworks plans. Fill in the slots for the horisontal struts as you go along. Don't forget that you can further cut a remainder piece (or, in other words, a 10-foot section can be cut three times). Don't forget that you need six vertical braces and three horizontal braces at the bottom of the tower.

There's nothing sacred about the number of modules in the tower. Windworks has six. You can have more. Don't decrease the number of modules if you're going higher, though. And don't stay with six if you're going to go even 10 feet higher. Don't let the vertical struts get too much longer than they specify or they'll not be as strong.

If you're shooting for a tower that's higher than 45 feet, I strongly recommend using a larger size EMT. I've used all the way up to 1-3/4 inch; It's harder to work with but you'll have a tower that's strong enuff to support a Jacobs. I doubt that the Windworks unit (which uses 1-inch EMT) will support a Jacobs wind machine. Larger diameter tubing is going to cost more, but if you've got a heavy wind machine, use it.

Before you commit yourself by cutting up that precious EMT, build a model of the tower you' ve designed. If it's ungainly, try again. Build one out of straws stapled together or lengths of wood (like bamboo skewers) glued together. The things are difficult to draw. You have to know trig to do this. One last point: if you have, say, 8-foot vertical struts in the base module this will not give you 8-feet of height to the horizontal triangle! It will be something less, becuz it is not literally vertical. At the base of the tower, the actual height gained will be about 3/4 of the actual length of the vertical strut. As you get closer to the top of the tower, the actual height gained will be closer to the actual length of the struts.

EXAMPLE : Okay, here's one that I worked out. Understand that there is nothing sacred about this particular one . . . I played around with the scraps and shifted the lengths of horizonal and vertical struts. This particular design had three 3-foot and one 6-inch piece of EMT left over; that's less than 2.5% waste and the leftovers are large enuff to use for other things. Realize, in working with the table below, that the leftovers are coded and used instead of a 10-foot section wherever possible. You need more info than this to build a sound tower. GET THE PLANS !

	QTY OF STRUTS	LENGTH OF STRUTS	TOTAL FEET	SOURCE OF MATERIALS		LEFTOVER SCRAPS		CODE
				# OF 10 FT. SECTIONS	SCRAPS	QTY	LENGTH	
VERTICAL STRUTS	6	10'	60'	6	–	–	–	–
	6	8'	48'	6	–	6	2'	(A)
	6	7'	42'	6	–	6	3'	(B)
	6	6'	36'	6	–	6	4'	(C)
	6	6'	36'	6	–	6	4'	(D)
	6	5'	30'	3	–	–	–	–
	6	4'	24'	–	(C)	–	–	–
SUBTOTAL ①		–	276'	33	–	–	–	–
HORIZONAL STRUTS	3	7'	21'	3	–	3	3'	(E)
	3	5'	15'	2	–	1	5'	(F)
	3	3'	9'	–	½ (B)	–	–	–
	3	2'	6'	–	½ (A)	–	–	–
	3	1.5'	4.5'	–	(F)	1	6 inches	(G)
	3	1	3'	–	¼(A)	–	–	–
	3	1	3'	–	¼ (A)	–	–	–
SUBTOTAL ②		–	61.5'	5	–	–	–	–
SUPPORT STRUTS	6	4' (v)	24'	–	(D)	–	–	–
	3	3'	9'	–	½ (B)	–	–	–
SUBTOTAL ③		–	33'	0	–	–	–	–
TOTAL ①,②,③			370.5'	38	–	–	–	–

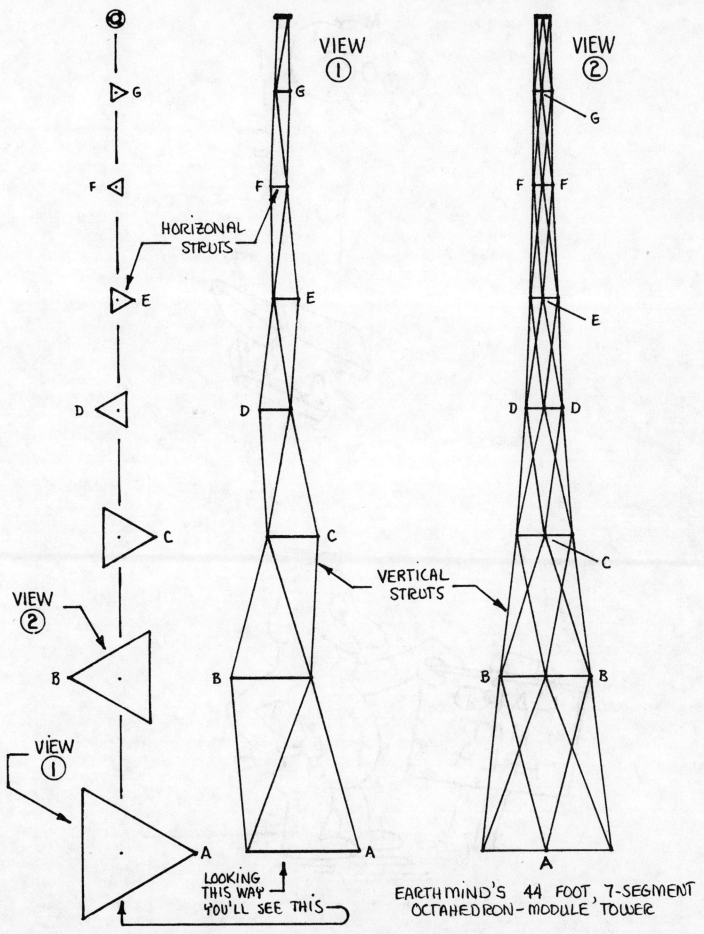

VIEW ①

VIEW ②

HORIZONAL STRUTS

VERTICAL STRUTS

VIEW ②

VIEW ①

LOOKING THIS WAY YOU'LL SEE THIS

EARTHMIND'S 44 FOOT, 7-SEGMENT OCTAHEDRON-MODULE TOWER

INSTALLING the WIND MACHINE

When it comes time to put the wind machine on the tower, there are only two ways to do it -- before the tower is raised and after it's raised. In terms of the work that's involved, the installation appears to be simpler by just attaching the wind machine and then raising tower and wind machine simultaneously, but keep in mind that this will make the raising a lot more dangerous (at the least) and somewhat more involved in preparation. The only time that I raised a wind machine and tower at the same time, it went smoothly and without event; I attribute that to both my knowledge and understanding of the precise way that it should be done (and a lot of ways it shouldn't), and the experience of having raised towers (without wind machines) three times before the attempt; besides, neither the tower nor the machine were particularly heavy. If you have not raised a tower and wind machine before, I would recommend that you <u>not</u> raise them together the first time around. I have included a section, however, on special considerations for this method at the end of the chapter; believing you shouldn't do this does <u>not</u> translate to "I'm not going to tell you how. "

Lowering a wind machine is essentially a reflection of raising one but, as most folks will raise one before they lower one, I'll describe the raising process thru most of the chapter. The last section -- Wind Machine Lowering -- will point out special problems of consideration for this process wherever it differs from raising a windplant.

If the tower is raised first, and the wind machine raised second, the method is fairly well restricted to the use of a machine-raising gin pole (not the same as the tower-raising gin pole). Again, the proverbial helicopter or crane could do the job, but if you're doing it that way, you don't need to know anything (unless you don't trust the pilot or crane operator). If neither of these methods is available to you, then the first thing that needs to happen is to understand what the gin pole is, where it goes, what it does, and how. Let's get to it.

The Machine-Raising Gin Pole

Quite simply, the gin pole used to raise wind machines to the top of the tower is a miniature crane; the only difference between it and the big guys is that it doesn't move around, it attaches to the tower, and it's something that you can put together yourself. If selected well, installed correctly, and operated within its limitations, it is reliable, strong, and safe.

Fig. 4-1 depicts the type and size of gin pole recommended for the installation of a wind machine like the large Winchargers of the pre-REA period. The latter is made of one and one-half inch to two inch water pipe, and measures 9 to 11 feet in length. A T-connector can be used to attach the horizontal member of this gin pole (don't use a 90° elbow as it is not strong enuff), but a preferred attachment is by welding. A brace must be added for strengthing the horizontal member and, by virtue of its position, must be welded. If you are doing this yourself, I recommend using an arc welder rather than a gas-welding outfit as the weld will be stronger with the former and the metal surrounding the weld will not be as weakened by the application of so much heat. So, if you don't have an arc outfit, take it to a place that does. An eyebolt (mounted as shown) will provide the greatest versatility for any kind of pulley used, but insure that it is large and that it is mounted as close to the brace as possible.

The Wincharger type of gin pole is suitable for the installation of any wind machine up to 150 lbs of weight. For larger wind machines, a Jacobs-type gin pole is recommended (see Fig. 4-2). This is an 11-foot-long, straight pipe, with a 2-1/2" inside diameter and should be of the seamless variety of pipe (not water pipe). When installed, a gin pole thus fashioned is incredibly strong and able to lift 500-600 lbs with no indication of unusual stress. (I admit my ignorance of what its upper weight limit truly is.)

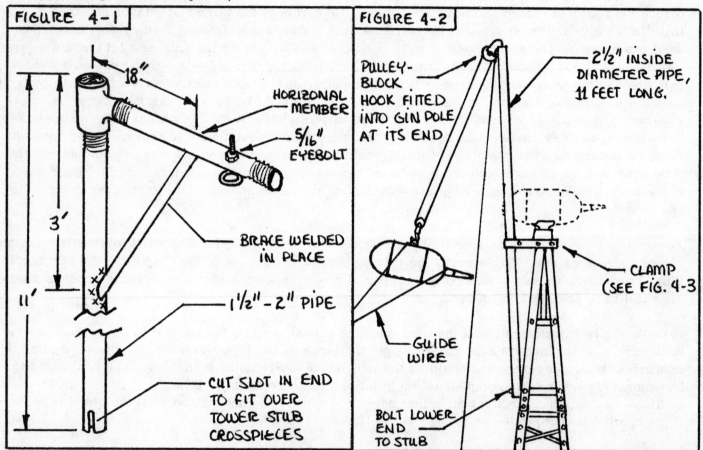

FIGURE 4-1

18"

HORIZONAL MEMBER

5/16" EYEBOLT

BRACE WELDED IN PLACE

1½" - 2" PIPE

3'

11'

CUT SLOT IN END TO FIT OVER TOWER STUB CROSSPIECES

FIGURE 4-2

PULLEY-BLOCK HOOK FITTED INTO GIN POLE AT ITS END

2½" INSIDE DIAMETER PIPE, 11 FEET LONG.

CLAMP (SEE FIG. 4-3

GUIDE WIRE

BOLT LOWER END TO STUB

Both gin poles attach to the tower at two points and will rise above the wind machine for about half of their length (see Fig. 4-2). The bottom of the gin pole is best secured by slotting it to slip over a cross-brace that is part of the tower itself. It must also be secured at a point below the wind machine mount but as far up the pole as possible. The greater the distance between these points, the more secure the gin pole will be during a wind machine-raising becuz it will have less of a tendency to shift or angle over to one side or the other as the force and direction of pull shift. By virtue of the shape of the tower, it is nigh impossible to secure the gin pole directly beneath the wind machine position without using some kind of "stand-off." Without it, once you've gotten the wind machine up near the top, you won't be able to mount it becuz the gin pole is in the way. It helps in this situation to visualize the clearance from wind machine to gin pole as though the wind machine is already in place. Fig. 4-3 illustrates three types of stand-off that can be used. The first is designed for a three-leg tower and is characteristically used for a wind machine of the Wincharger type (and weight). The second is the type used for a four-leg tower and for a class of wind machine like that of the Jacobs wind machine (and its weight). The third is a "gotta-be-desperate" method that I have used with some success a number of times. The latter is by far the most dangerous and the most difficult to use; while it makes for a faster setup, it will cost time and energy during the wind machine installation becuz it's not as stable. Use it if you are crazy, desperate, and fully paid up on your life insurance.

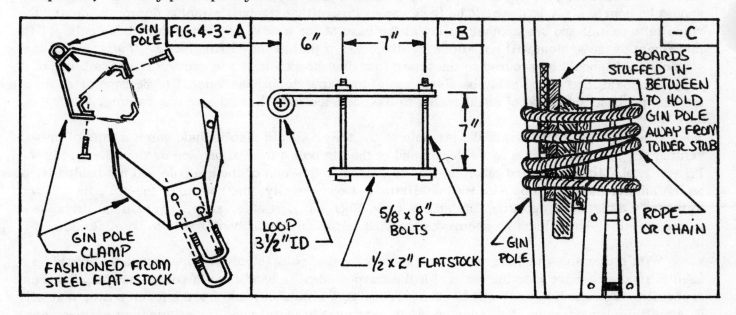

FIG. 4-3-A

GIN POLE

GIN POLE CLAMP FASHIONED FROM STEEL FLAT-STOCK

-B

6"

7"

7"

LOOP 3½" ID

5/8 x 8" BOLTS

½ x 2" FLATSTOCK

-C

BOARDS STUFFED IN-BETWEEN TO HOLD GIN POLE AWAY FROM TOWER STUB

GIN POLE

ROPE OR CHAIN

Machine-Lifting Physics

As previously indicated, the gin pole used for raising wind machines is essentially a small crane. To prevent unusual stress on it or on the top of the tower to which it is attached, there are a few general rules-of-thumb that should be followed:

1.   When securing the lower end of the gin pole, notch or slit the gin pole so that it fits over the crossmember; this will serve to prevent this end from moving inward or outward or from rotating. If crossmembers are not available to support the lower end of the gin pole, then bolt a sturdy piece of angle iron horizontally at the desired position. The situation may be that you have angled pieces of metal that are in the vicinity of this position but they don't appear strong enuff; you can, however, remove them and use the same bolt-holes for securing the angle iron. If no such convenience is present, then drill some holes and use quarter-inch bolts or larger. Here's one of those things that you'll want to do while the tower is still on the ground, so write it down as one of the items in the tower's pre-raise preparation list.

The angle iron that is used should not protrude more than about six inches from either side of the tower. This will prevent any collision of the wind machine during the raising with the angle iron piece. They're all tied together, folks. We used a similar piece of angle iron on an installation job and secured it only with some chain. This was quite safe for the raising becuz the wind machine was brought up on the gin pole side and swung around to be bolted on to the lolly shaft. A year later, however, we brought the machine back down for some work but, in this case, we removed it (along with the tail and governor) to the side of the gin pole. The obvious interference wasn't noticed until the wind machine was being lowered and it took a few seconds for the vehicle to get stopped, and we almost banged the angle iron crosspiece out of position. If it had moved a bit, the gin pole would have shifted to the side. This would have lowered the wind machine a bit more, pressing down onto the angle iron more, shifting the gin pole further: a very vicious cycle. The extra length of angle iron (about 18") had made a handy footrest for tower work. In lowering the wind machine we could have had both -- a 6" footrest and a noninterfering member -- by cutting off the excess 12". 'Tis what happens when you take siestas with the ole head.

2.   Fig. 4-4 illustrates another little point of consideration when using a machine-raising gin pole -- you shouldn't apply pull to the side of the gin pole any more than you have to. The pull should be nearly straight down. The best way to insure that the pull remains downward during the raise is to install and use another pulley at the base of the tower. By using this "base pulley," the movement of the vehicle will not affect the direction of pull at the "lifting pulley" (attached to the gin pole). It should be secured to the tower (not just hooked to it) to prevent the possibility of its release, should the raising cable be slackened at any time during the raise. (The rope or cable used for this purpose should be of equal rating to the one used for the wind machine raising.)

3.   The bottom attachment of the gin pole to the tower should also include some means of preventing any side movements of the lower end of the gin pole (toward one leg or the other). In the highest probability, the wind machine will be raised to the side of the gin pole and not behind it, or on the side of the tower opposite its installation. Consequently, the bottom of the gin pole will tend to move in a direction opposing this stress (see Fig. 4-5). Cable, rope, or chain should be used to prevent this, but it must be secured somewhat in the manner shown if it is to be effectual.

4.   With either the Wincharger or Jacobs-type raising pole, a cable, rope, or chain should be used to further secure it to the tower. If the third method is used for gin pole stand-off, this is a necessity. For the latter, it will be many wraps as a minimum, and for the former two, that will be a sufficient maximum. I've seen so much poor quality metal used for all kinds of clamps, etc., that I tend to overdo the number of ways it should be secured. It only takes a little more time and longer lengths of cable, rope, or chain, but it sure beats the idea of giving ceremonial last rites to your wind machine.

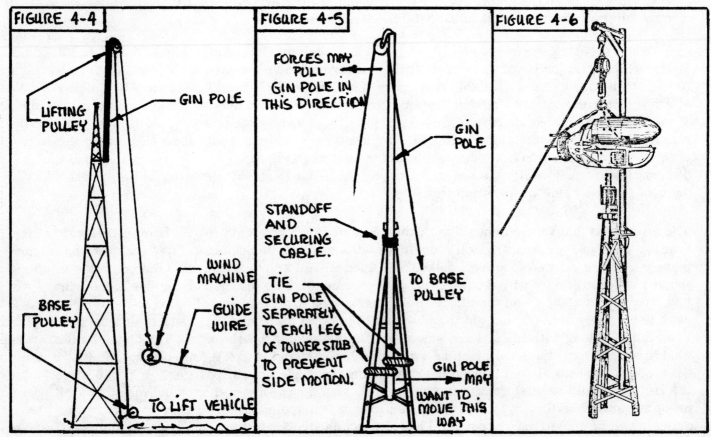

FIGURE 4-4

LIFTING PULLEY
GIN POLE
WIND MACHINE
GUIDE WIRE
BASE PULLEY
TO LIFT VEHICLE

FIGURE 4-5

FORCES MAY PULL GIN POLE IN THIS DIRECTION
GIN POLE
STANDOFF AND SECURING CABLE.
TIE GIN POLE SEPARATELY TO EACH LEG OF TOWER STUB TO PREVENT SIDE MOTION.
TO BASE PULLEY
GIN POLE MAY WANT TO MOVE THIS WAY

FIGURE 4-6

5. The gin pole length varies for different wind machines and the types of tower, but the idea is this -- secure the gin pole in such a fashion that it allows 18-24 inches more than the distance the wind machine must be lifted up to clear the lolly-shaft, turntable, or saddle (see Fig. 4-6). Do some measuring (in either case) of the width of the wind machine, the length of the lolly-shaft, turntable, or saddle, etc. If you're wondering why the extra 18-24 inches, remember that you will have a pulley attached to the gin pole (through which the raising cable will be strung) and must allow for any amount of "swing" that might occur during installation or removal. The straight (Jacobs-type) gin pole will need maximum allowance becuz the pulley attached to it will not be directly above the mount for the wind machine. You won't want the gin pole any higher than it really has to be but 'tis better to be that way than to come up short. You'll know almost immediately if you have underestimated in the case of lowering a wind machine; but if you're raising one, you won't know until after you've gotten it all the way up there.

6. If you have three single-pulley blocks, however, then consider using a mechanical advantage (or consider getting this many pulleys so you can use a mechanical advantage). A mechanical advantage is a lever arm; you won't do less work (by the physics definition of the word), but the amount of force that you have to apply to raise the wind machine will be reduced by one-half, one-fourth, or more (depending on which arrangement you use) and that spells less struggle, strain, and sweat (which is a layman's definition of work). With three single-pulleys, the best you will be able to do is one-half the force (see Fig. 4-7), but with two double-pulley blocks and a single-pulley block (for the base pulley), you can work up a mechanical advantage whereby you'll only have to exert one-fourth the force normally required to lift the wind machine (see Fig. 4-8).

The only disadvantage with using mechanical advantages in the pulley arrangements is that you will need a longer cable and the lift vehicle (if you still need it) must travel further in order to raise the wind machine to the same height. Let's illustrate the meaning here in an example. Supposing that you have a 54-foot tower and the top of the gin pole is 6' above the top of the tower (making it 60 feet to the top of the gin pole). If you don't use a mechanical advantage (Fig. 4-4), the cable will only need to be a little more than twice the tower's height in length and the lift vehicle

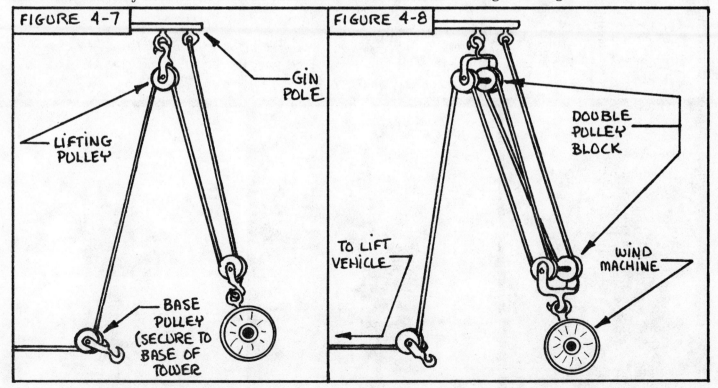

FIGURE 4-7
GIN POLE
LIFTING PULLEY
BASE PULLEY (SECURE TO BASE OF TOWER

FIGURE 4-8
DOUBLE PULLEY BLOCK
WIND MACHINE
TO LIFT VEHICLE

must travel out about 60 feet to get the wind machine all the way up there. For a mechanical advantage like that shown in Fig. 4-7, the cable will need to be a little more than 3 times the tower's height in length, and the lift vehicle will have to travel out about 120 feet to get the wind machine to the top. For a mechanical advantage like that shown in Fig. 4-8, the cable will need to be a little more than 5 times the tower's height in length, and the lift vehicle will need to travel 240 feet in order to raise the wind machine to the top. So you're not gettin' sumthin' for nothin'! The extra cable costs more and you'll need a longer path for the vehicle to travel (although you could stop, tie off the line, bring back the vehicle, and start off again). Another alternative here is to lift the wind machine by people power (Armstrong method). This would be hard to do if a mechanical advantage is not being used becuz you must lift the full weight of the windplant (let's say it's 240 lbs). If you're using the mechanical advantage in Fig. 4-7, that's reduced to 120 lbs, and if it's like Fig. 4-8, it's reduced to 60 lbs.

The Raising Cable

The raising cable must have a rating which will handle the weight of wind machine that is to be installed. If possible, it should have a snap rating (referring to the weight it will hold if the cable is suddenly tensioned) but it is not necessary if you can insure a strong, smooth pull. I've only used rope once to lower a wind machine (it was about three-eighths-inch nylon), but certainly prefer using my five-sixteenths steel cable with its hemp center. When raising a wind machine, it is easy to give the raising cable a little test without having to worry about what happens if it is not strong enuff, but this is impossible to do if you're lowering a wind machine without lousy consequences. More on that in the section dealing with lowering wind machines . . .

The raising cable will be secured to the top of the gin pole or to the wind machine, depending on whether or not a mechanical advantage is used. If it is attached to the wind machine, this will be at the ring-bolt or to a sling that supports the wind machine (See Fig. 4-6). If it's to the top of the gin pole, secure it to the eyebolt (along with the pulley's hook). Some pulleys have a hook underneath the pulley block which is attached to the center of the pulley, and this can be used also.

Wherever it's hooked, it should be secured with cable clamps if it's steel cable, or a strong and appropriate knot if it's rope. Keep the connections neat and prevent any dangling ends from any possible interference with the cable as it goes through the pulleys, or whatever, during the raise. Wherever a pulley is used, don't just use the hook! Secure a piece of line in addition to the hook around the same point to prevent the pulley from inadvertently slipping off when the cable is slackened. Always route the wire (or rope) over the pulleys in a neat manner (don't let 'em get all twisted); they should not cross but once at any point. If this is done on the ground, insure that the assembly is attached so they are not twisted during the installation. Think about where it is that it might turn (as the wind machine comes off) and you can compensate for situations where it might get messed up during the raise.

Guide Wires

Becuz of the gin pole's position, you should use a long rope (or wire) to hold the wind machine away from the tower once it is on the way up. If you are raising the wind machine without a tail, props, or hub, then one long rope will do it, and it should be secured directly to the wind machine,

With the gin pole installed, the Jacobs is readied for the raise. After a long look down, it's pulled out of the truck and the lift begins. After no more than a 20 foot raise, the inadequate gin pole bent and we thanked our last-minute decision to install a back-up wire. With a new gin pole attached, Jim pulled away and we got it up there. The author got some assistance from Ken in the bolt-up.

<u>not</u> to the pulley block to which the raising cable is attached.

The guide wire should be at least one and one-half times as long as the tower height. This will insure that the person pulling on the guide wire can get as far away from the tower base as may be necessary to hold the wind machine away from the tower without exerting tremendous amounts of downward force (and buckets of sweat) to do it. Of course, this person will be pulled toward the tower as the wind machine goes up (this is natural), but that individual can keep the brakes on sufficiently to do the job. The guide rope will only have to sustain, at the very most, a hundred pounds or so.

If you are raising the tail and governor at the same time, but not the props, then you should use two long wires for the wind machine, one attached to the front and the other near the tail. For the latter, tie it in such a way that you can get it off once the wind machine is installed; after all, the end of the tail may be a long way from the tower and you can't very well go scootin' out there to undo it. Fig. 4-9 shows just one of many ways this can be done. The reason for the two wires is so that it is easier to keep the assembly from turning one way or the other and jamming up on the tower (or marring your perfect paint job). On a perfectly windless day you can probably get away with only one line, but if you've got wind (or want to prepare **for** that eventuality), then run the two wires so that you can maintain perfect control.

Most folks who install propellers on the wind machine before it's raised are in too much of a hurry, as far as I'm concerned. There is simply too much hazard involved and, for most wind machines, the props are no manner of difficulty to attach once the wind machine is up there. (Usually it has been part of the design criteria for that wind machine.) However, this condition might not exist and for that reason I indicate the way to do it. The rope for the front of the wind machine should be well secured to the prop shaft or hub, and then the line should be secured to the tip of one of the props LOOSELY (see Fig. 4-10). Extra precautions are in effect here. Number one: use the two long guide wires (as in Fig. 4-9); this will prevent overstressing the blade by exerting bending forces toward the front or rear of the wind machine. Number two: the person or persons involved in pulling on this guide wire during the raise must always insure that they are pulling <u>only</u> directly out on the prop (they should have a perfect side-view of the wind machine from their position).

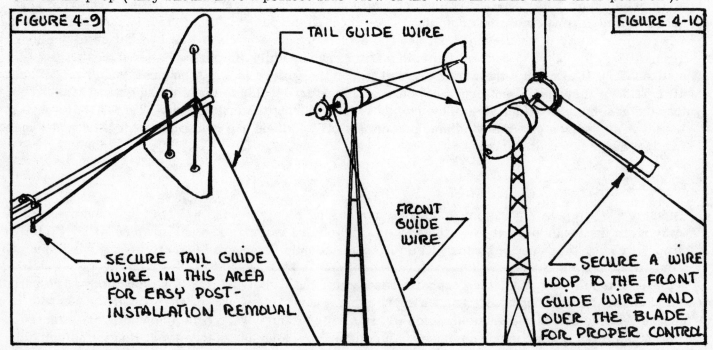

FIGURE 4-9

TAIL GUIDE WIRE

FIGURE 4-10

SECURE TAIL GUIDE WIRE IN THIS AREA FOR EASY POST-INSTALLATION REMOVAL

FRONT GUIDE WIRE

SECURE A WIRE LOOP TO THE FRONT GUIDE WIRE AND OVER THE BLADE FOR PROPER CONTROL

Understand that the guide wire attached to the governor or prop shaft is not attached to the blade tip at all; it is merely strung thru the loop around the blade. The purpose of doing it this way is to insure that the prop doesn't start spinning during the raise.

Backup Wire

Using a backup or safety wire for the raising cable is purely optional. I've only done this once, and it saved the day, as the gin pole started to bend over when the wind machine was a quarter of the way up; it would have doubled over and probably snapped, otherwise. We were using the wrong gin pole for the job and knew it. That had a lot to do with our decision to install the backup wire in the first place.

If you want to get maximum use out of the backup wire, then secure the pulley used for it as close to the top of the tower as possible (see Fig. 4-11 and accompanying photo). If you secure it to the gin pole, then you're only protected against cable breakage and not against the gin pole bending, slipping, or breaking. We secured one end of this wire directly to the ring-bolt on the Jacobs that we were installing, looped it over a well-secured pulley block near the top of the tower, and down to a truck. We looped the wire around a bumper support so that we could take up the slack as the wind machine went up. In this way, the most that the wind machine could fall was a few feet.

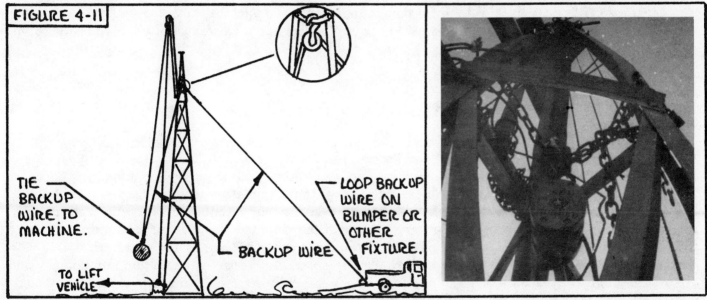

FIGURE 4-11

TIE BACKUP WIRE TO MACHINE.

BACKUP WIRE

LOOP BACKUP WIRE ON BUMPER OR OTHER FIXTURE.

TO LIFT VEHICLE

After the machine reaches the height of the backup pulley, the backup wire will need to be slacked off so the raising cable can pull the wind machine up the rest of the way. The backup wire can remain attached to the wind machine but, of course, the wind machine will fall a distance before all the slack is taken up and the backup wire may not be able to sustain the shock of sudden tension. One can be fairly assured, however, that if the wind machine can make it 90% of the way, chances are better than ever that it will make it the remainder of the distance.

Personnel

The number of persons required to raise a wind machine is the same here as it is for a tower-raising. I'd put the minimum at 3 -- one in the lift vehicle, one at the top of the tower, and one holding the guide wire. If you have two guide wires (tail to be raised with the wind machine), then add one person. If you are insane enuff to raise the props with the wind machine, add one other; this person can help to hold the guide wire for the front of the wind machine to eyeball its progress. If it might get windy, add two more people -- to help with the guide wires and to stand close to the lift vehicle so that messages can be relayed very clearly and quickly. If the wind is over 10mph (and I'm talking about gusts), invite them in for coffee and then send them home. If you're still go (it's a calm day), and you're running a backup wire for the raising cable, you'll need someone to take up the slack in this cable (around an inch) and hang onto it if the main raising cable setup goes haywire. If you've got people to spare, then get someone in there to take pictures and maybe get a cassette recorder on the set. This last thing may sound corny, but I would give a lot at this point to have a recording of the raises that I've been involved in.

Final Setup Check

When you're actually ready to raise a wind machine, go back through all the points mentioned in the chapter thus far, and write down all of the applicable ones. As in the case for tower-raising, don't substitute this information for your own head. I'll probably think of sumthin' I should have said when the book's out and it's too late. When you've set up all the equipment -- pulleys, raising cable, backup cable (if used), guide wires, vehicle positions, etc. -- then you should go over the setup and procedure with someone who's not familiar with it and let him/her doublecheck it.

A pre-machine-raising pow-wow is just as necessary as the tower-raising one previously suggested. The danger zone is still quite wide; even though the area that might be impacted by a falling wind machine is small, a snapped and loose cable can strike out like a rattlesnake, so keep spectators back at a safe distance.

Doing it

Shades of tower-raising! Do it!

When you've completed the "acid test" for the raising cable, give the GO signal again. Easy does it. The rope tensions and she starts doin' the anti-grav thing again. Up and up and up. The tail is swinging toward the tower so give the signal or yell to the guideline tenders for the tail to hold it a bit. They shouldn't have to actually pull out on it becuz they're allowin' it to slip through their fingers or movin' forward as the thing rises. If the machine is out from the tower more than a few feet, have them both slack off a bit. No sudden pulling here or the other end will surely swing inward. Watch the pulleys carefully. A simple kink in the rop or cable can jam up easy and rip a pulley loose or cause a cable or rope to snap. Everything flows like honey right now, though, so keep her going. Higher and higher into the sky. Guide-wire tenders movin' in now as the wind machine gets higher. Still taking up the slack on the backup wire. A shout from the top of the tower. The wind machine is almost up to the point where the backup wire's pulley is secured. Give the signal for SLOW. And another shout from above. It's there. Give the STOP signal. Check with the top-o'-the-tower watch and have the folks tending the backup wire ready to give up slack as the wind machine raises. But no more than necessary. It may not be much of a backup at this point, but it is sumthin'. And that's better than bare-fistin' it any day. Everything understood? Fine! Run over and talk to the driver. A nice and slow lift cuz the backup wire tenders have to match the raise now. And back to it!

The author balances the tower on his ear while adjusting some side guy wires in preparation for the raising of a restored, 32 volt, 1500 watt Wincharger at Earthmind. The farmhouse roof served as the gin pole and Jim Davis located his winch-equipped Toyota on the other side of the house. Nessie guided the machine's tail until it was high enuff, and up it went! Governor and blades were installed later and the author checks blade-tracking, gives it a lube job, and watches (cautiously) as the tail is let out (to the operating position). Then it's a quick scramble down the tower as it revs up.

The top-o'-the-tower tender takes it from here. A GO SLOW signal and it's rising again. Now it's up above the top of the tower. Dead slow at this point. A STOP signal from the tower tender. He looks the situation over. Nope, it won't quite clear. Raise it a mite -- maybe a foot or so. She inches upward. The STOP signal again. Nope, an inch or two higher. Steady back-up of the lift vehicle. Okay, STOP. That's it. Set emergency brake on the vehicle and block the wheels if it seems necessary. Kill the engine on the vehicle and keep it in gear (if it's a stick shift), or Park if it's an automatic.

At this point, a break is in order, unless everyone is primed and ready. There might be a need for two people up there for the bolt-up, so figure out who's going to do it. Get rigged up with the necessary stuff -- tools, good-and-strong safety belts, bolts, nuts, lock washers, etc. -- for bolting it up. Put 'em where they are easy to get out (back pockets are better than front pockets, incidentally).

The long climb up. At the top, a shifting around until the two people can work together and not be in each other's way. Get both safety belts secured and checked. Check the amount of slack afforded by the wind machine's position. How much can it be moved to one side or the other? Will it swing over and directly above the saddle (or to the top of the tower)? Don't expect this to be very much. The wind machine will be very close to the gin pole, and there won't be much rope to play with. Yell down to slacken off on the raising cable a bit so that the wind machine will start moving down on the top of the tower. If the saddle and lolly-shaft are attached to the wind machine, you'll have to guide them into the recess for the lolly-shaft. It's a wee bit more tricky sometimes than just lowering a wind machine down onto the saddle and bolting-up, but not impossible. If you're using a large mechanical advantage, then you may have to shake the blocks a bit and, in general, jerk the wind machine around a bit to insure that the raising cable isn't hung up. If ya don't do this, and they are hung up, the lift vehicle may give a tremendous amount of slack before they suddenly let go and fall the distance afforded by the accumulated slack. It can crush fingers, arms, and heads, or it'll at least scare the dickens out of you. If the vehicle is perceptively moving but the wind machine is not lowering, call a HALT and have them back up a bit to take the tension and work at those cables a bit to see if you can free any binding. When it does start moving down, push on it sideways until you're holding it over the top of the tower and keep coming down. This is exhausting work. Jim has a favorite expression for this. "It's like trying to install or remove a V-8 engine 50 to 60 feet up in the air." It'll have you sweating in no time. Take lots of breaks. No place to get in a hurry!

You may have to jockey the wind machine up and down several times during the last few inches until you can get a bolt started and on its way. Keep the fingers away from between tower and wind machine as it can suddenly slip on you and catch you a good one. When you do get a few bolts home, get the rest of them in there. Get 'em turned down tight before you release the raising cable connections or the pulley blocks. When that's done, the guide lines for the tail and the governor can be removed. If you have the props attached, keep the retaining wires for both of them attached until you can get the pull-out chain in operation. Without electrical wires attached to the wind machine, there will be no "load" condition to hold the prop in check and it can get to a very high RPM before you have a chance to sneeze. If the wind is turbulent, this will be a real chore because the guide lines will find it difficult to keep it pointed out of the wind. At that point, however, two mistakes have already been made -- raising the wind machine with props, and raising it on a windy day -- so whatever happens next is deserved. If I have gotten myself into this jam, I'd straddle the wind machine, get my safety belt on tight, and start yelling for someone to please hurry (although probably not in that vernacular) and get the pull-out chain secured and operating.

Installing the Pull-out Chain

Most wind machines are provided with some means of automatic feathering -- spoilers, governors, furling, etc. -- whose aim it is to slow the wind machine in high wind conditions or once the prop (or whatever) has reached a certain RPM. In addition, most wind machine are provided with a means whereby the aeroturbine's revolutions are manually stopped. This may be the only system installed (no automatics at all) and it can also be a means to completely shut the windplant down (instead of just the limiting effect of automatic devices). The good wind machine designs incorporate both; in this manner, the windplant provides for unattended operation with a capability of complete shutdown for maintenance or repair work (as required). Some existing wind machines have electrical shutdown devices, but most have a mechanical affair which is cranked by hand at the base of the tower. Whether it applies a mechanical brake or pulls the tail around (so the windplant is side-facing the wind) doesn't really matter; what is important is that some means is required to connect the crank at the bottom with the appropriate device at the top. This is a long wire with a short section of chain at the lower end (for winding onto the crank) and a swivel at the upper end so that the activated device at the upper end will do the job without twisting the wire excessively (which will occur if the windplant revolves into the wind more in one direction than the other). Fig. 4-12 illustrates these connections.

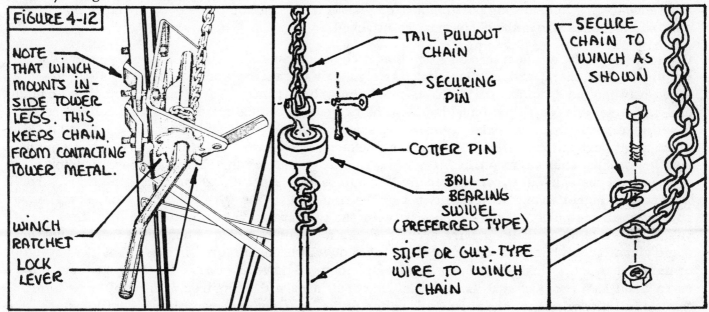

The swivel at the upper end is attached to another wire or chain that then connects to the brake or tail pull-out; it usually travels up through the center of the lolly-shaft so that the windplant is still free to turn. The Wincharger and Jacobs pull-out arrangements are somewhat similar (see Tail-Furling in CHAPTER 2) but you must know -- for these and other wind machines -- whether the tail is pulled into place (like the Jacobs) or pulled out of place (like the Wincharger). This and the tower height determine the length of pull-out chain used. Once established, the wire should be connected to the swivel. Be sure to lubricate the swivel with some heavy grease before you do this. If you can afford it, get a ball-bearing swivel as the ElCheapos don't work at all under tension.

The lower end of the pull-out or brake wire should be connected to some chain. The winch used here will have a small diameter spool; if wire is secured there directly, it will not take very long before the wire will be frayed and weakened by the tight turns it must take going onto the spool and the straightening that occurs when the wire is unspooled. I guess if you used stainless steel aircraft cable, it would do the job without being fatigued; but then you run into a problem in trying to cut it to length (you wouldn't believe what it does to wire cutters!). So chain is wound up on the spool instead.

To find the length of chain required for the crank is not all that difficult. First, route the pull-out wire down and into the vicinity of the pull-out crank. Pull it tight, give an excess of 9-15 inches, and cut off the excess. Loop the wire into the hole in the crank spool or attach it to a pin located there. Now rotate the crank clockwise (when viewed from the handle end).

When the pull-out wire is just tight, notice how many turns of wire have been made on the spool. Now, crank the handle around (in the same direction), making sure that the turns are going onto the spool side by side and neatly. As the wire is spooled in, watch the tail swing out and behind the wind machine (for the Jacobs-type) or out of this position and into a side-facing position (for the Wincharger-type). When it's straight behind or side-faced (respectively), mark the wire at a point where it is just starting to go onto the spool (a small piece of masking tape works well if wound tightly). Now, unwind the crank until the tail is back in its original position. Mark the wire where it just starts to come off the spool (at about the same number of winds you turned it before the tail began to move) and take the wire the rest of the way off the spool. The distance between the two markings (of tape) is the amount of wire that must be spooled to bring the tail from side-facing to operating position and/or vice versa. The top piece of tape marks the approximate point where the chain must be attached.

Get some good chain. Requirements are that it be able to sustain several hundred pounds of force. Get closed-link chain, and not the S-link variety. Don't get it so large that it won't clear the space between the spool and the crank-n-spool supporting frame. Once you find some, get one and one-half times the length you found between the two pieces of tape markings on the pull-out wire. It will take more chain than wire to make the same number of turns on the crank spool and a little extra won't hurt all that much. The stuff isn't exactly cheap, so I'm providing a way to keep the cost low without sacrificing utility. Once you're ready to attach the chain, you have to determine where to cut the pull-out wire. Generally this can be done right at the upper tape marking. You'll want it a bit higher than that in reality but by the time you tie the wire onto the chain, it will have shortened all the more. If the distance between the two tape markings was more than three feet, you might move up the pull-out wire about 3 inches for every extra foot and cut it there. Just do some visualization here and what you're tryin' to do will become more obvious. You'll want the chain to make a few turns on the crank before it starts to move the tail of the wind machine, but extra won't hurt provided that the spool is wide enuff to take the required number of turns to bring the tail full around. Loop the wire through one of the links and just twist it a bit until you check the amount of chain left over (below the crank). It should be anywhere from 6-12 inches. Okay?

Now tie the pull-out wire to the chain (like that shown in Fig. 3-36 of Chapter 3). Cut off the excess or twist it neatly around the wire until there is none sticking out more than a few inches. Don't want to get it caught on anything!

Because of the tremendous lever-arm of the crank, it would be wise to mount a sign at the base of the tower as to which way the crank should be turned to furl the windplant or to bring it into operation. Someone familiar with the cranking procedure for the Jacobs must reverse this process if a Wincharger is in use. Never know when you might have to tell a stranger to furl the windmachine (becuz you are otherwise occupied) and mistakes can be disasterous. We will be operating windplants of both types here so we plan to install these signs just so that we don't get confused. If it's dark, raining, and so windy that you must furl the windmachine, it can get done backwards very easily. I recall a conversation with a gentleman at one time where he commented that there were only three things that he couldn't remember. The first was the names of people. The second was the names of places. And he couldn't remember the third one! Have I made my point?

The pull-out crank, wire, chain, pulleys, swivel, and all connections associated with this function should be checked periodically for fraying, loose hardware, and rust. The swivel and chain should be lubricated with grease whenever necessary. Check the little ratchet-arm on the crank for wear. This is the only thing that keeps the windmachine furled or open and it will eventually wear out.

If the crank at the bottom of the tower is used to operate a brake on the windmachine, much of the above procedure applies but you will find that it will take less turns of the crank to engage or dis-engage the brake mechanism. The mechanical-brake assembly at the top will need close attention as it doesn't take much rust or dirt to muck-up the movement of the parts in the assembly, especially for releasing the brake. If it doesn't completely release, a slackened cable will be the first sign but it may not always evidence itself thusly. A partially-released brake will very quickly be worn by the propeller's rotation. As well, sufficient friction here will generate enuff heat to ig-nite any residual grease, so keep surfaces and hardware in the vicinity of the brake clean and free of grease.

Installing the Governor and Props

If you raised the wind machine without props (and a governor, if applicable), then it's sumthin' you're gonna have to do. If you have a tail to install, do it immediately after you've installed the governor and props. This way you can control the wind machine a lot better; it will not be con-stantly trying to orient itself to the breeze. If you have installed the tail, make certain that you have installed the pull-out chain or brake cable and that the tail is furled or the brake set tight. Never install, remove, or work on the windplant if you can't stop the machine.

The gin pole will help bring up the governor and the props, too. You shouldn't have to struggle too much to get it attached with someone holding the raising cable from below, but you will have to lean out a ways to do it. Some governors will mount before the props are attached and some after. If yours is the latter, watch out for the blades! Even with the windplant furled, the blades of the prop can (and will) swing around freely (particularly in gusty winds where the wind direction is changing faster than the tail can follow). It doesn't take much of a movement on the blades to draw blood if you get wopped one. Sometimes the blade will move backwards and that sharp, trailing edge can slice you good. It it's moving and hits you with the rounded, leading edge, it generally won't cut but it compensates neatly by just knocking you out (if that's any consolation). Even with-out wind, the windplant will respond to any pressure that you exert on various parts of it and swing away from you at just the wrong time, so prepare for it and make your movements sure and thought-ful.

Just a word here on something I have observed before. Never tie a blade tip to the tower in an attempt to keep the windplant from tracking or the blade from revolving. If there is no wind at all, it looks functional. But even in a slight breeze, the blades will revolve as the windplant tracks and it will slip out of the rope or it will just try to do these things and bend or break a blade. If you've ever tried to push a tail sideways when the wind is blowing, you will understand quickly the amount of force it is capable of applying and the absurdity of such an effort will find no place in your actions. After all, the tail keeps the windplant oriented into the wind and that's no easy thing. The area directly behind the propeller is very calm even in high winds and yet this small movement of air is sufficient to keep the wind machine well oriented and, generally, very responsive to fluctua-ting wind direction. Take heed!

When the prop is ready to be attached to the windplant, you must decide whether to raise it assem-bled (if possible) or in pieces. If you have a one piece, two-blade prop and the governor installs later, there isn't any decision to make. If you have a hub on which 3 or 4 blades are installed, then you might possibly raise governor and blades together, or the governor first and each blade separately. Doing it on the ground is easier for assembly, but the idea of having a combination of the weight and cumbersome size of this fragile assembly being raised 60 feet and then attached is a bit too scary for me. If you do it (wind or not), attach guide lines similar to those used in the windplant raising and take it slow and easy. Aerodynamic surfaces don't like dings and dents.

If you take the slower one-at-a-time method of attaching the props, the gin pole will come in handy for raising them up there. Insure that the person down below is holding onto a guide line cuz it's easy for the blade to swing and collide with the tower. Attach whatever is used for a raising cable in such a fashion that you can install the blade without having to remove the raising cable to do so. In this way you account for that "whoops" that is bound to occur with at least one of the blades that you're installing. Some of the Wincharger and Jacobs blade-and-governor assemblies had a piece of tubing inside the blade which slipped over a piece of stock-rod sticking out of the governor. If this represents your situation, then you'll want to rub a light oil over the shaft before you try to install the blade. A gentle twisting movement will work the blade onto the shaft, but you may have to have someone located further down the tower (at about that point where the blade tip is) pushing up on it. The whole assembly will need to be prevented from moving to install the next blade and, unquestionably, the windplant will be trying to swing around one way or the other. It's a skillful and patient individual that gets these things on with a minimum of effort and time. Tighten all bolts immediately as each prop goes on, and install the air-brake if the windplant uses this type of governor.

Afixing the Tail

If the tail was not installed on the windmachine before the windplant was raised to the top of the tower, prepare to experience the fun of installing it afterward. The gin pole will be absolutely necessary to doing this, so leave it up there. Attach the cable (that is used to raise it to the top of the tower) as you would have for the guide wire (see Fig. 4-13). You might also attach a short piece of rope to the end of the tail that will mount on the wind machine, just for a little easier handling once you've got it up there. This is a two person operation -- make one a strong-arm and the other one with some brains (to figure out the best way to do it). Using only muscles with this job is the wrong way altogether becuz it is truly difficult to apply enuff force to counteract the tremendous lever-arm of the tail. By using a method similar to the one in Fig. 4-14, the attachment is just a matter of adjusting raising cable tension once the end of the tail assembly (that secures to the windplant) is at the attachment point. The strong-arm helps to prevent the tail assembly from pivoting at this point and swinging to either side during mate-up. Use the lift angle afforded by

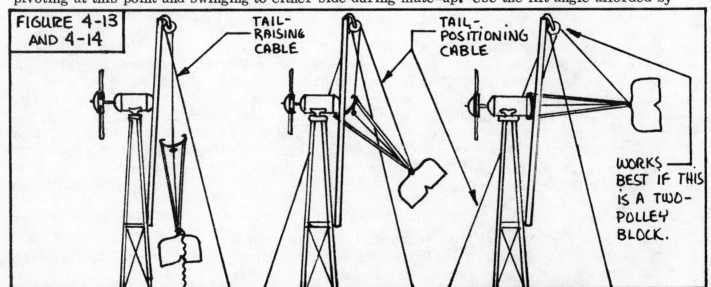

FIGURE 4-13 AND 4-14

TAIL-RAISING CABLE

TAIL-POSITIONING CABLE

WORKS BEST IF THIS IS A TWO-PULLEY BLOCK.

the gin-pole and raising cable and adjustments to the shorter piece of rope (which can be looped thru the eyebolt on the gin pole) to do the work and it will just be a matter of concentration rather than a weight-lifting contest. Don't expect it to be a fifteen minute job.

Once the tail is installed, attach the pull-out line and route it through the pulleys and holes to the position of the swivel. If you're trying to get the wire (or a chain located here) up through the center of the lolly-shaft, you may need to lower some wire through it from above and then tie it up and pull it back through. A piece of baling wire will work wonders here (if you're not the farmy type, try a coat hanger). If you find that you are getting nowhere while working on a tower, you're no longer tuned into it, so stop, lean back (with the safety-belt attached, of course), and think about it. This is no place to get hurried!

Blade-Tracking

The remaining thing to check is the blade-tracking. (This is different than windplant-tracking.) This is easiest done using a ruler or small stick at a position on the tower directly at the level of the blade tip. Do this on a non-windy day and preferably with someone at a higher point on the tower holding on to the tail to insure that the windplant does not change its orientation during the check. Secure the measuring device tightly to the tower (with the hand) and move the stick or ruler out until it just touches the blade. Pull it back a slight amount so that it will not scratch the blades. Give the blade a slight push to get the prop to rotate and bring the next blade into position (this movement may cause the windplant to turn if it's not being held -- if this happens, it'll screw up the test). All blades should be the same distance from the tower.

If there is any possibility that the blades are warped, take this into account by measuring the distances to the blade (from the tower) at points in line with the blade's tip and at its mid-point. Always correct for the middle of the blade first. If the blade is slightly bent near the tip, this will tend to straighten out and align itself with the rest of the blade when the centrifugal forces become significant. So . . . the distance to the blades should be the same at the midpoint of the blades even if they are not quite the same at the tips.

If the blades are not the same distance from the tower and it's only a two-blade prop, you're going to need to put a shim between the blade and the blade-mounting plate on the windplant. Insert the shim between the blade and mounting-plate on that side which has the blade that is closest to the tower. The shim can be a thin washer or piece of sheet metal or shim-stock. How thick it must be depends on how far the blades differ in distance from the tower. Try something, tighten it down, and re-do the test (at the tip and midpoint of the blade). Mark which blade was closer to the tower to begin with. It it's still closer than the other blade, you need to add more shim. If it is now the one which is further out, you need to insert a smaller shim in place of the one you installed. Keep it up until the blades are equidistant from the tower. That's it.

Make the same kind of measurements for a 4-blade propeller as you would for the 2-blade unit. If you find differing distances to the blades from the tower, then you should mark the blades before you attempt any adjustment. It will be important to keep track of which one is at what distance becuz in adjusting for one blade, you may change the distance of any or all of the other blades in the process. As well, with a governor assembly like the four-blade Wincharger, there are two sets of blades attached to the windmachine (see Fig. 2-5); one set attaches to the governor mechanism on arms that will move and allow the propellers to change pitch when governing is activated. The other set of blades attaches to a fixed plate which is located rearward (or closest to the wind machine); these blades do not change pitch as the governing mechanism activates. The only significance to this design is that any wind machine with this or a similar design of blade-mounting will require special attention when blade-tracking adjustments are made. For purposes of clarity in the following discussion on these adjustments, I shall refer to the blades mounted on the fixed and immobile portion of the governor as the fixed-blades and the governor assembly portion as the fixed-blade mount. The other blades will be referred to as the feathering-blades and the portion of the governor assembly to which they attach will be referred to as the feathering-blade mount. To further facilitate communication, let's label the blades A, B, C, and D. There are a number of out-of-track situations that might be experienced and I'll run through several of them to give you a feel for what might have to be done.

1. Let's begin with this oddity. You find, after careful measurement, that two of the blades are further away from the tower than the other two. It's the same situation when you check at the blade midpoints. It just so happens that two of the blades, say A and C, are equal in distance from the tower and the same goes for blades B and D, but the distance to A and C is different than the distance from B and D. Weird, huh? Not really. Look up and you'll find that A and C belong to one set (like they're both feathering blades) and blades B and D belong to the other (fixed blades). What do you do? Well, check to be sure that you have tightened both the governing mount and the fixed-blade mount to the propeller-and-governor mounting plate on the windplant. If you can see daylight in the cracks between all of these plates, chances are good that it wasn't machined right or that it's part of the design. As long as one blade in a set is not out-of-track (more or less distant from the tower than the other in the same set), there's nothing to worry about. It will not upset the action of the blades in operation.

2. What about this one? After some measuring at the blade tip and the midpoints you find that blade B is farther away from the tower than blades A and C (which are the same distance) and that blade D is closer to the tower than blades A and C. You're gonna need a shim here. But, you have to get the answer to a question first: are all the blades attached to one governing unit or are they attached, like in the Wincharger, to separate portions of a governor. If the former is the case, then simply insert a shim between the governor assembly and the governor and propeller-mounting plate on the windplant on that side where blade D is attached. If the answer to this question is the former—the blades are attached to a two piece governor assembly (with fixed and feathering blades) —you must then answer another question. (Hang in there—this all sounds a lot more complicated than it really is.) Are the blades that are out-of-track the feathering-blades or the fixed-blades? If the answer is the former -- the feathering-blades -- then you will place the shim between the feathering-blade mount and the fixed-blade mount on the side where blade D mounts. If these blades are the fixed-blades, on the other hand, you will place the shim between the hub mounting plate on the windplant and the fixed-blade mount. In this instance, you will have to loosen the feathering-blade mount to, in turn, loosen the fixed-blade mount and put the shim in. Make sense? Tighten down the assembly and again check the tracking. If blade D is still closer to the tower than blade B, you must add more shim, and vice-versa. Check each time to see that you are not causing the distances to blades A and C to change by whatever you do. Repeat until it is right and you're finished.

3. Supposing that you did your measuring at blade-tip and blade-midpoint and found that, say, blades A and B were closer to the tower than blades C and D. This can be a tuffy if none of the

Jim's Jacobs needed its commutator turned down; an attempt to do it with the EM tool (with the unit on the tower) failed, so we brought it down. Insofar as the Jacobs wind machine is balanced with the governor and tail attached, we left them on during the lowering. After attaching the twin guide wires to the Jacobs, we lifted it clear of the saddle and the author walked it down. Posing for the post-lowering (R to L): Ken, Jim and Clayton DeKorne, the author, Charles, and some neighbor helpers.

distances are equal but, for a moment, suppose that they are -- blades A and B are the same distance and blades C and D are the same distance . This should be compensated for by the insertion of a shim between the hub-mounting plate on the windplant and the fixed-blade mount halfway between the two blades A and B. If the distances are not equal between any of the blades, then you may have to first get the fixed-blades equidistant and the feathering-blades equidistant next. For this case, you'll probably end up with several shims -- one between the hub-mounting plate on the windplant and the fixed-blade mount and another between the fixed-blade mount and the feathering-blade mount. It'll be a time consuming event, so give a rest period in there somewhere or you'll end up saying to heck with it and not doing it right.

Proper blade-tracking is essential to good performance of the windplant. Without it, the windplant will vibrate and abnormally wear the bearings for the propeller shaft. As well, it can cause severe stresses on the propeller assembly in high wind conditions. If you're wondering how close the distances to the blades should be with one another, then go by this rule of thumb. With careful measuring, when you can no longer detect any differences with a standard ruler, it will be close enuff. If you can note the differences, you're not yet there.

Removing the Wind Machine

Bringing a wind machine down from a tower is far more exciting than puttin' one up, at least to the person that's gotta be up there to loose it from the tower stub. Extra precautions are in order here becuz there is little room for the small mistakes that a raising can "absorb". The entire proceedure is essentially the reverse of wind machine installation, but here's a few additional notes.

First, if the wind machine has the blades on it, I strongly recommend that they be removed. Fasten lowering wires to 'em before you detach 'em. Attach a guide wire to them so that friends on the ground can help keep 'em away from the tower as they come down. Consider removing the governor and tail. If the wind machine is balanced with 'em attached (the unit will stay horizontal when lifted clear of the stub or mount), it's your option. My preference is removing them, but I have done it the other way. (See photos.) If you've never done this sort of thing before, your first consideration should be to remove as much weight from the wind machine as possible.

Attach the main lowering cable and guide lines as indicated in the text for wind machine installation. I recommend installing the back-up wire; insofar as the pulley for the backup wire is installed in the tower (as previously indicated), it won't have much effect until the wind machine is lowered below the pulley position, but it could prevent an otherwise lenthy fall, hitting the tower as it goes.

For most wind machines, it will not be a matter of simply pushing the assembly sideways (off its mounting position) and lowering it. At the very least, you'll want to take up the tension in the lowering cable and, in most cases, you'll have to lift it a foot or more. This will call for some precision teamwork and it will be absolutely necessary to have good line-of-sight between the vehicle driver or winch operator and whoever is tending the top of the tower. Some good relay work or clearly understandable hand signals (like those shown in Fig. 3-39) will facilitate communication over possible engine noise. Be sure that no guy wires, electrical wires, or other obstructions will interfere with the lowering. You'll have much better control of the wind machine if you lower it on the windward side of the tower, but refrain if the wind is truly a nuisance.

Raising the Wind Machine and Tower Simultaneously

This procedure is not recommended for someone that has no experience with raising towers or wind machines; the special allowances required should provide sufficient reason for this statement. The first effect of raising tower and machine together is the tremendous increase of cable tension over that required to raise only the tower.   An example: If you have a 60-foot tower that weighs 2000 lbs (one ton) and a wind machine that weighs 250 lbs and you attempt to raise them together, you're going to need 25% more lifting force than you would with just the tower to raise.   And if the tension is initially 4000 lbs, another 1000 lbs is a lot !

Second thing: To mount the wind machine, you'll need to raise the top of the tower off the ground a bit (see photos). Whatever you use for a standoff is critical becuz , when you start the raise, there might not be enuff pull to raise the thing more than a few feet and it's going to settle back down on the standoff. If it's not wide or strong enuff, the wind machine will miss or crush it and that's very rough on the wind machine. Unless you have unlimited lifting capacity, you're going to have a real problem lowering the tower back down (should you have to) before the raising is completed.

Okay, I'll get off the negative aspects. Irrespective of the way you've attached the raising cable to the tower (pulleyed-sling or direct), you'll want to move this entire attachment closer to the top of the tower (to relieve internal tower stresses); this should be about half-way up from where you'd put it for raising only the tower. Double up the cables and doublecheck all connections. You've really got to do it the first time.   This will also mean double the anxiety but that comes with the package; if ya don't want it, don't do it. I've uneventfully raised a large Wincharger on a 40-foot, single-leg tower, but had a devil of a time with another (smaller) Wincharger raised with a 47-foot Octahedron-module tower. Quite frankly, I've lost interest in raising wind machines with the tower-- that's too much ganglia shock for me and just not that much less work (if any).

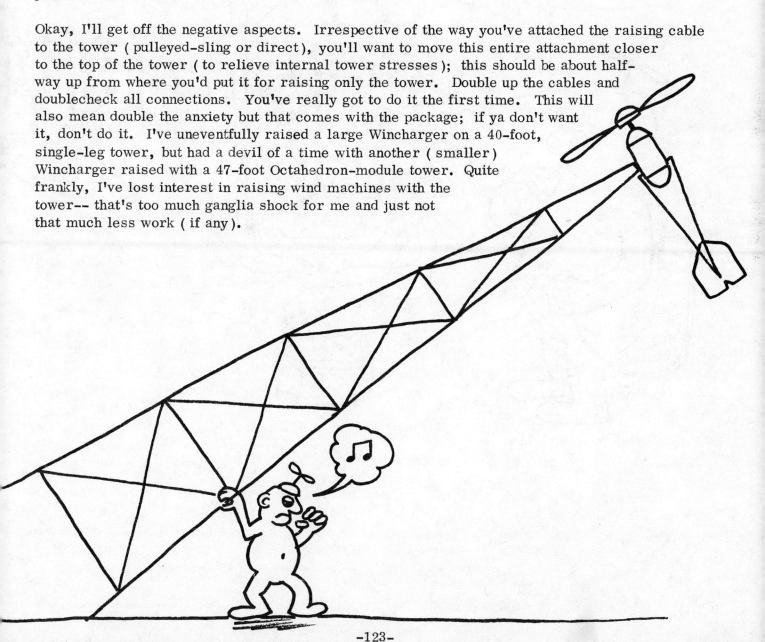

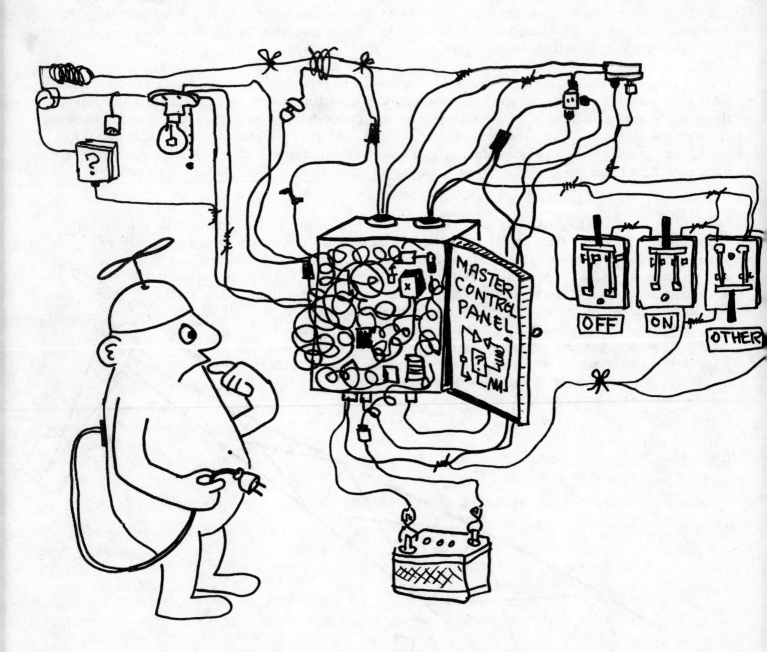

CHAPTER 5

THE CONTROL BOX

There is probably no single component of a wind-electric system that is more a mystery than the Control Box. Wires run in and out of it (depending on your point of reference) and it sits there on the wall, hopefully doing whatever it's supposed to do. Perhaps needles move in gauges, or lights turn On or Off (or just flicker) or, occasionally, it issues forth a series of machine-gun clicks, or a single click. If you are fortunate enuff to have an operator's manual for it, it will show a maze of circuit and wiring diagrams and there may even be a section that attempts to explain the individual components and what they are supposed to do. It may also tell you how to make some adjustments if this doesn't read this way, or your batteries don't seem to be full charging, or whatever.

Or maybe there isn't an operator's manual. You've found yourself a pre-REA wind machine and its control box looks like it was Grand Central Station for the BMU (Barn Mice United). So, you've cleaned it up but you're not sure if you've hooked it up right, or it doesn't seem to be operating. Pretty desperate situation. Call for help? Who? An electrician? Maybe one could take care of the problem-- a blown fuse or a simple adjustment. Then again, he might just play taps for your unit after a cursory inspection. What then? What if you don't even <u>have</u> a control box for the wind machine you have, or are presently building.

The point of this chapter is to detail the components of the wind-electric controls-- how they work and what they do, how they work together, what things need to happen, etc. -- and to provide sufficient information on how to replace a control box that you've acquired with something that will do the same job (particularly if there is no hope of getting the one you have to work becuz it's just one big hunk of rust now, having sat in the bottom of a creek for a number of years). If you're building a wind-electric system, this chapter will tell you what you must account for and protect, and how you can do it. There is no way that all of the information that would be necessary to fit all situations can be provided in the space that is allotted in this chapter, but it will be a start. If you have never worked with electronics, this will <u>not</u> make you an electronics technician or a qualified electrician; only hard work and study on your part will gain you that skill. But it will make you a competent operator of your wind-electric system (if you acquire a working knowledge of the information contained herein) and, at the very least, it will supply sufficient information on the wind-electric system control requirements to allow for some competent work on the system or the construction of a functional control box by those qualified to wire a house.

Control boxes for wind-electric systems are, for the most part, extremely simple devices. They do a variety of things, none of which is difficult to understand. If you can remember back to when you first learned to drive, you should recall that it seemed like there were too many things to do at once -- steer, clutch, shift, turn on the turn signals, headlights, etc. -- but now you don't give any of them a second thought. Yep, it's the same way with control boxes. In our society they are generally referred to as "black-boxes" but, while some of them are more complex than others, they can be reduced to the components that make them up. If you can recognize some of the parts, by a process of elimination, it is possible to determine what the other unknown parts must be. If you know some of the basic interrelationships between the components (or how they work together to produce some desirable effect), then they become the truly simple things that they are.

Most of the information provided here is not available to the library-going public insofar as I have determined. This unquestionably forms the largest reason for the very existence of this chapter. It comes, therefore, from my own work in the field and an extensive analysis of these systems. The Bibliography lists the few references for further reading on the subject that I know of. This chapter includes, as well, an in-depth description of the Jacobs and Wincharger control boxes; by the time you have absorbed the workings of both of these control circuits and the owner-built control box of my own design, you will realize the extensive similarities of all three, and the few differences among them. This in itself should be indication enuff that control boxes for different types and makes of wind machines still carry the same kind of components hooked in the same way; control boxes, therefore, differ in degree rather than kind. It should further suggest that once you've seen one control box, you have probably seen them all. And that makes it all the easier to learn!

The chapter would probably be better entitled "De-Mystifying the Control Box," but I see this as more than just knowledge. It's awareness and understanding and liberation. There are probably as many different reasons for using a wind-electric system as there are people using them, but if you are doing it becuz it seems more sane to generate your own electricity in a non-polluting manner, then you're doing it to liberate yourself. It seems to me that this pertains to many of the things that go on around us. There's an absurdity to trying to do everything for yourself, but the middle ground is the place to be. Maybe you don't have the knack or the inclination to take on electronics toward this fulfillment, but at least the information will be there waiting for you when the time is "right" for you to learn it. Filling up these pages with philosophy won't help much, so let's get on with it.

Building your own vs. buying one

If you have no control box, you'll have a decision to make: To buy one or to build one. As hope for unlimited power in the fire of the atomic reactor, or coal, or oil dims with the problems and limitations of using these sources of energy, more and more companies and individuals will begin building solar and wind-electric equipment. And that will make it all the easier to out-and-out buy a control box for the wind-electric system you have, or will have. If you buy the wind machine new, it will have a control box with it. Even if you have a vintage machine, chances will get better and better for finding one that will work with your wind machine. If you can do it and you can afford whatever it costs, it becomes your decision.

Buying a control box is like buying a new car for someone that nursed along an old clunker for a number of years before it finally died. There are generally a few vows that the individual will make and one of them is gonna be to take good care of that new car so that it doesn't end up like the old one. And that vow is generally the first one to get broken. Why? I don't really know for sure, but it seems to go somethin' like this: one gets kinda caught up in the beautiful workings of the new one and sorta gets to thinkin' it will take care of itself for a long time before any real attention needs to be implemented. Oh, sure . . . it gets washed a lot and worried about and fussed over when the wax job is put on. But that begins to wear off becuz it works so . . . so . . . Beautiful!

Newly installed windmachines and new control boxes get the same kind of treatment. A careful reading of the instruction manual. A schedule of changing the oil, lubing the zerks, and checking the gauges for proper readings. And a whole lot of "I'm gonna learn everything there is to know about this dern thing!" Maybe it happens and maybe it doesn't. That's avoided if the individual is directly involved in constructing the control box. Maybe a friend ends up puttin' the thing together cuz he's good at that sorta thing, but you're the one that bought all the components and you watch with a careful eye as he breathes life into it. And you learn what's what, what it does, and how to adjust the few controls and adjustments that it has. And you know what reading is right at what time (on the gauge) and what isn't. You KNOW when a fuse is blown becuz you KNOW it's doing what it's not supposed to, or it's not doing what it is supposed to, and you've checked these other things that could be causing it and they're okay. It all becomes amazingly simple and second-nature -- like operating a car, or a 27-knob stereo receiver -- and the thing functions year after year with trouble-free operation.

Another thing that helps the situation -- whether you buy or build a control box -- is to stockpile parts for it. This is more likely to occur with a home-built job than one that is bought. Not surprising in this latter case becuz the manufacturer is not going to suggest that you do this (it would make it sound as though there is something that is high-failure or apt to go bad quickly) and the new owner of the control box is not going to be thinking that anything will go bad with it, and will figure the part can always be ordered when it does go bad. This reminds me of a funny event which occurred one day when I was working on a Wincharger control panel and noticed a seal on the cover of the cutout relay. Consulting the manual, I was amused to read two items pertaining to the discovery. The first one indicated that this particular relay could not be adjusted by anyone but the company and that it should be removed and sent to the company if it was determined that it was not functioning properly. The second item was that the warranty on the entire wind-electric system was void if this seal was found to be broken when it reached the company. Sound familiar? The joke? Well, there was no company to send it to and there was no warranty to be voided becuz it had long run out. As I removed the seal and cover and proceeded to adjust the relay (correctly, I might add), it brought out some good laughter from the people present in the shop at the time. Stockpiling some of the more apt-to-go-bad components in the control box, therefore, will prevent a discovery that the company you purchased the unit from has gone out of business when you need that very specially-constructed-and-adjusted part somewhere down the years.

Control box functions

So . . . what does a control box do? Why, it controls, of course! And what does it control? Well, first of all it assures that the wind machine operates properly. A little vague, isn't it? So let's list some of the functions of the control box.

1. The control box allows the windplant generator to begin charging the batteries when it reaches a speed where this can occur. When it's below this point, it disconnects the generator from the batteries (for reasons that will be detailed later on).
2. The control box protects the windplant generator from putting out too much voltage or current. This can cause arcing or excessive heat in the generator and possibly a fire or severe damage.
3. The control box senses the condition of the batteries, allowing a high rate of charge when they are near exhaustion (from use) and a limiting action (less current , or "trickle charge") when the batteries are fully charged and no heavy-power consuming devices are being operated.
4. By virtue of the action described in #3, the control box protects the batteries from overcharging and undercharging.
5. The control box directs the current from the generator to the batteries and the load

(or anything consuming energy while the generator is charging). When the generator is not charging, the control box routes power from the batteries to the load (if any).

6. The control box indicates the amount of current the generator is producing (when it is charging); this will be a readout on the ammeter (which measures amps). If there is a load while the generator is charging, it will generally only indicate what percentage of the amount of electricity being produced is going to the batteries. If the load draws more current than the generator is producing, it will indicate what percentage of the load the batteries are supplying. (Don't get hung up on this here, it is more fully explained later on). When the generator is not charging, the ammeter indicates how much current the load is taking from the batteries. If a voltmeter is used in the control box, it indicates the voltage of the generator.

7. The control box serves as a junction box for the various components of the wind-electric system. Wires from the outlets (used for appliances), the wind machine generator, the standby generator, and the batteries are all connected to the control box.

8. The control box houses the gauges, relays, resistors, switches, fuses, and inter-connections of these components. Sound almost too simple to say? Not really. This serves to protect these components from dust, moisture, and physical damage.

The control box is a brain -- sensing voltage and current -- and it regulates by switching, routing, and limiting. It houses the controls which can be adjusted to insure optimum performance, efficiency, and safety of the wind-electric system. It's the watchdog which keeps you from having to sit there and do all of these things yourself. And that's liberation!

The Relay

If you look under the listings for the components in any control box, there is no doubt (unless it is all transistorized) that you will see various kinds of relays indicated. Generally you'll see things like "current regulator relay" or "cutout relay" or "voltage regulator relay" and the like, but this describes what they do, not what they are -- they're all relays, or more correctly, electromagnetic relays. Before you can understand how they do what they do, you must understand what a relay is. If you already know this, you can skip over to the next section now. Or you can hang in there and find out how much I goof up trying to explain this very basic electrical device. This section is presented in the spirit of trying not to make too many assumptions about what you know or don't know. I know how frustrating it is to hear someone talking about the many advantages something has -- say, the igjsuytoff, for example -- when you don't even know what it is. Oh, admittedly it can be fun guessing, but if you're told that it is an essential item to the installation of your phertoky, you might get worried!

The electromagnetic relay has four essential parts -- the coil, the core, the movable armature, and the contact points. The coil is made up by winding wire around the core. When an electric current passes thru the coil, it magnetizes the core. If you have ever wound wire around a nail, hooked it up to a small battery, and proceeded to pick up small tacks and metal objects, you've got the idea. This does the same thing. Only, in a relay, we don't want to pick up tacks and paperclips. We want to attract the movable armature, which is made of steel, attached to the relay by a hinge, and held away from the core by a spring. When enuff current flows through the coil to magnetize the core strongly enuff to overcome the spring tension in the movable armature, the latter will move toward the core. In most instances this will be a very small movement -- maybe only one-sixteenth or one-eighth of an inch -- but far enuff to do the job. (Spiffy, huh? The idea of using an electric current to move a piece of metal a tiny bit!) Why? Well, attached to the movable armature are some contacts. More contacts are attached to the stationary frame of the relay. Fig. 5-1 illustrates the arrangement of some of these contacts, but understand that these contacts are really little switches (like light switches). If you had some lights attached to the contacts, you could, by energizing the relay, turn off the lights or turn them on. Whatever you do when you energize the relay, the reverse will happen when you de-energize it (or stop the current from flowing through the coil). This is becuz the core will lose its magnetic properties when the coil current is stopped, and the spring tension on the movable armature will cause it to move back to where it was before the relay was energized. And whatever switch was opened or closed by the energizing action will then close or open (respectively). Got it?

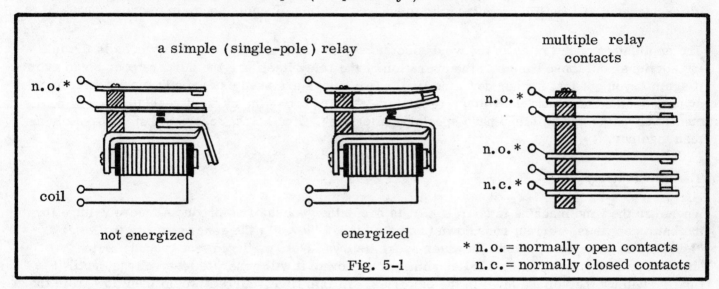

a simple (single-pole) relay

multiple relay contacts

n.o.*

coil

not energized

energized

Fig. 5-1

n.o.*

n.o.*

n.c.*

* n.o.= normally open contacts
n.c.= normally closed contacts

Some relays will only turn On one thing when the relay is energized. Others will turn it Off. By adding more contacts, you can get many things to switch On or Off. And many other relays will do both at the same time; that is, they will turn some things On and others Off when energized and the same things Off or On when de-energized. The strongest example of this multi-operational relay is the washing machine timer. You set this timer and the machine does all these different things -- turns On valves to let water in or pump it out, turns On the washing cycle or spins the thing, lets in cold water or hot water, etc. -- all with one switch (which is really a timer relay), and it does them again and again in the precise order required.

The washing machine-type relay is just one example of the hundreds of applications in which relays are used. But it's just a special kind of switch. Instead of having to turn various types of things On or Off, the relay will do it for us -- automatically and reliably. Becuz of its special nature, we can use a small amount of current to turn on a device that may draw a very large amount of current. The coil, then, can be hooked up in the control box to "sense" something, and turn on something else.

Relays have ratings, just like switches do. This will be a voltage and current specification for the coil and generally a current rating for each set of contacts in the relay (if there's more than one). Because the wire in the coil has a certain amount of resistance, only a certain amount of voltage needs to be applied to it before a sufficient current flows to the relay and, activates the switch contacts. If the amount of current flowing thru the coil is below the rated amount, it will not energize the relay. It will try, but it just won't be able to magnetize the core enuff to overcome the spring tension in the movable armature. If you put more voltage on the coil than the specified amount, you will eventually burn the thing up.

The relay's contacts are rated in amps. Any time that there is a lot of current flowing thru the contacts (as is the case for any switch), it will arc to some extent when you break the connection (open the contact points). If you allow more current to pass through the contact points than it is specified to carry safely, it may do this easily while the contacts are closed. However, as soon as you energize or de-energize the relay (whichever one breaks the contacts), this will result in an arc that will eventually (if not immediately) burn up the contacts and -- bing -- no more switch. There are, therefore, ratings that you must abide by if you want a relay to last very long in a specific application. You'll need to know them, as well, when you go out to get a relay that will work for whatever it is that you want it to do. There are a few tricks to the trade that will allow you to "modify" the operation of a relay in a specific circuit, but if it's underrated, it's underrated and its life expectancy is measured; in this circumstance, in microseconds.

The application of the relay in the wind-electric system will be exhaustively covered in the following sections, but these basics to the operation of the relay itself are the cornerstone; so go over it again if you get lost further down the line. Two relays are used extensively in wind-electric systems-- the cutout and the voltage regulator. A third one-- the current regulator-- will be discussed as well (becuz it may have special application). I will first describe them separately and then together.

The Cutout Relay

Whenever the wind machine is charging, it is becuz the generator is producing more voltage than the batteries; thus, current runs down from the higher "level" (the generator) to the lower "level" (the batteries) much like water seeks its own level, or the lowest ground, or the shortest path to it. When the wind machine slows down, it will generate less voltage, until it is finally "below" the voltage level in the batteries. At this time, current would then flow from the batteries to the wind machine's generator, causing it to turn like a "motor"; if this is not prevented, it would quickly drain the batteries. The way to keep reverse current from occurring is to disconnect the batteries from the wind machine generator whenever the generator is lower in voltage potential than the batteries. Simply said, but a bit time-consuming if we just insert a switch and do it ourselves -- this can happen hundreds of times in a day! So we use a relay instead, connecting the battery leads to one contact and the windplant to the other contact (see Fig. 5-2). When the relay is not energized, the contacts are open (and the windplant and batteries are disconnected); when the relay is energized, the contacts will close and charging will occur. If we hook the leads from the relay coil to the plus and minus power leads from the generator, the relay will sense the voltage coming from the generator and activate the relay when this voltage becomes great enuff for charging.

If you looked at a relay used in this application, you would notice that it has two windings of wire around the core (or two coils); one is a few turns of very large wire, and the other is many turns of very small wire. The small wire is what energizes the relay initially. The large wire is "series" wound; when the relay is energized, the current flowing from the generator to the batteries flows through this large coil, and this reinforces the magnetic field created by the smaller wire, insuring that the contacts are firmly closed. When the voltage in the generator becomes less than that of the batteries (the windplant is slowing down), current will momentarily flow in the opposite direction through this winding. The effect is that it will reverse the polarity of the core and neutralize the effect of the smaller winding. This will cause the relay to de-energize and the contacts to open, disconnecting the batteries from the generator.

You can't just stick any old relay in there and have it work correctly, though, and don't assume that the one you have (in a control box you've obtained) will be correctly operating. The relay must energize and de-energize at specific points (voltages) if you want to have an efficient transfer of energy and keep from having to replace the relay every so often. Usually this will involve the adjustment of a resistance (a rheostat, like R1 in Fig. 5-2), the air gap between the contacts, or spring tension. This involves bending tabs for tensioning the movable armature's spring, or bringing the contacts closer together or further apart. This is tuff going -- different relays have different means of doing this and the manufacturer's specifications won't always be available. If you want to have this done, get someone that knows how to do it or to show you how. Sorry, folks, I won't grant you the frustration that would result from any futile efforts on my part to explain it to you. I burned up a lot of relays trying to make these types of adjustments, and didn't learn the proper way until I found someone that really knew it, and had the patience to teach me. The whole problem stems from the fact that you can't always tell that you have adjusted it correctly when you do try. It may be many days, weeks, or months before you'll know you botched it becuz the relay just burned up. If you just replace the relay, you have to get one with similar specifications -- contact rating, coil resistance, etc. -- and it can be a tedious and fruitless search.

I wouldn't be saying this unless I could provide you with an alternative -- a diode. This is a marvel of the new age of electronics (although it is 25-30 years since its discovery and use), but the problem was that most control boxes (for vintage windplants) were built before they became commonplace. If the diode had been around then, it would have certainly been used becuz it is small (size of a grape), inexpensive (about one-tenth, or less, the cost of the cutout relay), super-efficient (does not permit any reverse current at all, period!), reliable (with a very long life), and has no contacts or moving parts. Anyone with a cutout relay should replace it with a diode and save themselves a lot of grief. If you are building your own control box, you can not only save on money, but use a smaller box. Use of a diode (to replace the cutout relay in a control box) is shown in Fig. 5-3.

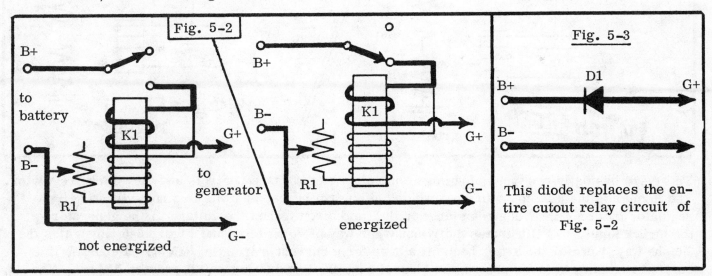

This diode replaces the entire cutout relay circuit of Fig. 5-2

When buying a diode for this purpose, you must purchase one that will have the proper current and voltage rating. Get a diode that has a current rating one and one-half to two times the maximum current rating of the windplant itself. Whatever voltage your windplant is operating at (6-12-24-32-110 volts), select a diode with a PIV (Peak Inverse Voltage) that is at least twice that voltage. Dividing the wattage of your windplant by the voltage at which it operates will give the maximum current rating. If you have a 1500-watt 32-volt windplant, the current rating of the windplant will be a little less than 50 amps. Therefore, the diode selected for the reverse current protection device (to replace the function of the cutout relay) should have a current rating of 75-100 amps and 75-100 volts.

If your windplant is using an alternator, you will not need a diode or a cutout relay to protect against reverse current; this is already protected against by the diodes in the alternator itself (which turns the three-phase alternating current into DC). I'd add one in there, however, just as extra protection in case one of the diodes in the alternator goes bad.

The Voltage Regulator

As a wind-generator increases in RPM, it will produce a voltage slightly higher than that of the batteries, and then remain at that voltage with increases in RPM becuz it is being "loaded" and current is being drawn from it. If the batteries are near fully charged, however, the voltage will continue to climb, and try to force more current into the batteries when you really want it to be giving less current to taper charge the batteries. To insure this happens, a voltage regulator relay is installed in the control box and all that it does is to sense battery and generator voltage and to vary the field current (and, thus, the generator voltage) in one of a number of ways. One lead from the field coils is connected to G+ _in_ _the_ _generator_; the amount of current flowing in these coils (which in turn affect the amount of voltage and current produced by the generator itself) is (or can be) controlled in the control box. If you want the maximum amount of power the genera-tor can produce at any time, you merely ground the field lead (at the control box) and the maximum amount of current will flow in the fields. If you want to limit the output, you can insert resistance between the field coils and ground to limit the field current.

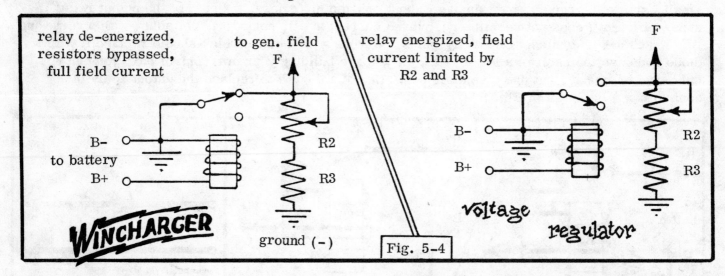

relay de-energized, resistors bypassed, full field current

to gen. field
F

B-
to battery
B+

R2
R3

WINCHARGER

ground (-)

Fig. 5-4

relay energized, field current limited by R2 and R3

F

B-
B+

R2
R3

voltage regulator

There are basically two types of voltage control -- step-voltage controls and the voltage regulator. The former is the kind found in most windplant control boxes, and this is a non-vibrating type regulator that only inserts a resistance in the field circuit when the voltage in the generator gets too high. Figure 5-4 illustrates the Wincharger way of doing this, and Figure 5-5 illustrates the Jacobs way; I prefer the latter becuz it allows for a current-regulating effect. Of course, if a current regulator relay is used in the control box, the Wincharger way is most sufficient. The true voltage regulator relay is a vibrating type (about 220 cycles per minute) and it limits the field current by simply opening and closing the contacts. Both types of regulator -- the step-voltage control and the voltage regulator -- have their contacts closed (and the field grounded) when the relay is not energized. When the voltage becomes too high, the relay coil magnetizes the core, and the contacts will open; this entirely opens the field circuit in the case of the true voltage regulator, but in the step-voltage control, the field current will pass thru the resistor which was bypassed when the contacts were closed. In the Wincharger step-voltage control, this will be the only resistance in the field but for the Jacobs-type control box, the total resistance in the field circuit is the sum of R2 and R3.

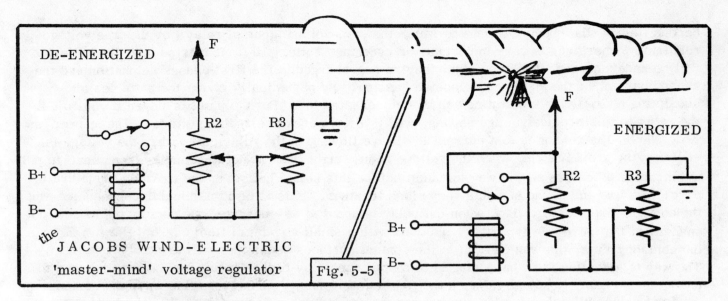

DE-ENERGIZED

F

R2   R3

B+

B-

the JACOBS WIND-ELECTRIC

'master-mind' voltage regulator

Fig. 5-5

ENERGIZED

F

R2   R3

B+

B-

The step-voltage control is preferred over the true voltage regulator in the wind-electric system; this is primarily due to the need for taper-charging the batteries. Lead-acid batteries will take an immense rate of charge initially but, as they grow closer to being fully charged, current must be limited to their "finishing rate." This value varies for the type and size of batteries used so the resistances should be fully or partially adjustable (rheostats). The step-voltage control will allow rapid charging initially (grounded field) and taper-charge (resistive field) when the battery voltage is sufficiently high.

A bimetal, thermostatic hinge on the movable armature is used to compensate some types of regulators for changes in temperature. This causes the regulator to provide a higher voltage when cold, compensating for the fact that a cold battery needs a higher voltage to take a charge. As both warm up, the voltage level required to energize the relay becomes less (as it should).

Okay, here's a few observations. First, I prefer to use the arrangement described in Fig. 5-6 for sensing battery voltage and, at the correct voltage level, energizing the step-voltage control. If the wires connecting the batteries to the control box were nearly perfect conductors there would be no need for doing this. But they're not and this is. Why? The voltage at the control box end of the battery leads will read higher than the voltage at the batteries (especially under heavy current flow). So the voltage regulator is sensing voltage at the control box and not at the batteries, which is where it should be doing the sensing. Becuz the amount of current needed to energize the step-voltage control relay is very low, these wires can be relatively small (#16 wire or smaller). Not a super-important item, but one that has always bugged me about all these control boxes! In fact, many high quality commercial battery chargers use separate sensing wires.

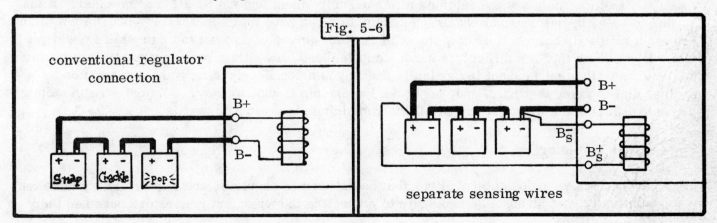

Fig. 5-6

conventional regulator connection

B+

B-

Snap Crackle Pop

B+

B-

B_S^-

B_S^+

separate sensing wires

Second item -- the precise voltage at which the step-voltage control relay (or the true voltage regulator) energizes is very important for maximum battery life. If it trips low, the batteries will be undercharged; if it trips high, they're overcharged. The first causes sulphation and the second burning of the plates or excessive gassing. By periodically giving the batteries an equalizing charge, the low setting can be compensated for. But the point is: even if you adjust the relay to this precise voltage setting, will it always energize at this voltage? The answer is: No! Why? The reason is that current is always flowing in the relay coil (when the voltage is still too low) and it's only when the voltage is just right that its field becomes strong enuff to pull the movable armature all the way in. Just before this point, however, the movable armature is part of the way in and the contacts very close together. This is of no particular consequence when the contacts are closing. But, when the relay is about to de-energize, the contact points will not snap apart but move slowly apart. And even with a small amount of field current flowing through the contact points, this can be fatal to the contact surfaces becuz they will arc and pit or burn. The way to keep this from happening is to install one relay in the circuit for the sensing, and to use a second relay to actually switch the field current (see Fig. 5-7); in this way, the contacts on the first relay will only have the current for the second relay flowing through them (which is going to be a heck of a lot less than the current in the fields) and the actual switching relay (the second one) will energize and de-energize with a snap and save those contact points. By inserting rheostats (variable resistors) in this arrangement (see Fig. 5-8), any adjustments -- precise voltage sensing, current limiting, etc. -- can be easily made.

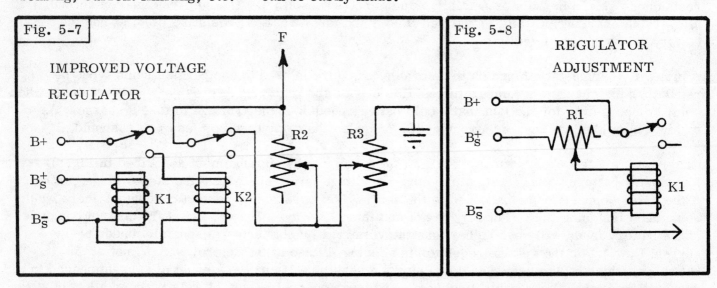

Fig. 5-7

IMPROVED VOLTAGE REGULATOR

Fig. 5-8

REGULATOR ADJUSTMENT

Author's Note: As you may have surmised by now, this is not casual reading-type literature; you may have to reread and study this information several times before it all makes sense. Keep looking at the diagrams and the sections which describe them and it will all become clear. It may appear to be a big jigsaw puzzle at first (schematics can have that appearance) but I'm not taking you for a ride and, believe it or not, the stuff is quite simple compared to other stuff I could get into. If you think that it's difficult to read, don't feel too bad. It's a bear to write! This medium has the limitation that I cannot immediately see if you are understanding some one point or another as I'm going through it and, accordingly, explain it another way. So, just struggle along! Try to get the big picture first and fit all the remaining pieces in afterwards.

The Current Regulator

I have never seen a windplant control box that had a current regulator, and this really irritates me. It is, admittedly, not an absolute necessity to protecting the windplant generator, but when there is a heavy appliance load and the batteries need charging, the voltage may not increase to a value sufficient to cause the voltage regulator to operate. As a result, the current can easily approach and surpass the maximum current rating of the windplant generator itself. Without any additional control, this can burn up the generator, peg meters, and blow fuses. The Jacobs control box did incorporate a maximum rate of charge resistance adjustment in the fields (R3 in Fig. 5-5) but this is not as positive a control as the current regulator itself. I strongly suspect that current regulators were not used in wind-electric systems for economic reasons. If you're constructing your own box, install one as it will provide for that once-in-a-blue-moon condition that will deprive you of energy becuz of a blown fuse, and allow the generator to "run away."

Note: The alternator has a built-in feature which limits its current to the maximum rating, no matter how much the load is trying to draw. As the current induced in the stator coils approaches this maximum, the field of each coil encroaches upon and partially cancels out the current in the adjacent coils. However, in cases where the maximum rated current for the batteries is lower than that of the alternator, a current regulator would still be desirable.

A simple application of the current regulator is illustrated in Fig. 5-9; it consists of a few turns of very heavy wire around a relay core. The coil is then connected in series with (between) the windplant generator and batteries. The field connection is then attached to one contact and the other contact is connected to a contact on the voltage regulator, which in turn is connected to ground. As the contacts for the two relays are normally closed when the relays are de-energized, it should be obvious that either one of these relays, when energized, will block direct grounding of the fields (maximum field current flow) and field current must travel through R2 (and R3 if it is being used). In the situation where overcurrent can occur (high winds, low batteries, high load), current flowing through the current regulator will energize that relay and open the contacts. As this will insert a resistance in the field, the current will immediately decrease and the current

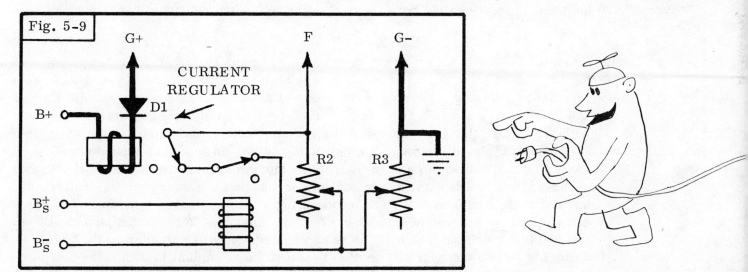

Fig. 5-9

regulator relay will de-energize, closing the contacts and allowing for full field current. If the condition persists, the current regulator relay will energize and de-energize as many as 200 times per minute.

As it might be difficult to find a relay that will energize for your maximum desirable current, an alternative to finding a current regulator relay would be the circuit described by Fig. 5-10; here you can use your own homemade coil of heavy copper or baling wire and insert a relay and rheostat in parallel with the coil. The small amount of resistance in the heavy coil will cause, at high current transfers, a small amount of current to go through the rheostat and relay and in this way the same effect is accomplished as would be in the current regulator relay itself. Adjustment of the rheostat will allow you to set the relay to energize at whatever current flow (through the generator) is in excess of its maximum current rating. The cost of the smaller relay, rheostat, and coil will be, in most cases, far below that of a genuine current regulator relay.

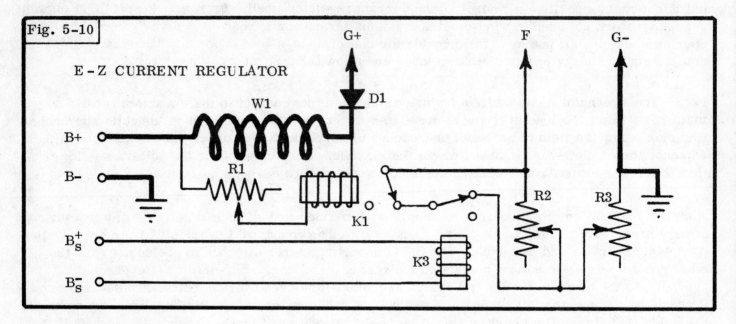

Fig. 5-10

E - Z CURRENT REGULATOR

Other Components

While you may find almost any kind of component in a control box (depending on how many "features" are included), most control boxes will have the following additional assortment of components.

1. Ammeter -- this is a gauge that will read out the number of amps of current flowing through it. You must know how it is hooked up in the circuit if you want to know what it is indicating. There are two types of ammeter. One reads current flow in one direction (and reads from left to right) and the other reads current flow in both directions; this latter gauge will have its needle in the center of the scale and it will read to the left or the right depending, also, on how it is hooked up. The most standard hookup for the two-direction ammeter is shown in Fig. 5-11. In this arrangement, it will show the amount of current that is flowing into the batteries and out of the batteries. If you are operating a load (motors, appliances, lights, etc.) it will not tell you how much current the windplant is producing and it will not tell you how much current the load is consuming; by noting which way the needle is deflecting, however, you will be able to tell if the windplant is producing more or less than the amount the load is consuming. If you are using the single-direction reading ammeter, the best place (in the circuit) to install it is shown in Fig. 5-12; this will only tell you how much current the windplant is producing, but you can guestimate the current consumed by a load by totaling together the wattages and dividing by the voltage used (12V, 24V, 32V, or 110V). If you subtract this from the meter reading, it will give you the amount of current going into the batteries. This meter will not read the current from batteries to load if the windplant is not operating. A way to get around this is to install a second ammeter (see Fig. 5-13) to read load consumption.

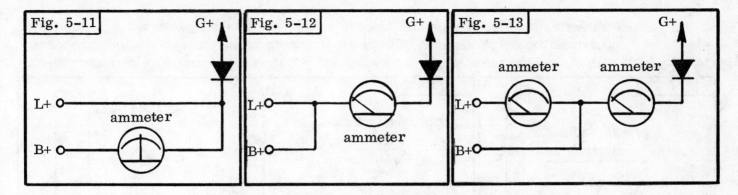

Fig. 5-11   Fig. 5-12   Fig. 5-13

Make sure you know what you're reading by checking out the way you install the meter. In the case of the single-direction reading ammeter, reversed connections can damage the meter. In both cases, use only an ammeter that will read the maximum current the windplant can produce or the maximum amount the load will consume without pegging the needle (if it doesn't outright wrap it around the travel-limit post) or burning up the insides.

2. Voltmeter -- this is also a gauge, but it's used only in some control boxes and is somewhat optional (since a good one can run $5 or more). Fig. 5-14 shows the proper location for this meter; in this way, it will read the generator voltage and, as the wind machine comes up to speed, you'll be able to see its needle rise until the reverse-current (prevention) relay cuts in. If it continues to rise much more, something is wrong. My own feeling is that I like to install a voltmeter in the control box becuz it can help indicate or isolate a problem; if it's hooked up as shown in Fig. 5-15, you'll be able to monitor battery voltage as well. Install the switch (for selecting battery or generator voltage readings) and mark which is which and you can instantly know what's happening with each. If the windplant is charging, the difference in the readings will be very slight (and probably not detectable).

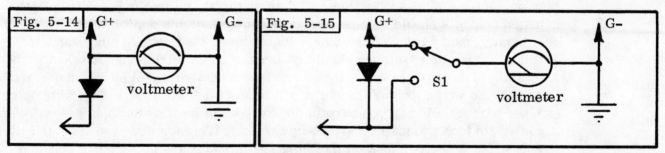

Fig. 5-14   Fig. 5-15

3. Fuses -- Despite the control features of the relays in the control box, you should install a fuse for the generator, the batteries, and the field. The generator (G+) circuit should be fused (as in Fig. 5-16). The batteries should be fused in case the load line shorts (wires or motors, etc.) or something in the control box shorts in its connection to the cutout relay or diode. (See Fig. 5-17). The field fuse protects against shorted wires or shorted field coils in the windplants. (See Fig. 5-21.) All fuses should be installed in rigid fuse-holders affixed inside the box; they should be located where they can be easily removed and replaced. The Generator (G+) fuse will be rated for something about 5-10 amps higher than the maximum ampere-rating of the windplant. The battery fuse will also be rated at this amount unless the fuse is located as shown in Fig. 5-17, in which case it should be rated for the maximum amount of current you want your load line to draw.

The field fuse will be a small ampere rating (the Winchargers used a 2-amp fuse and the Jacobs ,5 amps). Always stock spares as high wind conditions are more likely to blow fuses than shorts are, and you'll want to immediately replace them.

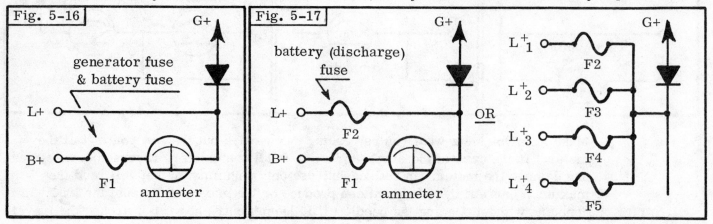

4. PTT switch -- Some control boxes have a Push-To-Test switch and this function will bypass the reverse-current relay and motor the windplant   (if you are using a generator; you can't motor an alternator!) This is a good way to check all sorts of things, but that's explained in the section on the Jacobs unit so it won't be discussed here.   The switch should be a heavy-duty, pushbutton-type switch (it will have a lot of current flowing through it), but it should be located inside the control box and not very accessible; once a kid finds out that it'll make the blades go "wound 'n wound," you're gonna have dead batteries real soon.

5. Control Box Chassis-- the term control box means both the container it is in and the whole unit (complete with components), but here (in using the word chassis) I am referring to the former. If you're building your own control box, get something that has a hinged face (or lid) if possible; a utility box (for circuitbreakers) may do, but see what's available. The ammeter(s), voltmeter, and frequently-adjusted controls should be attached to the lid so that you don't have to open it to see them. Fuses, relays, resistors, capacitors, PTT switch, and Manual/ Automatic operation switches should be located on the inside and attached to the side walls or back of the box. If you can mount another panel on the inside and locate all the wiring behind it, you've got a super-safe box (see Fig. 5-18), but exposed wiring will keep you careful and respectful so it's not absolutely necessary. If you've got kids around (or grown-ups that act like kids and have the curiosity to match), put a latch or lock on the thing. If this appears necessary, consider putting all of the adjustments on the inside so your dials don't get exposed to "Derdialemtwistum" urges.

6. Terminal Strip -- This is just an insulated connection board that allows you to secure the wires coming into or going out of the control box itself.   Leads for the generator (G+, G-, and Field), the Load (L+ and L-), the batteries (B+ and B-), the standby generator (Sb+ and Sb-), and other sensor-type wires should all have a place to connect with screw-type connections. From here, you can run wires to the gauges, switches, relays, etc., inside the box. This will make for easy connection during the installation, easy disconnection when testing something, and less chance of pulling an outside wire and ripping off a part of something vital (like relay contacts) inside.

7. Manual/Automatic Switch -- Any control box that has a voltage regulator should have one of these switches; it can be a toggle-type mounted inside the box. All that it does is to defeat the action of the voltage regulator, and this is necessary if you want to give the batteries their once-a-month equalizing charge (see Chapter 3 in Wind and Windspinners). If you have to do some work on the voltage regulator (like adjust its contact points), when you flip this switch to Manual, it will put full current to the field coils in the generator. You won't want it to stay there for long, though, becuz it will overcharge the batteries and permit fuse-blowing in high winds (becuz of the higher-than-normal voltage the generator will produce). Fig. 5-19 illustrates its position in a normal circuit.

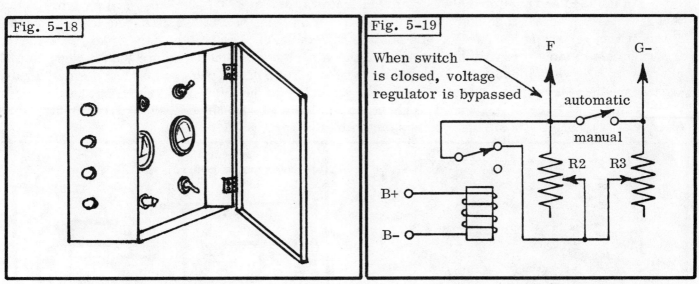

Fig. 5-18

Fig. 5-19

When switch is closed, voltage regulator is bypassed

8. Control box wiring -- Just a mention here on the wiring in a control box. If you have acquired one, check to be sure that the wire is not burnt, or so rotten that shorts are likely to occur. The copper will still be intact, but insulation can rot off and this should be checked. If it exists, tape it up or replace it with new. Use the same size of wire that's there or larger -- never smaller. If you're building your own box, use large wire for all the heavy-current stuff. It can be difficult to work with in the confined space, but undersized wire will waste a lot of the energy that goes through the control box. Make good contact and use terminal lugs (crimped and soldered for all connections). If the gauges and other controls are mounted in the control box, account for the swinging of the lid so that the wires are not bent sharply or pinched. (Route it to the lid at the hinge side). If you're using solid wire inside the box, any wire that has to move should be given a generous amount of room to do so or you'll metal-fatigue the copper (which is pretty soft stuff). Be sure that the lid and its components do not, when it's closed, short out the wires, or stretch them. Resistors and other heat-dissipating devices should be kept clear of other components and wires as they can burn thru insulation or cause fires. If you can do it, run all wires into the box from the sides and just punch out some holes in the top and the bottom so that ventilation is assured; if you put some screen over the top of the box (on the inside for neatness sake), this will keep the dust from building up too fast. Periodically clean out that dust; with a little moisture added to it, it can cause a resistive path to ground and this can drain batteries or lose some generated electricity if it doesn't out-right cause component failure.

A Simple Control Box

With the smaller Winchargers manufactured in the pre-REA period, a very simple and small control box was installed. Fig. 5-20 gives a wiring diagram for this unit and, compared to the ones we'll soon be discussing, you can see that there is not much to it. It didn't do an awful lot but then it didn't have to -- the wind machine that it was controlling was a relatively low-power unit and overcharge on one of these units is almost a joke.

Basically, the control box contains a cutout relay, an ammeter (two-direction type), two fuses (one for the load and one for the windplant generator), and a PTT (push-to-test) switch. Notice that there is no voltage regulator relay; the field coil on the generator is grounded at the windplant. Becuz it was relatively low-power, this control box counts on the spoiler (air-brake) installed on the windplant to slow it in very high winds. If the windplant does put out more than it ought to (in current), it blows the fuse. Truly a "poorman's" control box. If you are building a small windplant (capable of less than 400 watts), this will probably do the job well. The RPM that the propeller would achieve with these small units is phenomenal, but a six-foot blade can take a lot if it's fairly well balanced. Or at least you have to believe it can.

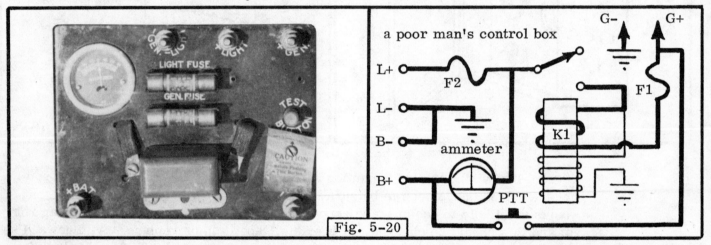

Fig. 5-20

Let's trace the path of current in this unit. The generator current goes through the heavy coil on the relay but is blocked by the open switch, so it goes through the smaller winding of wire on the relay. When the voltage from the generator is sufficient to begin charging, the current in this part of the relay will be sufficient to pull in the relay and close the contacts. Now the current will flow into the batteries thru the ammeter. When the windspeed drops, the windplant will slow; when it's at a lower voltage than the battery voltage, current will flow in a reverse direction thru the heavy wire winding and this will neutralize the magnetic field of the small-wire winding-portion of the relay and the contacts will open. If the wind is not present, and you want to be sure that all is okay with the windplant, you can hit the PTT switch and this will short the batteries out to the generator and motor the windplant; if it starts turning up there, all is okay. If it doesn't, the batteries are dead or the windplant is frozen up or has a broken connection somewhere.

The Wincharger Automatic Power Control Box

With the higher-power Winchargers, the simplicity of the previously discussed control box had to be abandoned. A voltage regulator was inserted to insure positive protection for the windplant and to keep the batteries from being overcharged. Extra resistors were added to provide a trickle charge capacity so that the batteries could be properly topped off without excessive gassing and heat production. Fig. 5-21 illustrates the wiring diagram for a control box of this type.

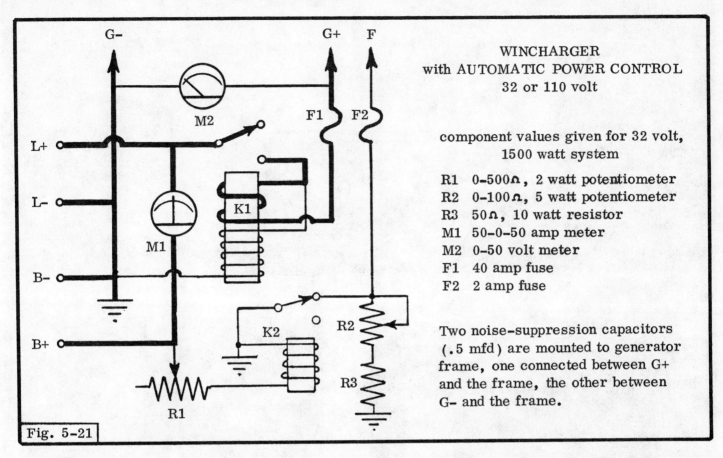

Fig. 5-21

WINCHARGER
with AUTOMATIC POWER CONTROL
32 or 110 volt

component values given for 32 volt,
1500 watt system

R1 0-500Ω, 2 watt potentiometer
R2 0-100Ω, 5 watt potentiometer
R3 50Ω, 10 watt resistor
M1 50-0-50 amp meter
M2 0-50 volt meter
F1 40 amp fuse
F2 2 amp fuse

Two noise-suppression capacitors
(.5 mfd) are mounted to generator
frame, one connected between G+
and the frame, the other between
G- and the frame.

The operation of the cutout relay is similar in this control box to the poor-man's control box. Two adjustable resistors and one fixed resistor are added to the circuit, though, and the field winding is brought down to the control box through the slip rings. Rl is a 500 ohm pot (which is short for potentiometer, or variable resistor), and it is inserted between the battery and the voltage regulator. By adjusting this control, it is possible to "set" at what voltage the voltage regulator relay will energize. R2 (also a variable resistor) and R3 (a fixed-value resistor) are connected between the field and ground. If the voltage regulator is not energized, note that its contacts are closed and these resistors (R2 and R3) are shunted (or bypassed) and the field coils in the windplant are provided with full current. If the voltage rises to a value where the voltage regulator is energized, the contacts will open and the field current will be limited by the value of R2 and R3. R3, incidentally, is inserted in there so that you can't adjust R2 to the minimum value and give the field coils no limiting effect at all. The network of Rl and R2 form what is called the trickle-charge adjustment, and this value will be determined primarily by what batteries you use and what finishing current will top them off without excessive gassing. Rl is the voltage regulator adjustment. The values of these resistors is determined by the value of relays used and the characteristics of the windplant itself (what voltage and current it produces), so don't duplicate this control box unless you have a similar or identical windplant.

These components were, for this model of Wincharger, mounted in separate boxes and connected via a 4-wire cable and 4-prong plug. If the voltage regulator needed servicing, the Automatic Power Control Box could be disconnected and shipped off to the factory for repair or adjustment. In this case, a dummy plug was inserted in the Main Panel at the normal plug-in for the Automatic Power Control Box, and this provided the Manual switch (of Manual/Automatic Switch fame) to allow continuing operation of the windplant while the other box was being repaired/adjusted. To give the batteries the equalizing charge, it was possible to adjust Rl to a value where the voltage regulator would not energize and, thus, allow full field current and maximum charging.

This particular control box also included such niceties as a voltmeter and a field fuse; it is missing a battery fuse, but does show the existence of an external fuse block (in the installation wiring diagram) for the various loads. It did not have a PTT switch although someone could push the contacts closed on the cutout relay and accomplish the same thing.

Other Wincharger models sometimes had control boxes with slightly different values of components, and some were more adjustable than others. The best way to insure that you have a wiring diagram for your particular model (assuming you have a Wincharger and that it has a control box different than the two already presented here) is to make one yourself. Use the ones provided here for a comparison (they won't be that different) and note any changes. This is a little time-consuming, but if you trace out the wires, see where they go, and what they connect to; you'll soon have a working diagram of your control box. If you have an earlier control box, you might think about adding some of the components found in the later units -- voltmeter, PTT switch, fuses, etc. -- to update it.

The Jacobs Control Box

The control box used with the Jacobs had some very basic differences when compared with the Wincharger units. Probably the most notable is the connection of the cutout relay in the negative portion of the circuit rather than the positive. The quality of components in the Jacobs box is most evident -- adjustable nichrome wire-wound resistors instead of carbon rheostats, copper strips instead of wires for interconnection of components, etc. While the negative side of the field coils (in the generator) is brought into the control box (like the Wincharger's), an adjustment is allowed in the field circuit for maximum field excitation (or maximum rate of charge), and this is an added feature; the windplant and batteries receive excellent over-current protection for most conditions. Unlike the Wincharger control boxes, the Jacobs box has a resistor in series with the small-wire winding on the cutout relay; while it is a fixed-value resistor, it would allow for some adjustment of the relay itself without messing around with the spring tension. This came in very handy when we decided to use the Jacobs 32-volt system with only 30 volts of batteries (five 6-volt batteries in series).

Let's trace the circuit out in the Jacobs control box. As the diagram indicates (Fig. 5-22), the positive generator lead and the battery lead are separated only by an ammeter (plus and minus reading) and a fuse. The negative generator lead, however, is connected to the main relay through the heavy-wire winding. The circuit is blocked at the contact points, but the current will flow through the smaller windings on the relay and the resistance Rl. When generator voltage is sufficiently high to magnetize the core in the main relay, the contacts will close and the negative generator lead will be connected to the negative battery lead, completing the charge circuit. The windings on the voltage regulator coil are connected across the generator leads and its contacts are normally closed, connecting the field to   G-   through R3 (the maximum charging-rate coil). When the voltage in the generator rises to a higher-than-desirable value, the voltage regulator will energize and the contact points will open. Now the field current will complete its circuit through the resistor R2 (the automatic charging rate control, which is set for the taper current required for the batteries used) and resistance R3. If the Manual/Automatic switch is switched to Manual, both the taper-charge resistor (R2) and maximum charge-rate resistor (R3) are shunted (or bypassed), and the windplant will put out whatever maximum current rate is allowed. A 10-watt, ll5-volt pilot light is hooked across the field and negative generator leads to show that the taper-charge function is operating; this serves as an indicator that the batteries are nearly full. In the 32-volt system, this bulb would be receiving a maximum of about 41 volts during taper-charge and would thus light only dimly. Latest-model Jacobs control boxes employed the dual relay voltage regulator as shown in Figure 5-7.

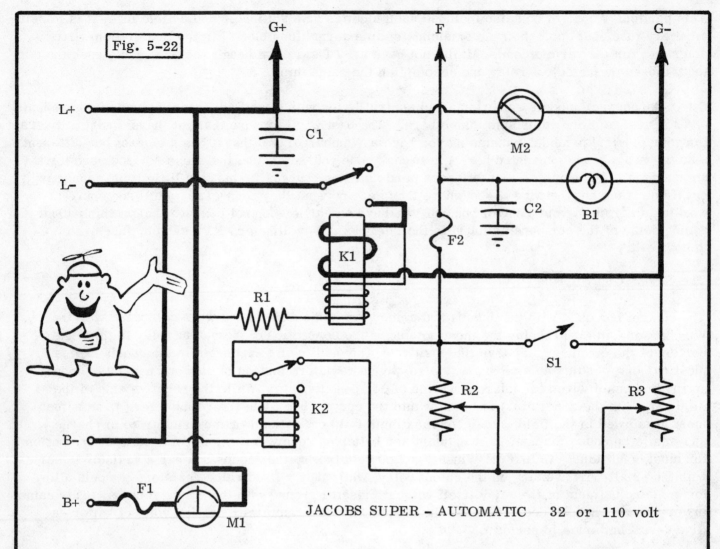

Fig. 5-22

JACOBS SUPER – AUTOMATIC   32 or 110 volt

Component values given are for a 32 volt, 1800 watt system. Ground symbols represent connections to control box chassis. No other connections to chassis.

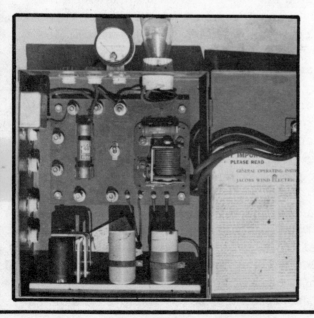

R1   100Ω, 5 watt resistor
R2   0–50Ω, variable resistor
R3   0–15Ω, variable resistor
K2   relay has 500Ω, 40 V coil & armature adj.
M1   50–0–50 DC amperes
M2   0–50 DC volts
C1, C2   2 mfd, 400 VDC, two–in–one capacitor
F1   60 amp fuse
F2   5 amp fuse
B1   110 volt, 15 watt bulb (glows only dimly)

A two–in–one, 1 mfd, 1000 VDC noise-suppression capacitor mounts on generator, connected between G+ and frame and between G– and frame.

While all of the control boxes discussed thus far have included most of the necessary control functions desired in a wind-electric system, each one of them is lacking in some respect or another, or they utilize components that could be replaced with more available, reliable, or inexpensive circuitry or components that would provide maximum protection and efficiency of energy conversion. Fig. 5-23 is a schematic representation of a circuit that would fulfill all of these requirements for the owner-built control box. A description of its components, functions, and combined effect follows, along with guidelines for component selection, construction, testing, adjustment and troubleshooting.

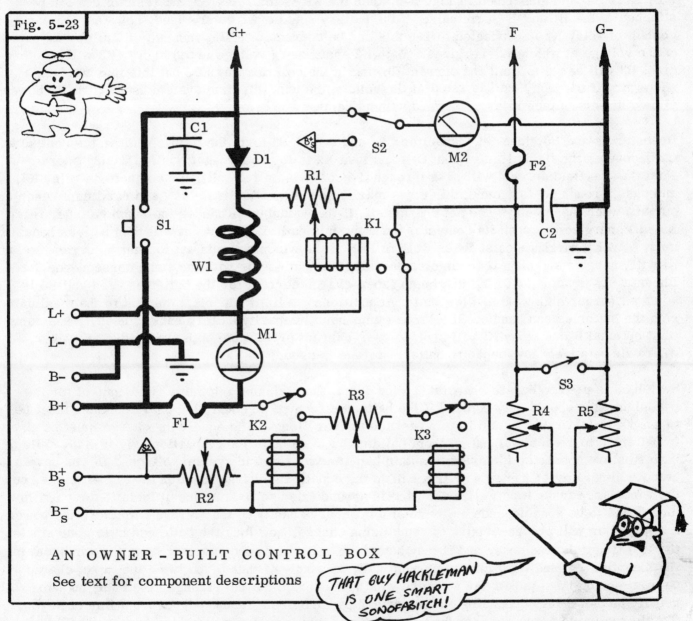

AN OWNER-BUILT CONTROL BOX

See text for component descriptions

THAT GUY HACKLEMAN IS ONE SMART SONOFABITCH!

The main power circuit (from generator to batteries) in Fig. 5-23 is essentially the same as that described in Fig. 5-10; in this instance, however, fuse F1, switch S1, and ammeter M1 are added to complete the requirements. The coil of wire W1, rheostat R1, and relay K1 form the current regulation function. A large amount of current flowing through the coil W1 will, depending on the adjustment of R1, energize relay K1 and cause the field current to be decreased. (It must pass through rheostats R4 and R5.) The optional PTT switch (S1) is added only for those wind-plants utilizing DC generators; this allows the windplant to be motored by the batteries for testing purposes. Without this switch, the same connection can be made with a temporary wire or a metal tool. The only additional component not previously discussed is capacitor C1, which is a decoupling capacitor and it will serve primarily to bypass noise pulses that can cause interference (in nearby radios, stereos, and your neighbor's TV). M1 is a plus-and-minus reading ammeter (from Fig. 5-11).

The voltage-regulation circuit in the home-brew control box is the same as that described in the text and by Fig. 5-7. If the individual windplant owner is unwilling to install battery-sensing wires ($B+_s$ and $B-_s$) as described in Fig. 5-6, then the wires for relay K2 and resistor R2 can be attached to the B+ and B- terminals. If the battery sensing wires are used, note that the common contact of relay K2 is connected to B+; this can be connected to $B+_s$ instead. R2 allows adjustment of the voltage at which K2 energizes. With K2 energized (voltage is too high), K3 will also ener-gize; R3 will serve to limit the current flowing in the coil of relay K3, but this may not be necessary if the relay coil is rated at the voltage the wind-electric system uses. It will, however, allow a lower-voltage relay to be used without damage.

Rheostat R4 and R5, fuse F2, capacitor C2, and switch S3 form the field circuit in the control box. C2 decouples the field circuit (like C1) and fuse F2 is to protect against field wiring shorts. Note that the field current will pass through the contacts on relay K1, the contacts on relay K3, and pass through R5 to ground; this gives maximum current to the fields (and maximum windplant output) when these relays are not energized. If the windplant produces too much voltage, relay K3 will energize and open its contacts, breaking this path; field current will then be less becuz it must travel through rheostat R4 as well as R5. If the windplant puts out too much current, relay K1 will energize and open its contacts, breaking this path again with the same consequence. Rheostat R4 is adjusted to the maximum taper-charge current for the batteries used and R5 is adjusted (under high wind and low battery conditions) to limit windplant current to the maximum rate the batteries can handle. If a large (amp-hour) capacity battery bank is used, R5 is some-what optional becuz relay K1 will provide over-current protection; both are needed, however, wherever relatively low-capacity battery storage is used.

Switch S3 is used to bypass rheostat R4 and defeat the action of automatic field control for the windplant; this should only be used if the batteries require an equalizing charge. Care must be taken not to leave this switch in this position for very long. The equalizing charge must be given to batteries to prevent sulphation from building up in some of them, particularly if many cells or batteries are connected in series to obtain higher wind-electric system voltages. If you have a standby generator (Chapter 6), this can do the equalizing charge function every 2-4 weeks, but the windplant can do it as well if the wind is around (no use wasting fossil fuels to do it). How long it has to be done depends on the total amp-hour capacity in the storage batteries, the power the windplant will produce during the equalizing charge, how long the batteries have gone since the last time this was done, and if they have been receiving good charging from the windplant in the meantime. Equalizing charge current will, as a rule of thumb, be twice the taper-charge current so you must pick a day when the wind is moderate but not strong. The charging time will usually be 5-15 hours depending on the various parameters already indicated. If this bugs you, the alternative is to use the standby generator and just insure that the thing is turned off after a while!

The remaining function in our homebrew control box is reading voltages; the circuit consists of voltmeter M2 and switch S2. One side of the meter is hooked to ground and the other to the common position on S2, which selects either the generator or battery voltage.   The switch should be set to normally read generator voltage.

Wires in the control box for the power circuit -- generator, battery, and load -- should be large in size and short in length (where possible); the thicker lines in the schematic (Fig. 5-23) represent these large wires.   Once you've obtained the components and installed them in the selected box, you'll need to make up a physical wiring diagram from the schematic.   Neatness is a real asset in the control box, so the wires may be longer than straight connections between points.   Indicate wire sizes and color on the wiring diagram, and it will make connections easier, correct, and save hours of checking after it's completed to find mistakes evidenced by an incorrectly-operating control box.

Constructing the Owner-built Control Box

If you're buildin' the control box yourself, save yourself some grief by planning ahead on it. Learn all the parts and the variations on components.   Find a box that's roomy enuff to fit every-thing in plus anything you may want to add later.   You're going to need a drill, a rattail file (to enlarge holes), some chassis punches (for the larger holes, like meters), and other small hard-ware -- bolts, nuts, washers, standoffs, etc.   If you want to save on buying the larger chassis punches that will be required, look for a small tool called a nibbler; it requires only drilling a small hole in the chassis to start and it functions by cutting out small bits of metal about 1/8th of an inch wide by 1/16th of an inch long.   This is a handtool and can only handle small metal thick-nesses and won't last long if you're cuttin' steel plate.

Figure out how many components will be mounted on the front plate and lay them out neatly on a sheet of paper which has the control box panel size lined off.   Leave adequate space between 'em on the front so that the knobs won't get in each other's way.   Insure that they won't interfere be-hind the panel as well, when mounted.

What you put on the front panel is pretty much up to you.   The meters should be mounted there so they're visible as you approach the control box.   The switch S2 (generator or battery voltage select) should be on the front so that you can quickly take either reading.   If you've got kids, you might want to put everything else behind the panel cover.   This is not as convenient as having R2 (voltage regulator adjust) and R4 (taper-charge adjust) on the front panel.   R1, R3, and R5 can also be mounted behind the panel.   On the other hand, if you've got the tools, space, and want a cockpit-type control panel, go to it.   Leave plenty of space for labeling the switches and rheostats. A sample lay-out is illustrated in Fig 5-24 for mounting all controls on the front plate.   While the fuse holders can be mounted in the front panel, a less expensive fuse block will neatly mount be-hind the lid.

Figure out where you are going to mount the resistors, capacitors, current regulator coil, etc. You can mount them to the controls mounted on the lid but I'd advise the use of standoffs; these are small, multi-terminal strips which are secured to the chassis and are insulated from it.   This avoids having a lot of loose wires free to jiggle around in the box and provides suitable lugs for keeping solder connections in place.   You can use the rigidity of the standoff and the wires coming out of resistors (for example) to hold the components away from the box itself.   Power resistors should be mounted away from other components, wires, etc., that may be affected by their heat. As heat will rise, locate them where something above 'em is not going to be barbequed.

It's normal for the Diode D1 to get hot in high-current operation -- too hot, unless it is mounted in some kind of heat sink.   This will be a finned hunk of aluminum which helps dissipate the heat when the windplant is operating. At the very least, you should mount the diode to the control box wall, but a heat sink will work better. These can be obtained from electronic places and may be pre-drilled to receive the size of diode for your control box. The fins or channels should be oriented so that air may freely travel vertically thru the heatsink. I recommend mounting the heatsink on the outside of the control box, but if it can't be done, put 'er in there. You have to insulate the heat sink from chassis ground so take suitable measures.

Don't forget that you must mount some kind of a large terminal strip inside the control box for the wires coming from the windplant and batteries (and standby generator, if used). The control box should be wired in such a way that to disconnect and remove it requires only unscrewing wire lugs from the terminal strip and removing whatever secures the control box to the wall.

Notes on Control Box Components

The values of components in the control box depend on what voltage and current your windplant will produce, the capacity of your storage system, and how fancy (and expensive) you want it to be. If you don't outright know how to proceed with the information I've provided thus far, then obtain a copy of some basic electronics text and, perhaps, a course in basic electronic construction (soldering techniques, wiring procedures, selecting and adjusting component values). Only a book-length treatment is going to arm you with all the information needed to build the finished box that you will want to install with your wind-electric system. So that you'll have some idea of where to start, I'll go thru a few of the parameters not included thus far. The terminology that I use may not be familiar, but once you find out what it does mean, it'll clue you to where to find any other info.

Relays

(1) The value of relay K1 will depend on the current rating of the windplant and not its voltage; in most cases, it will be a low voltage, low coil-current relay with a contact rating of 5 amps. Relays K2 and K3 should be rated at the windplant voltage or lower (never higher) and should also have a low coil current (high coil resistance). The contact rating of K2 need only be about 1 amp but relay K3 will have the same contact rating as K1 (5 amps).

Obtain sealed or enclosed relays, if possible; they will give better service if the contacts are not exposed to air or dust. I prefer the clear glass or plastic ones becuz you can see the contacts and this is helpful if you are trying to see the relay operate.

One way to avoid the cost of high contact (current) ratings for relays is to buy multi-contact relays (if you can find them less expensively) and to series the contacts. Do not confuse this with paralleling the contacts or you're going to crisp 'em right off. If you've got a relay of the correct rating for your control box and it has more than one set of making or breaking contacts (as required), you might as well connect them in series as well, to insure long contact life.

Be aware that relays K1 and K3 use "breaking contacts" (when energized they break a connection, not make one) and relay K2 uses "making contacts". When you buy the relays, the contacts will generally be discussed in terms of normally open or normally closed; this describes them not-energized. So . . . relays K1 and K3 will be listed as "normally closed" and relay K2 will be described as "normally open".

(2) The value (resistance) of all rheostats will depend very heavily on the field current rating and the windplant voltage. R1 is the only exception here; it's resistance will depend on the current rating of the windplant, the value of the relay K1, and the resistance of W1 (the current regulator shunt coil). Resistor R2 and R3 values depend on the windplant voltage, and the coil current and voltage of relays K2 and K3. Rheostats R4 and R5 values will depend on the amount of current required for the field coils of the windplant generator or alternator. An important point to re- member here is that, if you halve the field current to the windplant, you will not receive one half the power it produces at full field current (but sumthin' quite a bit less); this is becuz field strength is not directly proportional to field current. In terms of control, this simply translates to resistance values, for R4 and R5, of something probably less than 100 ohms. (Look at the values for the field resistances of the Wincharger and Jacobs units.)

Rheostats are rated not only for resistance, but in the power (wattage) they will dissipate (in the form of heat). R1, R2, and R3 will be 2 watt rheostats (or potentimeters, as they're some- times called) if the coil current of relays K1, K2, and K3 are around 100 milliamps. Rheostats R4 and R5 will probably be 5 watt or higher. To determine the required wattage of a rheostat, multiply its resistance by the square of the maximum amount of current that will flow through it; this is the I^2R value that we've occasionally mentioned. Always obtain a rheostat with a wattage rating twice that of the calculated value; this will give you a safety factor of two.

Non panel-mounting rheostats (called "variable resistors") are available and would make nice substitutes for the common rotary-types. These are large straight tubular resistors with a band of metal which is movable up and down the length of the resistor itself; a small screw is used to hold this band to a specific position. This is the type of resistor used in the Jacobs control box and it's practical, relatively easy to use, and is less susceptible to "derdialumtwistum". They're also less expensive than high-wattage rotary-types and easy to mount in the rear of the box.

(3) Coil W1 is a current shunt; it allows most of the current coming from the windplant to go straight through it rather than through the higher total resistance of rheostat R1 and the relay K1 coil. You must cut a length of copper wire (not too thick) or steel baling wire which will allow relay K1 to energize with rheostat R1 adjusted to minimum resistance while the current flowing through W1 is approaching the windplant's rated (maximum) current. When you've got this, increase the resistance of R1 so that the relay doesn't trip until the windplant reaches its full rated output. You don't want W1 any longer than necessary; it's wasting a bit of power to facilitate overcurrent protection and you want to keep that to a minimum.

(4) Switch S1 (if used) needs to have a large current rating. A large push-button switch is nice here, but if you can't find one that is large enuff (20 amps or more), use a less convenient knife switch. Switch S3 will need a current rating of 5 amps. Switch S2 will only require a current rating of 1 amp or less.

(5) A final note on control box wiring. If you want some real safe current capacity for internal wiring, consider flattening some small copper tubing and drilling holes in each end for bolt-together connections. By bolting all connections down to an insulated board, you can be fairly sure of a sound layout, even if you are not experienced with electronic soldering. These also make nice battery straps (between batteries in sets). They have very low resistance and good strenth and are less expensive than heavy wires with terminals.

Checking Out the Control Box

Okay. You've got a mint-condition control box. Or you have rebuilt a control box and you've tacked it up on the wall. Or you've got a homebuilt control box. You hook the wires up to their respective places. What now? You've got three ways to go. You can just let the ole wind machine rip and hope it does what it's supposed to do. Or you can get some test equipment on the thing--variable power supply, dummy loads, meters, etc.--and adjust everything down to the gnat's ass. Or . . . you can wait for the right wind conditions and adjust the control box bit by bit.

Seein' as how I have the test equipment, that's the way I'd go. Or I'd do it the third way. If I'm in a hurry, I might do it the first way. But you get what you get if ya do it this way. If you've wired the thing up wrong or have a bad component, it might get a little ruff. When I was in the Navy, we had a name for just firin' it up--it was called the "smoke test" and, if wrong, that's just exactly what would happen--lot's of foul-smelling smoke. That's not a recommended method for wind-electric circuits becuz the wind machine could be in some real danger. Assuming that most folks won't have the test equipment, I'll give troubleshooting and adjustment proceedures for the last proposed method--a bit at a time.

Troubleshooting and adjusting the control boxes for both the Jacobs and Wincharger systems is explained in their respective operator's manuals; if you've got one of these machines, get the manual. The Bibliography lists a source but, while out of print from the companies, they are now available from a variety of sources. I'd really like to include the information here, but I won't. Why? Well, anyone with those machines will need that service manual becuz it details a lot more about the systems than just control box adjustments and troubleshooting. Adjustment procedures for the owner-built control box will supplement the information found in those manuals. Troubleshooting and adjustment go hand in hand, but the former will be used whenever adjustments fail to allow proper operation of the control box and the system in general. So, we'll look at adjustments first.

Adjustments to the Owner-Built Control Box

If you're going to use the windplant to make adjustments in the control box, you're going to have to connect its leads and those from the batteries to the control box. Before you do this, set all five rheostats for maximum resistance. If the components have been correctly wired in, this will be at a zero setting, or one where the knob is at the maximum counter-clockwise position. When connecting windplant and battery leads, watch out for sparks and smoke; if you get either, disconnect immediately and check the wiring thoroughly. If nothing seems amiss, look for bad components. The number of things that can happen (that aren't supposed to) is truly unlistable. Assuming you have double-checked all wiring and all components are of the correct value and will function properly, let's proceed.

If you didn't barbeque your control box when connecting the windplant and battery leads, we're ready to begin adjustments. Make certain that the batteries are fully charged or these rough adjustments will be rougher than they should be. To adjust R2, move the knob clockwise

(hereafter stated as 'advance' the knob) and listen for relay K2 to energize (or visually watch this happen). When it does, note and mark the position where this happens. Move the knob counterclockwise (hereafter stated as "back off" the knob) until relay K2 de-energizes. Note and mark the position. Use pencil marks as these will only be rough adjustments. Advance R2 to the first mark. Relay K2 should energize. Back it off to the second mark. It should de-energize. Right?

Okay, R3's adjustment is next. Advance R2 until relay K2 energizes. Now advance R3 until relay K3 energizes. Note and mark this position for R3. Now back off R2 (not R3) to its second mark. When relay K2 de-energizes, relay K3 will de-energize. Now advance R2 until relay K2 energizes. Relay K3 should also energize. If it doesn't, advance R3 just a little bit more and it will cause relay K3 to energize. Erase the old pencil mark for R3 position and mark the new. Now back off R2 until both de-energize and advance R2 again. You want relay K3 to energize every time relay K2 energizes. That's it. Back off R2 to its original mark (so both relays are de-energized). Okay?

Let's adjust R1. This could be adjusted while the windplant was delivering its rated output but that's a bit dangerous (a bad time to find out you reversed a wire somewhere) so let's do it the safe way. Disconnect the windplant and battery leads from the control box (Battery + to G+ and Battery – to G–); in this way, the batteries will simulate the windplant. Connect a load to the battery terminals in the control box (at B+ and B–); this will simulate the batteries and allow current flowing into the load to pass thru M1. The load you connect should draw an amount of current equal (or very close) to the windplant's maximum (rated) durrent. Try using a good length of steel wire for the load. (For example, a 10-foot length of common baling wire will draw 50 amps at 12 volts; resistance will increase some as it heats up.) Or, connect enuff light bulbs, motors, etc. to pull the current.

When M1 indicates the amount of current at which you want relay K1 to energize, quickly adjust R1 until relay K1 energizes. You will be wasting a lot of power and heating a lot of stuff up in the control box. When you've got it right, mark the knob position (for R1) and reconnect the battery and windplant leads to their respective terminals. If, during the windplant's normal operation, you ever see the ammeter indicate more than what you thought you had adjusted R1 to prevent (by activating K1), you can make a fine adjustment on R1. Make a point of verifying its correct adjustment whenever the windplant is again delivering full power.

Rheostat R5 provides overcurrent protection for the batteries; if your batteries can't handle the windplant's current-producing capacity, you'll need to adjust R5, but this can only be done when the windplant is exposed to some pretty good wind and the batteries are near exhaustion (that is when the batteries will draw the most current). Additionally, R5 cannot be properly adjusted if relays K1, K2, or K3 are energized. With all of these conditions met, adjust R5 for minimum resistance (full advance clockwise) and then, observing M1, back off R5 anytime the current reading exceeds the recommended maximum charge current for your batteries. Take your time here and make only very small adjustments of R5. It's better to occasionally have the batteries receive a little more current than this value then to have them receive less than they could otherwise. Mark the final position of the knob becuz you'll probably end up moving this control frequently. When you're experiencing the low and infrequent winds of summer, you may want to move this control to minimum resistance (full advance) to take advantage of the relatively low amount of power available from the wind.

We've already gone thru a rough adjustment of rheostat R2 but a finer adjustment is required. This setting will depend on your batteries' recommended "finishing rate", maximum current rating, and "finishing voltage" and, even with this information, you will not have a precise indication of when the control box should activate the taper charge function. The value of voltage where you want relay K2 to energize will be that where a medium amount of current (say, twice the "taper charge" current) is causing the batteries to "gas" excessively.

Note: Normal gassing will cause a mist of fine bubbles in the battery and the electrolyte will appear milky. What I call 'excessive gassing' is when a hiss of bubbles (like in freshly-opened soda bottle) can be heard without putting your ear right up to the battery (and the battery feels warm to the touch). Really too much is indicated by what looks and sounds like a rolling boil (and the battery feels hot). Tiny bubbles will normally accumulate in pockets and suddenly rise to the top with a "blurk". If you're concerned with heavy gassing, give the battery a pound with your fist to release any more accumulated gas. If it continues to "gurgle," yer boiling. (Rolaids, anyone?) If you ever spot a fine spray of liquid around the battery caps (even though they are on tight), they've been excessively gassing or boiling behind your back.

A rough adjustment to the voltage regulator will be made initially but progressively finer adjustments will be made as the battery conditions and experience dictate. Arm yourself with a lot of good battery information; the more you know, the longer you'll be able to stretch the life of the batteries. (See Wind and Windspinners, and Bibliography.)

A control identification sheet should be posted near the box or taped inside the lid. It lists the controls and briefly explains what they do. The importance of the sheet comes in explaining which way the control needs to move to accomplish the desired adjustment. An example: If you back off R1, you increase its resistance. The effect will be to decrease the sensitivity of K1 to windplant current; hence, it will take more windplant current (thru winding W1) to cause K1 to energize . If you advance R1, the reverse will happen. Got the message?

Meaningful terminology for control labels is highly recommended. Keep it brief, or the label won't fit in the space surrounding the switch position. The second rule is to use something that works for you. A few examples here: 'Current Regulator' might be a good name for rheostat R1, but 'Max. Windplant Current Adj.' might be a better description since R5 is, in effect, also a current regulator (for the batteries). So, maybe call R5 'Max. Battery Current Adj.' R2 is 'Voltage Reg. Adj.', R3 is 'Slave Relay Adjust' (or no label), and R4 is 'Taper Charge' or 'Finishing Current Adj.'. Switch S1 can be called 'Push to Motor' (not abbreviated). Switch S2 can be called 'Voltmeter Sensing'. Label its positions: 'Gen.' for generator and 'Bat.' for batteries. Switch S3 has been labeled 'On/Off' (Jacobs) or 'Manual/Automatic' (Wincharger), but this is consumer oriented and not very explanatory. I'd label the switch positions 'Regulator In' and 'Regulator Out'. Aw heck, if you can remember what they are, label switches Ignite, Liftoff, Destruct, LOX/NOX mixture, Roll, Telemeter, etc. You too can play NASA.

Troubleshooting

Troubleshooting is a precise application of logic. The first thing that you have to do is become aware that there is indeed a problem. This may be a simple visual awareness (curling smoke, sparks, no ammeter reading, etc.) or an audible one (a sound like bacon frying on a stove, machine-gun clicks, a popping sound, etc.). Assuming that you know (or are willing to learn) enuff about your wind electric system to notice differences, it will be a contrast or comparison of what it should or should not be doing with what it isn't or is doing. When you've got the necessary stimuli that things are awry, your next step is to stop it from receiving further damage or exposure to the malfunction. This will generally involve pulling fuses (if they're not already blown), snapping switches, disconnecting leads, shutting down the windplant, or whatever.

The next step in the process is to isolate the problem. This may not be difficult if you've got a crispy resistor or blackened relay staring out at you from the innards of the control box. But it won't always be this obvious, or major. Try to remember what was or was not happening and write it down. If you can't pinpoint the problem by direct application of the information that you have, try a process of elimination -- what it couldn't be. It's sometimes difficult to separate observations from conclusions but try to do this or you may cast aside a possibility that will take you lots of blind alleys and hair pullin' to finally come back to. Check for possible incorrect component values, improper wiring, shorts (in wires and components), incorrect rheostat adjustments. Consider the possibility of more than one problem occurring simultaneously. Realize that whatever burned, arced, or whatever may only be a symptom, and not the cause of the problem.

Okay, troubleshooting takes practice before you're good at it. Don't just look at the control box; you might have windplant, battery, or interconnecting wiring that's causing the malfunction.

A small VOM (volt-ohm-milliammeter) will help with resistance and voltage checks; this is a good investment anytime you're working with electrical/electronic stuff. It's available at a wide range of prices from any electronic supplier.

When you've run the gauntlet of tests and troubleshooting, you are ready to fire it up. Make the necessary connections to bring the control box "back on the line" and watch for any recurring problem. Make a point of observing its functions under different conditions (full or discharged batteries, high or low wind conditions, varying load).

Maintain the control box and the wind-electric system hardware. Make up a schedule of hydro-meter readings, voltage checks, lubrication of the windplant, replacement of water in the batteries (use distilled water only!), cleaning dust out of the control box, cleaning the tops of the batteries, etc. Preventive maintenance will keep you "in tune" with the system and insure its long service to you. Freedom from dependence on utility power is only guaranteed by your active involvement in producing it for yourself. Without personifying a wind-electric system, it does seem a trait that, when unattended, it will command your attention in its own way.

An afterthought: In adapting an alternator to a windplant, consult Wind and Windspinners for required information on field excitation.

CHAPTER 6

AUXILIARY ELECTRICITY- GENERATING EQUIPMENT

The Standby Generator Unit (hereafter designated SGU) is a must for utility-free wind-electric systems. Powered by a source of power other than wind, it serves in many capacities. At the very least, it provides extra emergency power. Or it will charge the batteries while the wind-electric system is being installed, repaired, or waiting out the doldrums. Or it can give the batteries the required equalizing charge (every 2-4 weeks). Or it can give a different kind of electricity (like 110 VAC, 60 cycles instead of the 32 VDC you're using). So it's more than just a luxury.

The size of SGU (power rating) depends very much on your unique situation. If you are only using wind energy as a supplement to utility power, it can be a simple battery charger that converts the utility power to the DC voltage required to keep the system's batteries charged. If you have the wind-electric system but not the utility power, it can be a small and simple engine-generator. If you have larger power needs occasionally or need the SGU while you build the wind-electric system, the SGU used will be larger and more sophisticated.

SGU Capacity

Most of the SGU units of the pre-REA period (like the Delco Light Plants) were in the 750-1000 watt range, so this is a good starting place. The power needs of the people of that era were, however, much less than our present consumption which is, for the most part, wasted by the habits we have acquired, the appliances we use, and the inefficiency of present-day energy systems. Don't think that you will need to install an SGU that puts out the same kind of power the windplant produces; it need not be anywhere near this capacity. A windplant will need to produce a lot of power when it is operating becuz it will have to make up for low wind or calm spells. The real test of a wind-energy system -- the windplant and the SGU -- will be during the calm months of the year; if the two units will get you through the doldrums, you've got a winning combination.

Lower power units will tend to be more efficient than higher ones. That's becuz lower current will not unduly waste power in the wires and the batteries themselves (as heat). But the power rating required will depend on the voltage being used in the system and the minimum and maximum current requirements of the batteries used. For example, with a 110-volt system and a minimum current rating of 10 amps (for the batteries to charge), this will mean 1100-1200 watts of SGU. A 32-volt system with the same minimum current requirement (10 amps) can use the same size wire as the 110-volt system, but the SGU will only be a 400-watt type. If you want the same wattage (say, 1200 watts), this will mean 4 times the current (40 amps) with the lower voltage (32 volts) and the wire will need to be 4-8 times larger to prevent large I^2R losses.

If you want the SGU to deliver 110 volts of AC at 60 cycles for direct consumption (like with table saws, shredders, arc welders, etc.) instead of the DC required (at whatever voltage) for the batteries, you will probably need two generators. In this case, the SGU should be designed so that one generator can be removed and replaced by the other for use. Or build two SGU's. Most alternators can deliver 110 volts DC (with very little additional circuitry) as well as lower voltages for the batteries if necessary, but few generators will do this. Alternators can have their diodes removed to provide AC, but it's three-phase and not necessarily at the frequency required (60 cycles) so that's pretty much of a hopeless possibility for most situations.

The SGU Prime Mover

The power source for the SGU generator can be from a source other than an "engine," so I have indicated my awareness of this by not giving this section the title of "The SGU engine." "Prime mover" encompasses other types of motive force. Steam, air pressure, water (hydroelectric), and mechanical-muscular (hand-or foot-operated pedals or animal power) are alternatives to the engine powered by diesel fuel, gasoline, propane, methane gas, coal gas, wood gas, hydrogen, or kerosene. (I'll refrain from the insanity of considering nuclear power.) The Stirling engine is now approaching practical development; this is an external-combustion engine that can use any of these fuels or the direct application of solar energy. However, gasoline or diesel engines are the most available to the most people. If this turns your stomach (as it does mine), take consolation in the fact that it will be infrequently needed and that it can possibly be replaced with another non-fossil fuel as engines are perfected to use these other sources of energy.

The power requirements for the SGU must be determined before the engine requirements becuz you will need to match the engine's capability to the requirements of the generator. One horsepower is equal to (approximately) 746 watts of electrical energy. This is theoretical nonsense, however, becuz a one-horsepower engine will not give you 746 watts of electrical energy. Why? Well, most of the energy goes into heat losses, vibration, noise, and by the time you've coupled the alternator to the engine, you'll have lost more in the transmission and the inefficiency of the alternator itself. What this all means is that you must get an engine that will produce 2-4 times the horsepower than the horsepower equivalent of electrical energy that you may want to produce. And another little factor enters into the equation -- the speed of the engine. Engines don't deliver their horsepower rating except at a certain RPM. If you operate the engine at the lower RPM, you get less horse-power and, consequently, less electrical juice.

When you have decided what power rating you want from the SGU, divide that wattage by 750 (that's close enuff to 746 watts) and you will have the horsepower equivalent. I'd then multiply that figure by 3 to figure in all the conversion losses. If the losses turn out to be smaller than that, then you'll just end up with a little more power than you needed.

This might be a good place to indicate that you can purchase SGU's in a variety of power ranges, both new and from surplus sources. Some of the new ones are quite compact and the prices, while steep, are not always unreasonable. As I have never purchased any of these units, I haven't the slightest idea of what kind of quality they boast, but then I prefer to roll my own. If you've got the bread and the willingness to learn how to work on one of them, they might be a good investment. As most folks will have to build theirs, I'll concentrate on that.

The power ranges for SGU engines will fall into one of two groups: Under 5 horsepower and over 5 HP. If you've calculated over 5 HP, then you'll need to look at the section under MOSGU. If you're under 5 HP then we'll talk about the HESGU.

The HESGU

The HESGU (Horizontal Engine Standby Generator Unit) is just a name that I'll use for an SGU using a lawn mower-type engine; it is not a standard name, so don't expect anyone to understand what you are talking about if you mention it. Lawn mowers of the rotary type have a vertical shaft; this type is not recommended becuz an alternator or generator would have to be mounted with its shaft up and down and its bearings won't permit this kind of operation for very long. Turning the engine sideways won't work either; the carburetion and lubrication will be all wrong and the engine will either not start or it will quickly overheat. Go-karts and mini-bikes and other small-engined machines are sources of horizontal-shafted engines in addition to the nonrotary type of lawn mower. Many small bike and lawn mower shops will have some of these engines around.

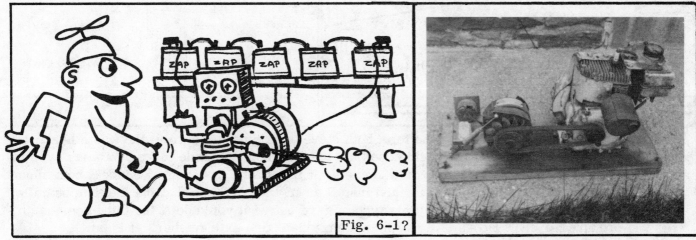

Fig. 6-1?

Making the HESGU is not a major undertaking (see Fig. 6-1 and accompanying photo). Some kind of framework will be required to support, position, and secure the engine and the alternator unit; this can simply be a short section of 2 x 8 plank. The engine should be bolted tightly to this surface but the alternator/generator will need to be secured to a pivot which is, in turn, bolted tightly to the surface; this will allow proper tensioning of the V-belt or gear-belt. Direct coupling of the two shafts(generator and engine) is possible, but I don't recommend this unless you can machine an accurate coupling and provide adequate speed.

A spring can be used to hold the tension on the alternator/generator. If you add in a turnbuckle, then you can adjust the tension, but keep the spring in there becuz it will give the assembly some "give" when the power is switched on and the alternator bucks a bit. An alternative to the spring and turnbuckle is to use the weight of the alternator/generator as the tensioner (see Fig. 6-2). If you're going to mount two different generators, you may want to adapt the mounting pivot so that it will receive either one.

If you're going to mount the HESGU inside the house, garage, or a shed you must make provisions for exhaust and you may have to add an air-intake hose for the carburetor. You should also check the engine for exhaust leaks or an open crankcase or, at the very least, only run it when doors or windows are open and the enclosure is well ventilated. The exhaust line can be made of water-pipe (check building codes for this if it applies) but it will get hot, so know what you're doing. A home-brew muffler is described by Fig. 6-3.

Lawn mower-type engines are very noisy so you may want to consider putting the HESGU inside a large box. Of primary concern here will be to fireproof the thing, especially if the box is made of wood. I'd line it with fiberglass insulation (on the inside) and then cover that over with foil to reflect the heat. Leave plenty of clearance to the top and sides of the box, and place a large inlet

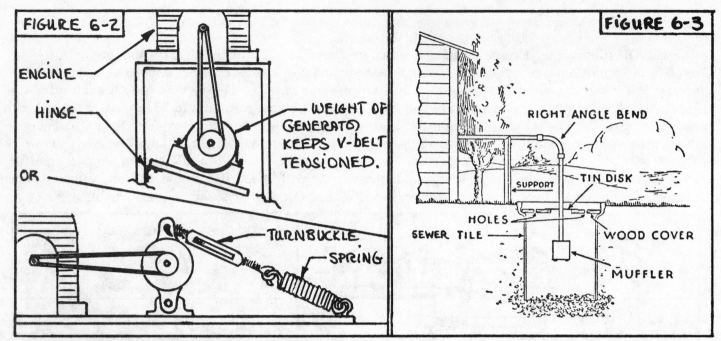

FIGURE 6-2

ENGINE

HINGE

OR

WEIGHT OF GENERATOR KEEPS V-BELT TENSIONED.

TURNBUCKLE

SPRING

FIGURE 6-3

RIGHT ANGLE BEND

TIN DISK

SUPPORT

HOLES

SEWER TILE

WOOD COVER

MUFFLER

pipe at the bottom and a vent pipe at the top (both stove-pipe type) to extract the waste heat. If you are absolutely positive that the engine does not have carbon monoxide leaks, you may even be able to use the heat to warm up a shop or whatever. If the HESGU is mounted inside a box, mount the gas tank outside, run the fuel line in, and install an in-line valve so that the fuel can be cut off in case of fire. For any installation of this type, figure out what you'd do if the thing does catch fire, and prepare for such a possibility with an appropriate fire extinguisher, at least.

All engines have a red-line; this is the rated RPM above which the engine is likely to explode, throw a rod, or burn up. To get maximum efficiency from the engine, you'll need to run it at an RPM about four-fifths of red-line or whatever speed below that level that the engine is delivering the power you need. The alternator or generator used with the HESGU will need to achieve a certain RPM before it begins to deliver power, depending largely on the battery voltage. It will also operate more efficiently at higher speeds than at lower ones. So it's not just a matter of matching power for proper operation but speed, as well. The gear (for gear belts) or pulley (for V-belts) that is mounted on the engine and generator/alternator will need to be in some proportion (or ratio) with each other. This will mean a larger or smaller gear or pulley on either the engine or the alternator/generator and which goes where is very situational. I rather doubt that it will be any more than a two-to-one ratio either way, if that's any consolation.

I keep indicating alternator or generator becuz either can be used in the HESGU. I fancy alternators for such a small SGU becuz I've worked with them more than I have generators. The general consensus seems to be that generators are more efficient, but there is little doubt that alternators are more compact and will deliver more power per lb, cost less, and will deliver higher voltages than most automotive generators. The power-producing part of the generator is rotating, so the power can only be conducted by using brushes and they wear out as do the commutators. Alternators, on the otherhand, have their power-producing coils mounted stationary in the alternator housing and eliminate this wear, arcing, and heat buildup. The generator unit, however, does have one possible large advantage over the alternator in the HESGU and we'll look at that now.

Automatic HESGU

When the batteries need an equalizing charge or you need some additional power, you could just trudge out to the HESGU and pull the ole rip cord to start it. Or . . . you could hit a switch and

-158-

start it. Or you could have it start automatically when the battery voltage gets too low or when a large load is switched on. If you've got an alternator in the HESGU, you're going to have to install a starter motor to automatically turn the HESGU engine over fast enuff to start; this gets complex. If you are using a generator in the HESGU, however, you might be able to use that to start the engine. How? Read on!

Any generator is also a motor, or can be. You should know this by now after reading the control chapter becuz provision must be made there (if the windplant is using a generator and not an alternator) to disconnect the batteries when there is low wind so the batteries do not "motor" the windplant. While we have not yet discussed the SGU controls nor how they are connected to the windplant control box, it will suffice to say that the same provisions must be made to insure that the batteries do not "motor" the SGU if it uses a generator. If we bypass the diode used for this purpose, we will motor the generator in the HESGU. And this can turn over the engine sufficiently to start it. Once the engine starts, it will rotate the generator to an RPM where it will produce electricity (as it is supposed to). At the very least, then, you will be able to hit a switch to start the HESGU engine and, with the right circumstances, you can hook up the system so that it will sense either low batteries or a large load and switch on automatically. Many of the Delco-type Light Plants of the pre-REA period were designed to do just that. The control box on the Light Plant, however, was a complicated affair becuz there are all sorts of desirable features in doing this and a lot of necessary ones. What if the Light Plant failed to start? Would it run down the batteries? What if the Light Plant's engine needed to be choked to start? Or what if it was cold and manifold heating was required? What if the Light Plant was out of gas? A Light Plant is not a computer, so some sort of sensing would have to occur if the automatic function of the HESGU were to operate properly under a variety of conditions. The control box for the Delco Light Plant is called the Sentry and I'll list both its sensing capabilities and functions.

1.   The Sentry sensed battery voltage and initiated the START function whenever the battery voltage dropped below a certain point. It initiated a STOP function whenever the battery voltage reached a pre-set level (to prevent overcharging the batteries). A manual switch was provided in the control box to override this sensory capability so that the plant could be started and stopped manually. This switch was intended to permit giving the batteries their necessary periodic equalizing charge.

2.   The Sentry sensed load conditions. If a heavy load was switched on, it would initiate START before the batteries were drained to the point where the voltage-sensing function (in the Sentry) finally started the SGU. It would also prevent the SGU from starting if a surge current occurred; this will happen whenever large motors are started but, as the normal current they require is far less, it is not desirable to have the SGU start.

3.   When low-battery voltage or high-load conditions dictated starting the SGU, the Sentry would initiate the START function. This involved bypassing the antimotor relay (which is a reverse-current prevention relay or a cutout relay, as we have discussed previously), removing the ignition-shorting contacts (which help to stop the engine when it comes time to do so), kicking in a set of starting coils on the generator (which give it more torque), bypassing an ignition coil resistance (to give a beefier spark), activating a cranking switch cutout heater coil (this will, if the engine fails to start, disconnect the starting function and prevent complete draining of the batteries), activating the automatic choke (for a richer fuel mixture), and activating an electric heater in the manifold to warm the carburetor air to assist starting. If the engine did start, and gained speed, it would then remove the bypass of the antimotoring relay, cut out the cranking coils in the generator, bypass the cranking switch cutout heater coil, remove the bypass on the ignition coil resistance (for normal spark), disconnect the manifold heater and allow normal charging

functions. When the batteries were charged or the heavy load was removed, it would sense these conditions and deactivate the antimotoring relay (disconnecting the generator from the batteries) and activate the ignition-shorting contacts (to ground the spark), and the engine would die.

Believe it or not, it was all done with four relays and few other components; sounds like a lot, but all very simple and to the point. You wouldn't think so if you saw the schematic for the control box or looked inside the unit, for sure, but I've indicated all of this to let you know it can be done and was done forty years ago. It's beyond the scope of this book to go into the how and wherefore of such a control box, but I've included a schematic of the Sentry box (courtesy of Delco) for the curious and inquisitive (see Fig. 6-4). The Delco company is still around, but they don't make light plants any more, so they won't be able to provide you with any information, parts, or working units. If you're interested in obtaining a copy of the theory, operation, and servicing of one of the Sentry control boxes, look under the Control listing in the Bibliography; this manual will provide information on construction and operation if you are interested in building your own.

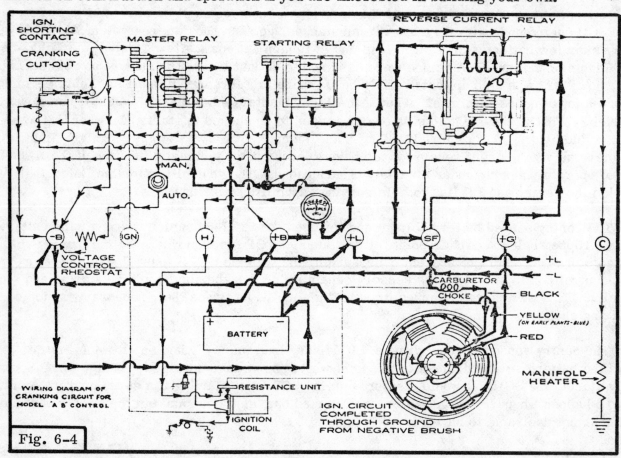

Fig. 6-4

DELCO SENTRY CONTROL BOX

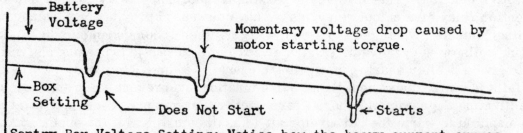

Sentry Box Voltage Setting:-Notice how the heavy current surges momentarily lower the box settings and prevent the engine starting on the majority of the power load cycles.

The HESGU Control Functions

Control of the HESGU is situational and will be as complex as what you expect it to do for you. If you're satisfied to go out there, set the choke, yank on the start cord, and set the throttle by hand until the proper amount of current is showing on the windplant's control panel ammeter, you're only going to need a few things -- a diode (for reverse current protection), a field control circuit, and maybe a fuse -- and the installation will be straightforward. If your wind-electric system utilizes 12-volt battery banks, the HESGU will be operating not unlike a car's electrical system and the voltage regulator will take care of the field control functions. Fig. 6-5 illustrates this basic setup. This same wiring diagram will apply to any HESGU which is using a generator or alternator that is designed to put out the voltage of the wind-electric system batteries; i.e., a 32-volt generator (and its voltage regulator) will interface with a 32-volt battery bank. A switch will be needed to turn on field current (like the ignition switch in a car does) after the engine has been started to prevent unnecessary drag in starting.

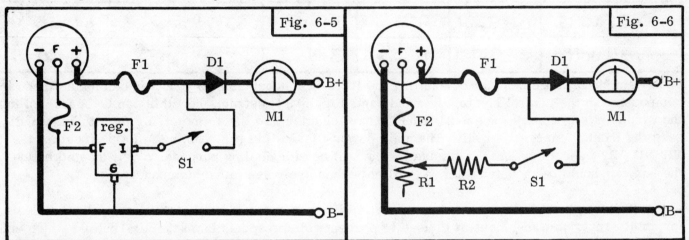

If you have an alternator that is not designed to operate at the voltage of the battery banks, special consideration must be given to the field control circuit. This is due to the fact that, while an automotive alternator is capable of operating at higher voltages (than the 12 volts used in the automobile), its field circuit is not designed to operate at anything but 12 volts. If the alternator is used, say, in a 32-volt system, its field must not be operated at 32 volts or it will fry. The simplest means of getting 12 volts from 32 volts (for the fields) is to put a resistor (or rheostat) in series with the 32 volts and adjust it to give the field 12-14 volts (see Fig. 6-6). A voltmeter can be used to adjust the rheostat, or the current in this circuit can be measured (with an ammeter) until it reads the same as it would if 12 volts were connected to the field.

Note that a voltage regulator is not shown in Fig. 6-6. A 12-volt regulator will not normally be usable in a 24, 32, or higher-voltage system without replacing its bias resistors or adjusting the tension on the relay (which only works for some of the heavy-duty voltage regulator relays). Unlike the automobile environment, however, the SGU will be operating at a constant RPM; if the charging rate is watched, a voltage regulator is not necessary. Remember: When you want to give batteries the equalizing charge, you bypass the windplant voltage regulator. You can't take great liberties with either the windplant or the SGU when this is happening becuz of the danger of over-voltage or over-current, but the situation is identical whichever one is doing the equalizing charge.

Fuses are required in the power circuit (F1) and field circuit (F2) in the schematics, Fig. 6-5 and Fig. 6-6. Fuse F1 should be rated for the maximum current rating of the generator (or alternator) or just above the maximum current (below the alternator/generator rating) that you expect to generate. Fuse F2 should be rated just above the normal field current consumption;

insure that this fuse is inserted in the circuit when you make the adjustments on rheostat Rl or you risk frying the field coils before the HESGU is ever brought into service. Fig. 6-7 is a table which lists the values for Rl and R2 for various voltages when a 12V (approx. 3a field) alternator is used. It is desirable to use two resistors -- one fixed and one variable -- in the field circuit whenever higher voltages are used; otherwise a large rheostat must be used to dissipate the additional heat. By using the two resistors, the fixed resistor can serve to dissipate most of the heat and the rheostat can allow the fine adjustment of field current without being physically large.

OPERATING VOLTAGE OF SYSTEM	RESISTANCE		COMPUTED WATTAGE		SAFE WATTAGES	
	R1	R2	R1	R2	R1	R2
12 volts	0-5 Ω	N/A	3 WATTS	N/A	5 WATTS	N/A
24 volts	0-5 Ω	4 Ω	3 "	36 WATTS	5 "	50 WATTS
32 volts	0-5 Ω	7 Ω	3 "	60 "	5 "	75 "
36 volts	0-5 Ω	8 Ω	3 "	72 "	5 "	100 "

If this simple arrangement for controlling the HESGU is acceptable to you, you can mount these few components in the control box for the windplant; Fig. 6-8 illustrates how this can be connected into the windplant's circuitry (see 5-23 from Control chapter) so the ammeter for the windplant will read the HESGU current as well. The main power-dissipating resistor in the field circuit of the HESGU (R2) should be located outside the control box for cooling purposes or, if located inside the box, it should be mounted where it will not excessively heat other components.

Diode Dl is required for antimotoring protection if a generator is used, but it must also be inserted for an alternator arrangement; it is used to prevent voltage spikes from the alternator (which can blow its diodes) if Fl should blow. This protection is not afforded if the field circuit is connected to the main power line at any other point than between the diode Dl and fuse Fl.

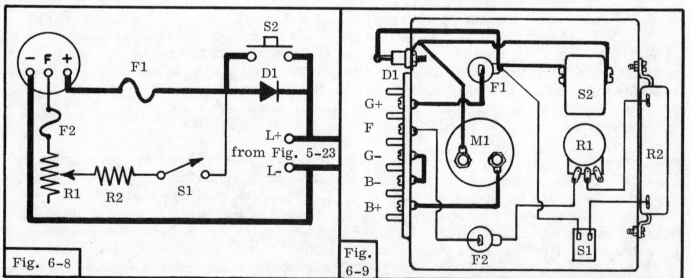

Fig. 6-8

from Fig. 5-23

Fig. 6-9

A separate control box for the HESGU is shown in Fig. 6-9; a separate ammeter (to the windplant's control box) monitors SGU output current. A toggle switch turns on field current and the rheostat (Rl) is used to adjust field current; the power-dissipating resistor (R2) is mounted behind the panel. Power and field fuses are also mounted here. Throttle and choke controls can be mounted on this box much like they are on lawnmowers. A PTS (Push-To-Start) switch can be added to either circuit if a generator is used for the HESGU and not an alternator. This should be a circuit breaker or knife switch becuz it must handle a large amount of current when it bypasses the antimotoring diode. This can also be the manual-start switch if the generator is large enuff to motor the engine to starting speed. The Delco Light Plants utilizing the Sentry automatic-start unit had generators equipped with dual field coils which gave the required torque necessary to overcome the drag in the engine caused by cylinder compression. If your engine has good compression and your generator doesn't have a lot of "oomph," you may be stuck with the manual start. If you're bound-and-determined to automate the HESGU, it'll mean a beefier generator or smaller engine or a combination of both.

If your situation calls for higher power or automated functions -- starting, stopping, and control -- then take a look at the MOSGU.

MOSGU

No, this is not some Eastern-based, philosophical sect. MOSGU (Multi-Operational Standby Generator Unit) is again my own terminology and it refers to a large SGU which has some additional features. Anyone installing a wind-electric system in a remote area is going to need power not only to construct and install this alternative energy system, but to supply electricity, heat, and light for the facilities in the interim. Most of us could not afford to purchase a SGU of the size required to take care of all these functions, little knowing that we may already possess one. Okay, what am I talking about? Why, an automobile engine, of course! Before you pooh-bah the idea, read on.

Suppose that you removed an automobile engine from its natural habitat and placed it into a box that is specially built to mount and accommodate it. Now, suppose that you connected a panel to it that allowed you to remote-start and otherwise control the functions of the engine from a distance. Further, suppose that you hooked up a number of umbilical cords to it -- hoses for the cooling system, electrical wires from its generator or alternator, ducting into the space around the engine, and an exhaust pipe -- and buried the unit. Right away I think you will see that this would have some advantages. The noise problem is minimized. The environment of the engine is closed and dust and weather protection can be assured. Where do the umbilical cords go? Well, the exhaust would be opened (after passing through a muffler of sorts) to the atmosphere. The cooling system is hooked to a tank which also happens to be a household hot water tank. The ducted tubing serves to remove waste heat from the engine and, operated with a blower (which can be an adaptation of the fan on the engine itself), the ducting can be terminated in your shop or habitat to provide space heating. The exhaust will vent a lot of heat, so let's extract some of that, and generate some steam (from a water jacket) to be used for cooking. And we'll hook up some batteries to the generator or alternator on the engine and use that to supply a stored energy for use when we need it. Since the engine will not be used to propel a vehicle, we can seriously consider adding a few more generators and alternators to the engine itself and gain a lot more electrical power that way. Maybe, we'll even add a 110 VAC, 60-cycle generator to the engine and, by regulating the engine speed about a certain RPM, we can be assured of a large, utility-size electrical capacity for emergency or occasional use.

Well, that may all sound a bit abstract but the idea is there. In an automobile, the heat is always considered a nuisance and is got rid of while driving. What you may not realize, however, is that an automobile engine is very inefficient if we were to consider the percentage of the energy that results in motive power from the original quantity of gasoline that fuels it. An approximate figure would be 5-15%. Not very good for a society which sees itself as being practical and pragmatic, is it? The rest of the energy goes into making noise, vibration, and heat. In cold weather, some of the heat would be used in the interior of the vehicle, but this is really a very small amount compared to the total amount of heat the engine produces and wastes. In actuality, of course, the engine wastes nothing. It is we--who design, build, and operate the engine-- that waste the energy that it produces from the gasoline. And it is we who can change that habit when we have need and otherwise see the light. Copy?

Keeping in mind that an automobile engine is more efficient as a heater than it is as a source of transportation, we have only to make a few modifications, and we can make good use of that energy and the gasoline that produces it. A conservative estimate of the efficiency of MOSGU is about 85%, and that is a five- to tenfold increase in efficiency. We'll take it all slow and easy as we go through the various components of the system so that you can actually fabricate a working system from it.

The MOSGU Engine

Selection of the engine to be used with the MOSGU is pretty much a matter of situation. If you can't afford to go out and find one that will be ideally suitable for use, then you may have to do with the one you have access to. If you have a car that you're not using and plan to have hauled away, then it may be what you'll use. Used cars may go for a pretty fair amount out of a used car lot, but the money those folks pay for the cars is really not all that much. Trade-in value of any car will be higher than the cash value it might have, so check out the situation carefully. If the engine is pretty well shot, then get rid of it. The most basic requirement for the MOSGU engine is that it be in good, if not excellent condition. The environment of the MOSGU is certainly a lot easier on an engine than the automobile is, but one that won't last more than a few more days on the road isn't going to last a heck of a lot longer when used with the MOSGU.

It's going to take a certain amount of energy to set up the engine for use in the MOSGU, so start out with something this side of junk if you're going to get any benefit from using it as an SGU. I offer the following parameters for those of you that might have access to various engines, or are willing to scout around for one that will provide reliable service.

Engines of small physical size and small horsepower are much preferred to the gas-guzzling V-8's found in most Detroit monsters. For this application, a 40HP engine is more than sufficient, and anything over 100HP is wasteful. I will grant that it doesn't matter all that much whether it is wasteful or not becuz the advantage of the MOSGU is that it does make use of the waste heat. But small is beautiful -- whether it's the engine you select, the money it may cost, or the amount of energy required to carry out some of the other little necessities. To be effective, the MOSGU must be located in a closed environment, and that means getting the engine out of the vehicle and into the receptacle that houses the MOSGU. A 40HP engine is work enuff. A V-8 is absurdly unmanageable. A 4-banger (4 pistons) is much preferred to a V-8. If it can't be helped, a 6-banger is the next choice. There are good 2-bangers around -- very small cars and motorcycles use these -- but I suspect that becuz of their relative scarcity, they will be more expensive than a good four- or six-banger. I don't know much about motorcycles, so check with someone who does for more info on that size engine. Maybe that person can swing something for you.

You may find a real neat engine, but if it's an obscure thing and parts are not available or take a long time to arrive (they come all the way from Kabul, Afghanistan or the like), forget it. If you're not the mechanic type, you must keep in mind that you'll have to have someone work on it, so avoid the situation where their first question is: What is it? Seriously consider getting a shop manual for the vehicle that the engine came out of; this will seem to be a waste of money when you consider that 75% of the book deals with the rest of the vehicle. But when it comes time to do work on the engine, it will be indispensable. You might consider stocking some of the more often replaced parts of the engine -- the points, plugs, condenser, oil filter, rotor cap, rotor, air cleaner, brushes for the generator and starter motor, a carburetor kit, etc. It would be a good idea to do a thorough replacement of many of these items prior to the installation of the engine in the MOSGU. This will not only insure that a period of time will pass before you must do these things, but will also familiarize you with the engine. Don't throw out the parts that you replace; keep them for spares. If you do the overhaul before you install the MOSGU, do it while the engine is still in the vehicle to insure that you've done it all correctly. With the number of things that must be done to get the engine operating satisfactorily in the MOSGU, you're probably going to forget to make some small connection somewhere and you don't need to have any more problems than necessary; if it is operating all right in the vehicle, it should operate right off in the MOSGU. If it doesn't, it helps to know what isn't wrong with it!

As indicated before, give some thought to using an engine which is going to be easy to remove from the vehicle (if it is not already out of the vehicle). You will need to construct some kind of a mounting stand for the MOSGU engine, and there is no sense in making it any more difficult than necessary. The mounting stand will experience some vibration from the engine, but for the most part it will not nearly experience the kinds of forces exerted on it in the MOSGU as it would a vehicle. Think of all the bumps, dips, corners, etc., the vehicle (and, consequently, the engine) experiences, and you will have some appreciation for the more gentle environment the MOSGU offers. (Even if you don't appreciate it directly, the engine will, and the longer life it will render will eventually bring you around.) An engine that is being revved exerts a lot of twist that the mounts in the vehicle must absorb, and this will be eliminated in the MOSGU (except when the engine starts). Don't figure to just set it on a table or sumthin', though; a rigid stand will insure that couplings to the engine are not damaged or broken. In earthquake country, this is a must.

While you're carefully considering the difficulties in removing the engine, check out the way it is mounted in the vehicle. Most front-of-vehicle engines have a mount on each side toward the front of the engine and depend on the connection to the transmission for support in the back. (It is the transmission or bell housing that is shock-mounted to the frame.) Rear-mounted engines are secured in a variety of ways. If you can't see how it's done, ask someone who does (or might) and you'll be better off. After all, you're going to want to secure the engine in the same manner inside the MOSGU. Why? Well, becuz of all the engine's paraphernalia on the bottom side (particularly, the oil pan), there are only a few places that you can support an engine adequately and still have access to the need-of-servicing areas.

Author's Note: This may be getting too complex for you, particularly if you realize that such things are not areas in which you hold any expertise. To that I can only say: Maintain. The specifics are little things that can be worked out, but the IDEA of it all is not always going to come from someone who is capable of doing it. It takes all kinds of people to make the world go 'round. I recall mentioning the idea of the MOSGU to an auto mechanic at one time. Just in the most general terms, he quickly caught on and started telling me all the different things he could do to make it work, and even gave me a few more ideas. Most auto mechanics would accept the challenge of such an idea if you don't have the skills to carry it out for yourself. If you can paint the MOSGU picture to 'em, they'll paint the real MOSGU. Sort of a reverse Van Gogh (or from the painting to the painted). End of Author's Note.

Water-cooled engines will afford a much easier connection for generating some hot water for showers and kitchen functions, but an air-cooled engine is likely to be smaller than most water-cooled monsters. A water-cooled, four-banger engine is the optimum type of engine for use in the MOSGU, but I think I would choose the air-cooled engine before I'd choose a larger, water-cooled one. The specific engine that I would choose for use in the MOSGU would be the Volkswagen

engine (which is air-cooled). I'd certainly have to figure out something for extracting heat for (in turn) heating water, but the other advantages of the engine -- ease of removal, efficient, lightweight, good design, easy to tune and repair, and small horsepower -- make it a desirable choice. But that's me, and what I'd do.

Front-of-vehicle engines have one advantage over most rear-of-vehicle engines that is desirable in seeking out an engine for the MOSGU -- easy access to the generator or alternator on the engine. This is important if it is your desire to obtain a lot of electrical energy from the MOSGU. For most automobiles, only about one horsepower of electrical energy is available; this translates to a little more than 700 watts. While this is enuff for most vehicular requirements -- lights, air conditioning, ignition, blowers, radios, etc. -- this is far below the level that could be obtained in the MOSGU installation. If the engine no longer has the requirement of supplying motive power, it can use all of its generated horsepower to produce electricity. A 40HP engine is theoretically capable of producing a little more than 28,000 watts (or 28KW) of electrical power. It will, however, deliver nowhere near this amount of energy becuz of the relative inefficiency of the engine, alternator, V-belt connections, I^2R losses, etc. I mean, after all, if it was efficient enuff, it would generate little heat, right? As it turns out, with due consideration of these inefficiencies, we might expect the engine to produce 5000 watts if a suitable generator was available. Most don't have access to that breed of generator, however, but there are a number of ways that this figure could be approached. A car equipped with an alternator can have the voltage regulator removed to substantially increase the power it otherwise puts out. (It will put out the same current at a higher voltage.) A car equipped with a generator can't do this becuz the generator would burn up. An alternative to both is to mount additional generators or alternators onto the vehicle to increase the power output. Access to the existing generator and the pulley-drive that couples it with the motive power of the engine will be necessary to do this. Anyone familiar with the auto engine will quickly realize that a suitable attachment can be made at the transmission end of the engine. In the MOSGU installation, the transmission is not essential. For the more enterprising, I leave the use of the power of the transmission for other mechanical work (such as operating a pump, lathe, etc.)

Finding the MOSGU Engine

If your situation doesn't stick you with whatever happens to be immediately available, then you're going to have to go out and find an engine to use in the MOSGU installation. This is a haphazard affair at most and a time-consuming one at least. My first tendency would be to check with various shops as their owners will have tucked away engines that were replaced or overhauled and never picked up. Generally, the engines will not be in a vehicle and this makes it difficult to know if the engine is truly dead or capable of being revived. If you know the guy, there's less chance of getting ripped off in this situation. But friends who are also mechanics or shopowners tend not to sell such items to good customers becuz it destroys friendships or loses them customers if they can't make good on a bad engine they've sold you. If you find an engine that's out of the vehicle, it will make it easier to install in the MOSGU, but you should have them make suitable connections to the engine where it lies and have them start it for you if that's possible. Some places will, or can do it, and others won't, even if they could.

Along the line of the MOSGU-type equipment is this 110VAC (single-phase), 3000 watt standby generator that we located and purchased during our October 1974 expeditions. Sure was heavy! It had thrown a rod (evidenced by a gaping hole in the engine wall), so Bill Hart and the author began its disassembly for repair and further inspection. In miniature contrast is the horizonal-axle, lawnmower-type engine used with the HESGU. Compare the realtively new-looking large SGU with the ancient, kerosene-fueled standby generators we also brought home last year.

Yards that specialize in tearing down vehicles for their component parts are a good place to go. If you don't know anything about these beasts (the engines, I mean), take someone along that does, or pray like the dickens that the person you're talking to doesn't see you as one big lollypop. Surprisingly enuff, I don't find many individuals in the business who have a motto like "Pray for ignorance and prey on ignorance," but then I know, most of the time, when someone is trying to snow me. Just keep remembering that an engine that _does_ run isn't necessarily a good one, and an engine that _doesn't_ run isn't necessarily a bad one.

(Author's Note: An observation here that might be useful, particularly to a woman that wants to install a MOSGU. I've often speculated on this without coming up with a good reason, but I have noticed less of a tendency, on the part of auto wreckers and shopowners, to try snowing a woman on the subject of automobiles. Maybe it's becuz a man pretends to know a lot when talking with these folks and they enjoy snowing him becuz he thinks they won't. A woman is generally far more honest about her ignorance on the subject, and maybe this takes the fun out of it and breathes some Good Samaritanism into the mechanic. This is surely nothing to count on, but it should indicate that any woman stands a fighting chance of coming up with a good engine. I'll probably get some mail on this one, but I mention it becuz alternative energy installations are just as capable of being installed by women as they are by men. End of Author's Note.)

If you do manage to find an engine (in one of these yards) that's still in the vehicle, try to find out why the vehicle is being scrapped. If the transmission was shot, or the rear end went out, or the side of the vehicle is caved in, the engine is probably all right. Check with insurance companies; many times they will sell you a whole car that's "written off" because of some damage that was in excess of what they thought the vehicle was worth to repair. If you get into this scene, you may have to bid for the car as the auto wreckers will certainly do, but you can get a fantastic buy. Be careful, as you can get stung, too!

Check with engine rebuilders as they have many engines that would be good for use in the MOSGU installation. They are generally the recipients of the engines removed at auto-wrecking yards, and they are choosy about what they take. Don't go into it blind, though; check with some auto-wrecking yards and find out how much they get for the engines. Expect to pay twice that amount (at the most) from a rebuilder for an engine that's not yet rebuilt.

Looking back over this, I think the best option for anyone looking for an engine in this manner is to establish a good relationship with someone in a shop or yard, and have them on the lookout for something that will do the job. If you can't afford a lot of money for it, indicate this. You're going to have to offer more than what he can get elsewhere, but if you're not in a big hurry, it can be worth the wait. If you indicate that you have a standing deal with other yards as well, chances are good that you'll hear from him sometime during the same year.

If you've got the money, might as well buy a rebuilt engine. You can really choose this way and, of course, there's not much wait (unless you're real choosy and he doesn't have what you want at the time you inquire). Generally auto engine rebuilders have a guarantee for a certain number of miles and a certain period of time. There won't be an odometer (mileage indicator) hooked up to the MOSGU, so time is what you'll be fighting. If this is your situation, don't buy the engine until almost everything else is ready; this way, you get the full benefit of the guarantee and can check out the engine's operation extensively in your application.

Installing the MOSGU Engine

The first order of business here is the engine-mounting stand. If the ideas and possibilities are not just popping into your head, line up someone with welding equipment to build you one. A good carpenter will be able to make a strong and rigid stand. Make the mounting stand high and roomy enough to allow easy access to anything you might have to get at (oil pan, valves, plugs, generator, etc.) If the stand is made very rigid, it will not be difficult to mount additional generators to the engine.

The MOSGU environment (or housing) should be given considerable attention and forethought. My own preference is for a buried unit, but it does represent problems which are an order of magnitude above simply putting it into a storage shed or above-ground container. It must, however, be a closed environment if the waste heat is to be effectively utilized. A large shipping crate will do admirably, but a home-built version will work as well. It must be very well insulated or you'll end up heating up the great outdoors and the noise will drive you wiggy. There are all kinds of possibilities, but let your imagination carry you where it will. Just so that we can get anywhere with it, I'll pretend that we (meaning you and I) have come to an agreement that a shipping crate is ideal (becuz we have one, so we'll go on from there. Say that our shipping crate is 6ft x 6ft x 6ft.

The housing for the MOSGU must be insulated, fireproof, accessible, and (preferably) soundproof. Our shipping crate won't meet many of these criteria "as is." You may have to check on the building, electrical, and safety codes for your area, but what you'll first want to do is figure out where you are going to put it. If it's above ground, get it near the habitat so that you don't have to spend a fortune for the insulated unbilical cords that tie it to the house. It's not much different for the underground installation but, for some locations, the ground will serve to insulate the ducting and pipes to some degree. Supposing that you decide to dig the hole for the crate, dig it at least 7-8 ft. deep becuz you'll want a foot or more of earth on top of the MOSGU enclosure to maximize the insulation afforded by the earth. The hole must be properly prepared to receive the crate to avoid flooding or moisture accumulation; this will depend on the type of earth in your area. Contact anyone that might be familiar with these conditions and have them advise you of ways to insure proper drainage. As well, insure that the MOSGU habitat is structurally strengthened, as it will be exposed to side and roof pressure of large magnitudes. If you can't seem to get that all together, plan on installing it above ground, in the basement, or in another building.

The habitat must be waterproofed if the wood is to survive long exposure to the earth or to the elements. As well, it should be insulated inside with fiberglass or the like, and then lined with foil to reflect heat from the engine and to prevent exposing combustible surfaces to the engine heat. A battery must be installed in the MOSGU for engine-starting purposes, but all of the other batteries used to store the energy it produces should be located out of the engine compartment. There is no reason to expose them to the heat and extra provisions would be required to vent the hydrogen and oxygen they liberate under heavy charging or discharging. Combined together in certain ratios, hydrogen and oxygen are highly explosive and the added heat and electrical sparks from a nearby engine is the sure-fire additive. Sorta like having your own underground blasting facilities without anyone knowing when the test is to occur!

If you locate the entrance to the engine housing at one end and the engine at the other, you won't have to drop down onto the engine when you go into the compartment. A side entrance to the compartment is a good option to a top one, but this will mean extra digging if you're on flat ground. If the MOSGU housing is located on the side of a slope, this will work admirably.(See Fig. 6-10)

Figure out where you are going to install the warm air ducts, hot water pipes, and the conduit in which the electrical wires are contained. Also determine where the exhaust vent will be located and the fresh air intake pipes. You'll need two of the latter -- one for the carburetor, and the other for the air that you will draw into the house or shop after it has been heated by passing it over and around the engine. You must also provide a fuel inlet for the engine; you could install the gas tank in the compartment, but I wouldn't. Most gas tanks in vehicles are not where they will receive a lot of heat from the engine and for good reason: It's not only dangerous but, as well, the heat tends to vaporize the gas, and you've got all those icky fumes which compounds the danger. So locate the gas tank above ground, separate from the MOSGU housing. A small line can be led to the compartment and the engine.

Before the engine is installed in the housing, take it down and get it steam cleaned. If you're going to try and extract waste heat from it, there is no sense in having to smell the accumulated oil, dirt, and road tar that coats most auto engines. You must also periodically inspect the exhaust system and the crankcase breather functions for leaks. If you can't take the time to do this, forget about getting warm air from the MOSGU housing. Carbon monoxide is odorless, tasteless, colorless, and deadly! At the very least, it'll give you headaches, nausea, and can cause permanent brain damage. Get that engine checked out! Or do it yourself, if you know what you're doing. You may have to install a modified system for crankcase breathing in the engine; when in doubt, run it to the outside of the habitat. This will be one of those things that you must check periodically on the MOSGU system. Heat and time will have their effect on most anything.

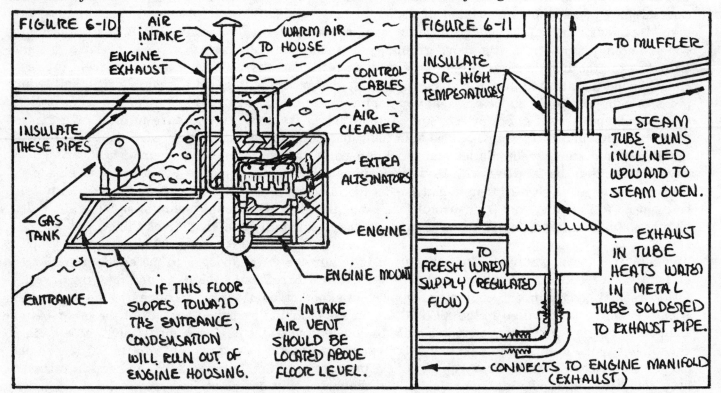

The ignition coil and the voltage regulator are often mounted to the engine compartment wall in an automobile, so make sure you get these if you remove the engine from a car. The generator or alternator are the other two necessities, but they'll be attached to the engine unless they have been stripped off. Mount these on the engine frame, or to the wall of the MOSGU housing. Before you install the engine, have the necessary work done to mate up other generators if you are going to do this. It might be a real bear to do it down in the compartment after the engine is on its mounts.

If the engine is water-cooled and you want to use this portion of the MOSGU for heating some water, then the radiator will not be needed at all. The setup will require the addition of some high-temperature water hoses (like those used in dishwashers and washing machines) and a length for the output and return hose sufficient to reach your hot water storage tank. If you don't plan to use this function, you might as well leave the radiator in the engine housing and use the fan to draw the air down into the compartment and push it into the house for space heating.

Hot water may be derived from the engine regardless of whether it is air-cooled or water-cooled initially. This is probably best accomplished by a close-proximity water tank or a heat-exchanger of sorts. Precisely how it could be done is extremely situational, but the desired end is to extract the high-grade heat before it is radiated into the surrounding air in the compartment. The water will need to come in contact with some portion of the engine, and this will be limited to nonelectrical locations and ones which will not crack the block. This may have to be a watertight seal so a bolted or welded addition may be necessary. The oil pan could be set into a pan of water, but only if the seals are tight -- essence of engine oil is not exactly a desirable part of your shower. If you're real particular about the quality of water you bathe in, the water-cooled engine will provide the best service, since a radiator can be installed in your hot water storage tank to provide a heat-exchanger that will not contaminate the water you use.

The highest-temperature output from the engine is generally the exhaust. Extracting heat from it is not difficult, if you build an apparatus like that shown in Fig. 6-11. If you expose a large amount of water to the exhaust pipe, you'll end up with hot water. If you expose only a very small amount of water, you'll invariably end up with steam. This could be real handy for cooking as the steam could be transported via heater hoses or insulated pipes to the house and used there in a special oven. This will take some thinking becuz you must be able to replace the amount of water that's converted to steam, but at a rate that insures that it doesn't cool off the super-heated water, or the steam will stop. An electrically-controlled valve in the engine housing might control the rate of water flow to this apparatus or a water valve in the house could be turned on to regulate the flow. It'll take some practice to first get the steam coming, and then keep it coming; but it would be an exciting prospect and one worth the effort to get it working, and keep it working. Some condensation will occur in the pipe before it gets hot enuff to get the steam all the way to the cooking apparatus but if the pipes are inclined upward a small amount, the condensed water will just run back into the exhaust heat-exchanger. Don't let any dips occur in the line, though, or the steam will be blocked.

Engine Start and Ignition Control

A desirable feature to the MOSGU is remote starting and control of the engine. Most of the required items can be obtained from the vehicle the engine was removed from, or any auto-wrecking yard. The key-type combination ignition and start switch will be the best bet, but a pushbutton switch and toggle-switch will replace that item if necessary. The generator, oil pressure and temperature "idiot lights" that most cars are equipped with should be used if their sensors are installed. But if possible, these should be replaced with an ammeter, pressure gauge, and temperature gauge becuz of the greater amount of information these instruments will provide about engine operating conditions. Fig. 6-12 illustrates the idiot light arrangement and the gauge arrangement. Most engines are easily converted to the latter, if they are not already so equipped.

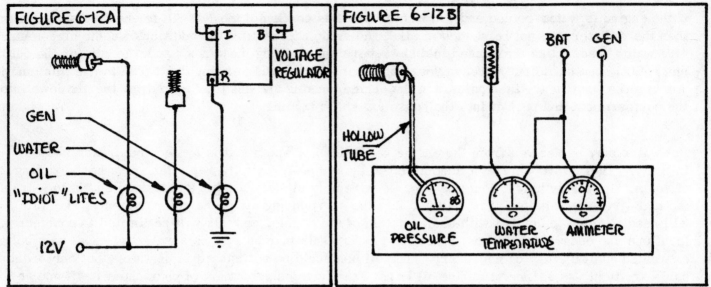

FIGURE 6-12A

GEN
WATER
OIL
"IDIOT" LITES
12V

VOLTAGE
REGULATOR

FIGURE 6-12B

BAT   GEN

HOLLOW
TUBE

OIL
PRESSURE

WATER
TEMPERATURE

AMMETER

If the vehicle is equipped with a manual choke, you must make some kind of an allowance for this, and run a similar setup in the house. This will be more difficult than the automatic choke found in later model autos. Some automatic chokes are really electrical in nature and not just a bimetallic coiled spring arrangement. One of the neat things about the Volkswagen is that it has an electrical choke and this makes for an easy choke-control from the remote panel. Learn what type your engine has and provide the necessary coupling for it. Manual choke types will be difficult to install unless you can find a long wire-in-cable of the type that was originally used with the engine. Chokes are pretty much of an auto-oriented thing, anyway; there has, in fact, been alot of contro- versy over the effect that so much raw gas has on an engine. If your engine will start, an advanced throttle will keep it going, and since you don't need to start "driving" right away, you can probably get along without it. Let the engine warm up a bit and then take it up to the speed you operate it at.

The gas pedal isn't going to be of much use to you, unless you get some kind of a thrill sitting at the console and driving your standby generator, but the linkage will be necessary and you should run some kind of throttle-control into the house and the remote panel. This can be a lever like the manual choke mechanism. You could install a small DC motor (low-RPM type like those found in clock drives) so that you can advance or back off on the throttle by using a suitably-connected center position, double-pole, double-throw (DPDT) switch. Another way to hold the throttle at a certain position is to preadjust the linkage adjustment on the engine and count on this to keep the engine at an approximate RPM. This latter method will be insufficient if you are varying the amount of load on the electrical generating equipment on the MOSGU.

The final feature required in the remote control panel is some sort of engine speed indicator. As the speedometer in an auto is operated from a sending unit attached to the transmission, this will be of no use to you when you discard the transmission for the installation. A tachometer (which electrically reads the engine's RPM) is the best choice. A second one might be to run a small DC motor (of the slot-car variety) on a drive belt, but you will need to calibrate this device to a tachometer if the readings you get on the voltmeter are to be translated into RPM. In the last couple of years, the market has been flooded with dwell-tach meters (or gauges), so inexpensive ones are available and will do nicely for the information that you are trying to get. Basically, an RPM-reading device will help you in three ways when used with the MOSGU. First, it will tell you when the engine is started. Second, it will allow you to adjust the speed of the engine whenever a certain amount of electrical energy is required. Third, it will prevent you from advancing the throttle of the engine to the point where it will be in danger (past its red-line, or safe-operating RPM).

The only difficulty with operating a standard automobile engine from a remote location is that it is difficult to tell when the engine is "ready to start." In learning to drive a car, we acquire this information by "listening" to the engine. When it starts to "hurry up," we let the key slip back into the ignition position and the starter motor disengages. Unless you install a small intercom between the remove-control panel and the engine housing (which isn't all that bad an idea, by the way), you may not hear it. So it's a bit of the GGM (guess-and-by-golly method) to know when to let go of the starter function. The tachometer will show a slightly higher RPM when the engine begins to start (after all, we listen for the engine to race a bit, when we turn it over, and use this as an indicator) but it will not always be noticeable and you might not respond fast enuff. A fancy remote-control panel is, of course, not necessary to the operation of the MOSGU; you could install it just inside the engine compartment. That could be a bummer, though, if you have to run out into the snowdrifts to turn it on. Then, too, it'll impose a self-limiting use of fossil fuels, so it may not be all that bad. At any rate, you'll acquire the sense of knowing when it's ready after you've worked with it a while. For temperamental engines, this will probably mean a few months or years!

A fuel gauge is a nice addition to the remote panel, but it might also be located near the gas tank. Most of these units are electrically sensed; but if you build your own tank, you must install the sensor; use a U-tube (clear tube that shows the level in the tank), or use a dipstick. The neat thing about the MOSGU engine is that it will generally be run at constant RPM and you will quickly learn the gasoline rate-of-use (if you keep records of ON-time) and will know, in this manner, when the gas tank is going to need to be filled.

I make a strong suggestion that anyone using a MOSGU installation keep records of the engine's running time, when it's refueled, and what it is used for. This is the sort of habit that is wisely acquired for anyone using an alternative energy source becuz it puts the user in touch with the reality of their own consumption or needs. This will help match the wind-electric or solar energy installation (in terms of output) to the required energy for existence and the level of comfort an individual wishes to maintain (come hell-or-high-water). Additionally, by doing a bit of math, the MOSGU user will acquire the ability to "think" in terms of BTU's, HP (horsepower), and Watts (electrical unit of power). Knowing that a gallon of gasoline, when burned, releases 127,654 BTU's won't mean an awful lot if an individual does not know how many KWH (kilowatt-hours) of electrical energy this will yield and how many BTU's are required to heat a room of a given size or efficiency. 'Nuff said.

If you are going to generate electrical energy from the MOSGU instead of just heat, then you will need to add a few more controls to the remote-control panel, or some similar location. If you find that the alternator or generator already attached to the engine will suffice for your electrical requirements, additions to the remote-control panel will not necessarily be required. The voltage regulator that came with the engine will automatically charge the battery in the engine housing (used to start the engine) and allow you to use any additional electricity (at that voltage) that you may need. This will be limited to something less than 300-400 watts in most cases (or whatever the total wattage of headlights, blowers, radios, etc., add up to in the vehicle the engine came out of). If you wish to charge additional batteries, you should use a switch on the control panel to cut them in and out. While you would not be in any danger of hurting the voltage regulator or the generator/alternator on the engine if you added more without this switch, you would run the risk of running down the battery required to start the engine if it and the others were discharged together. The switch will serve to isolate the starter battery from the others when you are using the energy in the batteries (when engine is off). As well, it will insure that this battery will be the first to be charged when the engine is started, after which the others can be switched on to also receive a charge. A diode will partially automate this function (and prevent discharge of the starter battery when the others are being used), but the switch would be required to permit first topping off the starter battery.

Most alternators are capable of being operated at much higher voltages (see Chapter 2 of <u>Wind and Windspinners</u> for a detailed analysis of this function), but the automotive voltage regulator will not be usable unless it is a heavy-duty type that can be adjusted to this voltage. I have repeatedly operated a standard, automobile alternator at 24 volts (and full rated current) with no negative effects and suspect that most will survive, as well, at 36 volts. This will give, at 24 volts, twice -- and for 36 volts, three times-- the power capability of the unit when operated at 12 volts. (If a generator is used with the engine, this cannot usually be done without burning it up. Therefore, if the alternator is originally rated at 42 amps, at 12 volts it will deliver 500 watts (42 x 12), at 24 volts it will deliver 1000 watts (42 x 24), and at 36 volts it will deliver 1500 watts (42 x 36). An amazing array of factors come into effect here which will limit these figures somewhat -- I^2R losses, eddy current losses, additional slippage in the V-belt, etc. -- but the idea is there.

The addition of a second alternator or a third alternator will double or triple (respectively) the expected output wattage at these various voltages, but additional requirements will come into effect -- engine speed will need to be increased to prevent loading, the V-belts should probably be replaced with gear belts (to prevent slippage and friction losses), higher voltages should be used (to prevent heavy I^2R losses), and the batteries will need to be located close to the engine housing for the MOSGU (to avoid the high cost of large-size wire).

Author's Note: There are many factors to consider in generating high quantities of electrical power from the MOSGU, particularly if it exceeds the 1000-watt figure. A complete understanding of the nature of electrical energy--how it is produced, at what wattages and voltages, with what horsepower requirements, with what I^2R losses, heat, friction, and slippage losses, and with what effect on the design of controls, use of batteries, etc.--will be required for a full appreciation of why it is done this way or that way, and how much this can be compromised before dangerous combinations are produced. An exhaustive treatment of control, batteries, and electrical generation is given in <u>Wind and Windspinners</u>, which is meant to be a companion volume to this book, and the information will not be repeated here. Nor could it be, for it took a minimum of 45 pages in the first book to deal with these subjects. End of Author's Note.

As in the instance with the owner-built (wind machine) control box, if you don't already have an idea of how to proceed with building the MOSGU, you've got some homework to do. You may need to consult basic texts on mechanics, engineering, electronics, electricity (including wiring), and surplus catalogs for the relays, generators, regulators, etc. Or, it may simply be a matter of consulting someone you know who would be able (and willing) to help. . . . Steam ahead.

CHAPTER 7

WIND MACHINE DESIGN NOTES

This chapter is dedicated to a clear understanding of a <u>few</u> wind machine design parameters. It is <u>not</u> intended to be a complete design guide, just some notes on matters that seem neglected in other works that I've seen. If you're buying a wind machine, it will help you to evaluate the different makes and models. If you're doing a "homebrew", it will provide an outline of the basic factors which affect final shape, type, and operating characteristics. The chapter, as it progresses, will move from the general to the more specific.

An observation at this point. If you're prototyping your own wind machine, expose it to the hardcore analysis of others around you, especially those working in the alternative energy field. Don't be afraid that someone is going to steal your idea and patent it. When such paranoia reins, knowledge is set back for years! I've noticed a tendency on the part of folks just started in alternative energy to assume that their first idea is the "breakthru" that everyone else is struggling to find. I guess this stems from a belief that people working in the field for a number of years are now so consumed by the details that they miss seeing the proverbial "forest", and that they're unaware of the innovations that were introduced to the field back in 1908. Correctly applied criticism will refine any good idea and will, except for the very stubborn, junk out any wild ideas that will simply not work. Anyone working extensively in the same field is probably the best person to confront with your idea; they'll also be the least likely to steal an idea, mostly becuz they're thoroughly wrapped up in their own ideas and have more than enuff work to do. I've heard some ingenious suggestions but my response has been to convince the individuals to develop them him/herself.

Power Rating

This is a much-discussed yet little-understood characteristic of windplants. How much energy you need is not expressed by the power rating of the windplant. If you want to know if a particular power rating of windplant is going to work for your situation, you must involve yourself in a bit of calculation and some basic soul-searching regarding your own use and waste of energy. There's no rule of thumb here; the size of wind machine for your situation involves a dozen parameters. <u>Wind and Windspinners</u> is dedicated to the determination of the factors involved and how they interrelate, and I refer you to that if you find yourself confused by this information. Realize that salespersons have a job that depends on how much they sell; if we could get them to write down in the guarantee everything they say when they're trying to sell a wind machine (or whatever), there'd be a lot less claims made of their products. On the other hand, if you go in there with little or no knowledge of the subject, you're not going to understand a manufacturer's claims even if they are true. You can't blame a good company for selling to a customer who's too ignorant to know the product won't work for his situation.

Let's look at an example. You're told that a certain wind machine puts out 2000 watts. Your next question should be: from where? The reason? Some manufacturers describe, for their wind machines, the power at the blades rather than the power out of the generator. Okay, so it's a gimmick to sell the product; if they indicate this in the specifications sheet for the wind-plant, it's up to you to spot it and if you don't, it's your problem. If they rate the power at the blades but don't tell you that, you've got incompetence or a con going; report 'em and then take your business elsewhere. Gonna be a whole lot of wind-electric manufacturers in the years to come; with a bit of consumer action, we can get rid of the rip-offs.

Windspeed Rating

If you don't ask at what windspeed the wind machine will deliver its full rated power, you ought to have your hand slapped and be sent home with a note. The power rating of a windplant is just so much nonsense unless you know this info as well. Many windplants currently being manufac-tured are rated to deliver full power at a 25 MPH windspeed; this rating is useful only for those areas of the world experiencing very high average windspeeds. It is unfortunate that many people in the USA are ordering some of these wind machines when they will rarely reach full power in their area. The Jacobs windplant of yesteryear was designed to deliver its full rated power in an 18 MPH wind; above this windspeed, it would continue to deliver the plant's rated power, but the governor mechanism would limit it to this amount. There are quite a number of wind mach-ines on the market now but I've already noticed that many do not specify at what windspeed they deliver their rated power. Many will specify at what windspeed they begin to charge but this will tell you very little, so beware. Don't be afraid to ask and get it down in the guarantee.

I've mentioned the more desirable windspeed rating to some folks and had them shrug at the 7 MPH difference between 18 and 25 MPH as though it didn't matter. Then I had them guess at the power output of a 2000 watt machine rated at 25 MPH when exposed to an 18 MPH wind. They were a bit shocked when they heard only a piddly 746 watts. The conversion factor, incidentally, is .373 and it's obtained by cubing the two windspeeds and noting the ratio of the answers. It will vary somewhat with other factors -- increased efficiency of the wind machine as it approaches its rated windspeed, and the different wind velocities that you're comparing -- but it'll give you the ballpark figure. Specification sheets might include a power curve that will help you find the power delivered at various windspeeds but not all will provide this curve. Realize that most folks that have plans, kits, or complete wind machines for sale don't figure they'll sell 'em if they note the disadvantages as well as the advantages.

Voltage Rating

Here's a tuff one. Generally speaking, you'll want a high voltage rating (like 110 volts) from the wind machine; maybe you can get it higher (like 220 volts) but in most cases it'll be at lower voltages (like 6, 12, 24, 32, or 36 volts). Let's look at some determining factors:

1. High wattage systems require higher voltages; this keeps I^2R losses to a minimum and wire size relatively small. Conversely, low power systems may utilize lower voltages.

2. Higher voltage systems mean more batteries; a 110 volt system will require 56 two-volt cells, or 19 six-volt cells, or 9 twelve-volt cells. This is roughly four times the number of cells required for a 32 volt system, 5 times the requirement for a 24 volt system and 10 times the required batteries for a 12 volt system. The size (and cost) of electrical wire needed for each will be smallest for the highest voltage, increasing as the voltage becomes smaller (if the watt-age remains the same).

3. Most homes (in the USA) have 110 volt appliances; this makes a higher voltage system more practical in terms of using presently-owned appliances. Becuz of the camper-craze there's a lot of 12 volt and some 24 volt stuff floating around, so if you figure that most of the stuff you have you're willing to do without, then consider the lower voltage units (if it suits your situation all around).

4. To avoid prohibitive costs of long lengths of large size electrical wire, use higher voltages (if you can't locate the windmachine and/or the appliances close enuff to the batteries). Wind and Windspinners gives a few examples in which the power losses in electrical wires are figured for varying wattage and current figures; if you won't figure it out for your own situation, at least look over the examples so you'll know what you have to account for and why.

AC vs DC Systems

Most wind machines deliver DC (Direct Current) rather than the common household AC (Alternating Current). Couple of important reasons why: you can't store AC in a battery and it's wasteful (in a wind-electric system) to try to provide the very specialized AC used in the household -- 60 cycle AC. That doesn't mean, however, that it's not being done; you can find 60 cycle inverter systems.   One system uses the utility line as the storage bank; if you've heard about a way to run your meter "backward", the cutie that does it is the synchronous inverter. Another AC wind machine presently under development gives you AC when the windplant operates; if you don't use it, it rectifies the AC to DC and has the battery bank store the power. When you want to use the power, the DC is inverted and made into AC. It allows you to use the 110 volt, 60 cycle AC appliances but it wastes a little of the stored power becuz it's not as efficient to make AC out of DC as it is to make DC out of AC.

While most people will probably want the convenience of this special kind of power, it's full of holes as far as I'm concerned. The synchronous inverter may eliminate the need for a storage bank but there's a limit to how many people can use this system, it requires continuous connection to, and dependence upon the utility system. There are advantages to using AC (easy transformation of voltage), 60 cycles (timing), and 110 volts, but there's nothing sacred about it, so check it out before you automatically decide that's what you need or want.

Most of the wind machines we acquired (of the pre-REA type) are 32 volts. Well, on the same trip we acquired light bulbs, motors, tools, appliances, an inverter, and an arc-welder that all operate at 32 volts and that's what we're starting to use. Okay, we do have to worry about wire sizes (or higher I^2R losses) and avoid long wire lengths, but we've got some advantages. The lower voltage system is not exposed to the restrictions (codes) that the higher voltages must comply with (in terms of wiring, conduit, etc.). A straight-across-the-board comparison of the amp-hour rating of our 32-volt battery bank might be the same as the 110 volt system but we have several packs in parallel; this allows us to alternately charge and use different sets of batteries. We can also poke our greasy fingers around anywhere we want with little fear of shock. A 110-volt shock is far more dangerous than a 32-volt shock, but realize that either can kill!

The greatest advantage that I can see from a wind machine that produces AC is the possibility of transferring its power over large distances (thru wire, of course) by stepping it up to a higher voltage and then back down when it's where you want it. The wind machine's electricity-producing unit must be an alternator (a generator won't do this) but, unless it's designed to produce the AC, internally-mounted diodes will need to be bypassed to provide AC (instead of DC). Automotive type alternators are three-phase; this will require a special delta-type transformer, or three separate ones, if the voltage is to be stepped up. The transformers and control circuits (to insure proper operating conditions) would be extensive and probably not feasible in terms of the cost/ benefit ratio, but thought I'd mention it for anyone who wishes to work on it.

The Aeroturbine

A wind machine is an aeroturbine; as the word suggests, it's an air-driven turbine. Mechanical energy from the wind. Hook it to a generator or alternator and you can produce electricity if you do it <u>right</u>. But first, you're going to have to consider the types of aeroturbines available. I neglected to say, "you have to decide on a type...", becuz if you're just starting out in all of this, you can't make that decision (intelligently, anyway). And there are so many other things to learn about, but line'em up and bowl'em over. The more you learn, the more you'll realize how ignorant you are (by seeing just how much there is to know); if ya get to where you think ya know it, you've taken a wrong turn somewhere!

Okay, there are two classes of aeroturbine: the vertical and the horizontal axis machines. And they're pretty well defined by the name. The vertical axis machine rotates about a vertical shaft (or axis) and the horizontal axis machine -- yep, you guessed it -- rotates about a horizontal shaft. The sail-wing, wind-sail, prop-types, Chalk turbine, farm water-pumpers, Dutch wind-mills, are all horizontal axis machines. The Savonius rotor, Darrieus rotor (alias "eggbeater"), and the hybrid-types are all vertical axis machines.

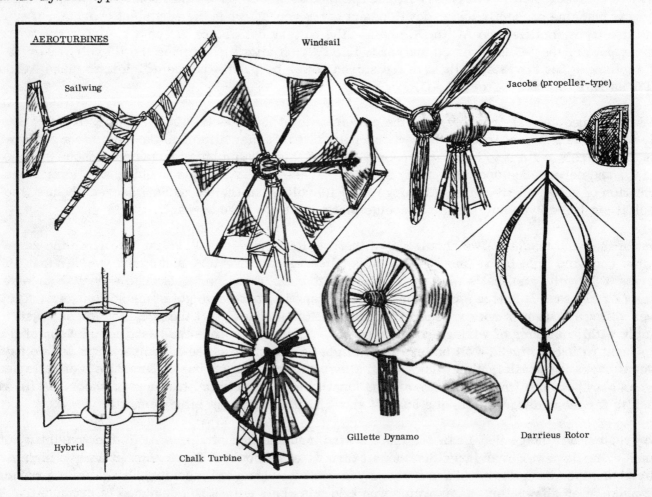

The differences? Through the ages, the prop-type (horizontal axis) has been the more favored aeroturbine. The vertical axis machines are less efficient; the calculated maximum power they can extract is less than for a horizontal axis machine. That may be true or it may be hogwash.

(it was once considered impossible to fly and pass the sound barrier).   Recent work with the vertical axis machines is showing their value. Keep in mind that efficiency is only _one_ of the criteria for selecting a wind machine. The vertical axis machines may win out now becus they're easier to construct, generally cost less, are omni-directional (don't have to "point into" the wind) and don't need slip rings (to transfer the power). I don't care to convince you to use one over the other--that's too situational and I know it even if you don't. Just don't get any ideas that there is some kind of intrinsic worth to the prop-type horizontal axis aeroturbine. More is known about them than the vertical axis machines becuz of their extensive use; in order to honestly evaluate 'em under the same conditions we gotta know as much about the vertical axis jobs. It's kinda hard to tell when you're there, tho, unless you've got a Certificate of Knowledge and Whizdom from the Cosmic Energy Society.

But which one you choose is gonna affect a lot of other things. To spark some thinking along those lines, let's look at some different aspects of the two classes of aeroturbines. First we'll cover the horizontal axis windplant (HAW) and then we'll look at hardware for the vertical axis windplant (VAW). I won't get too specific here, however; there are too many types of each class to allow a discussion of them to be any thing this side of a book-length treatment. The Bibliography lists some sources of information various types of wind machines; as well, the list of other bibliographies and sources will point out further information.

The HAW: Some notes on Tails, Blades, Governors, Turntable, and Slip Rings.

The HAW Tail

A horizontal axis aeroturbine must be positioned to face the wind if it is to extract the available energy. This is accomplished in two ways: by adding a tail, or designing the aeroturbine so that its blades run "downwind" (without a tail). Becuz of its need to "orient" into the wind, the "upwind" windplant can be shut-down (prevented from operating) by side-facing the props or tail. See the Jacobs Tail-Furling section in Chapter 2 for a description of the recommended system. A tail that is higher than it's wide will provide the best response. If the windplant is tailless, shut-down can be provided by manual activation of a change of pitch governor (See: HAW Governors).

HAW Blades

I have no specific information on the most desirable number of blades for the windsail-type of HAW, but the highest speed units are two-blade props. Becuz of the gyroscopic vibration these props can experience during change of direction, a three-blade prop is used on most good HAW windplants. As indicated, Wincharger made four-blade props but these have proved to be one too many. A good two-blade prop is a little more efficient than a similar three-blade, so consider the addition of small counterweights on a cross-arm perpendicular to the prop to get around the gyroscopic vibration problem of the two-blader. Consider the cost/benefit ratio before committing yourself to any type or number of blades.

A variety of materials and blade-making processes can be found but I can only recommend sources rather than information itself. If you want efficient blades, they're going to be (generally) more expensive and more difficult to make. This is becuz they need to be "twisted" and tapered from the root to the tip; this brings many portions of the blade into high efficiency at the same RPM (design RPM). The weight of the blade assembly must be kept low if the unit is to survive the stresses imposed by centrifugal forces. Larger diameter props are restricted to **lower** RPM than smaller ones. The shape, size, and efficiency of blade used depends on the average annual windspeed for your area and the highest windspeed to which the blades will be exposed. Many wind machine designers specify different blades for different local windspeeds. A low wind area will generally use a wider blade set at a larger pitch angle than one used for a high wind area.

Precisely balancing the blades is essential to optimum operation and long life of a windplant. It is better to balance blades dynamically (at operating RPM) but this is difficult, dangerous, or outright impossible unless you have the equipment. Static (motionless) balancing is the more common method of balancing blades and a knife edge or preferably bubble floats are used here. The biggest problem here is the setup -- serious attention and forethought can eliminate introducing error but it's a tedious process. Best results are usually obtained by suspending the entire prop assembly from THE center (indoors where the air is still) and adding small metal weights where necessary. Weights placed on fast-traveling portions of the prop should be curved to an aerodynamic tear-drop shape. Don't be in a hurry to let it fly until you've done absolutely the best balancing job you can. It's worth it.

HAW Governors

There are many types of governor too, but the best seems to be the change-of-pitch type; it's the only one that not only limits the generator output but relieves wind-pressure (of the wind force) on the blades, windplant, and tower. The governor used for the Jacobs units is among the best. If you homebrew one, provide for adjustments of the governor-activation RPM and response. Use big bearings in the main hub and tapered-roller bearings (or some thrust-type) in the propellor-attachment arms. Otherwise you'll be replacing them, or littering the countryside with your precious blades (and windplant). Learn how to calculate centrifugal forces. It's essential that variable-pitch blades be coupled together so that they all change pitch at an equal rate.

A much simpler governor design is the automatic side-facing (furling) prop assembly. If the prop shaft is mounted off-center from the turntable shaft, high wind forces on the prop will cause it to pivot about the turntable shaft and face more or less out of the wind against the tension of an adjustable spring. The tail pivot and spring are, of course, necessary anyway, for shut-down with a manual pull-chain, except that automatic side-facing will necessitate a low-friction tail pivot to prevent rapid wear, and a stiff spring or rubber cushion to absorb the shock when the prop springs back into working position. The tail pivot spring can be avoided by tilting the tail hinge slightly so that when side-facing occurs, the tail folds slightly upward, against gravity. Adjustments can be made by changing either the hinge angle or the weight or length of the tail.

Some side-facing systems employ a side, or "pilot" vane on an arm parallel to and just behind the prop. Unlike the off-center mounted prop shaft, this will affect governing regardless of the electrical load on the generator and may be a wise alternative if you are afraid of excessive no-load prop speeds.

The little Parris-Dunn windplant of the 1930's employed an upward-facing rather than side-facing system (no pilot vane). This may afford additional protection against sudden gusts that often sock it to the machine from the side. The direct drive generator tilts upward against gravity with the aid of a spring, and lands on a rubber cushion upon its return.

HAW Turntable

This should be loads of fun! It'll bring out the creativity in you. First, it's got to support the windplant structurally. Second, it's got to mate to the tower you're using. Third, it's got to have thrust capability to handle the windplant weight and allow responsive wind-orientation by the windplant. Fourth, it's got to contain the slip-ring/brush assembly to provide for attaching the wires coming from the generator itself and the wires going down the tower and into the control box.

A slip-ring/brush assembly can be avoided by using wires composed of thin strands for flexibility, and a plug and socket at the base of the tower, so that you can untwist them occassionally. Such wires will usually last at least a couple years if they don't rub anywhere. Not a bad idea if you have a prevailing breeze of a steady direction.

HAW Slip-Rings

If you're building the conventional type slip-rings, cut some heavy wall brass or copper pipe with a hacksaw into rings and slide them over some micarta tubing or sumthin' similar that will fit over or into the turntable tube. The Winchargers had thin brass rings that were held away from the turntable so that the connecting wires (to the rings) could pass under them (instead of through the wall of the turntable tube). This was done this way becuz they had a shaft thru the tube and couldn't run the wires through it without interference. But . . . their rings could be easily damaged and many that we found were dinged or not perfectly round or downright smashed and they're nearly impossible to straighten. So design the turntable assembly around the slip-rings and get 'em tight against the tube on which they mount.

I recommend using genuine carbon or graphite brushes instead of copper or brass ones on spring-arms like those found in the Winchargers. I don't think that the same kind of pressure (brush to ring) can be maintained in the copper/brass brush and they would often get misaligned and short to another brush or slip-ring. As well, it is much harder to get the copper brushes "arced" to the same contour as the slip ring itself; if this isn't perfectly done, electrical arcing and pitting will occur. Changes in brush tension (if it's a non-carbon type) change the position of the arced metal and this will cause the same effect. The carbon type are, therefore, easier to work with, more efficient, and less likely to need attention. Brush assemblies scrounged from an old motor or generator can be well adapted to this purpose.

THE VAW: Some notes on Orienting, Governors, and Support Assembly

VAW Orienting

Vertical axis windplants do not require wind-direction orientation; they are omni-directional; this may be thought of as being oriented into the wind irrespective of the specific wind direction. However, if a Venturi shroud (or wind focuser) is used with the wind machine, a tail may be required to keep it properly oriented.

VAW Governor

A good governor mechanism for a vertical axis machine is not an easy thing to come by, at least not for the S-rotor type windplant. A centrifugal unit coupled with the impellers or blades will help somewhat but there is really no direction to orient them in which they won't be affected by wind action . With the Savonius type, this represents a genuine problem; many designs have been offered but none tested to a satisfactory or publishable state. Here the Venturi shroud might come in handy in itself, however, as a windblock. One truly intriguing idea, other than those offered in Wind and Windspinners, is to have the impellers fold in on themselves and create a cylinder of sorts. Manual shut-down represents more of a problem becuz you can't side-face the machine into the wind. A trip lever might allow full activation of a normally activated centrifugal governor but I'd work with separate units -- one for automatic and one for manual; if one fails, you've still got the other.

VAW Support Assembly

The VAW's tend, becuz of their lower efficiencies, to be physically larger than the horizontal counterparts. There will be an optical illusion as well; the HAW blades (if of the high-speed type) appear very thin but many people do not realize that at operating speeds these blades are moving so fast so as to appear, to the wind, to be a large circular wall. The VAW, on the other hand, will generally expose a lot of frontal area (unless it's a Darrieus type); a 1500 watt prop-type windplant may only have a 14 foot diameter blade but an equivalent power Savonius rotor would be 18 feet tall and about 8 feet in diameter. The point (before we forget it all together) is that the support assembly for the VAW will be much more involved than the HAW.

Becuz of their need for support at both the top and bottom of the main shaft, VAW units are difficult to mount as high as the comparable-powered HAW. Fig. 7-1 illustrates the way it can be done on a conventional tower but we've lately come to the conclusion that it's better to "tailor" the tower to the machine than vice versa. Given the versatility of the octahedron-segment tower (see Chapt. 3), we designed one to fit our newly-designed 18-ft by 8-ft Maxi-rotor (see Fig. 7-2). By building the rotor inside the tower, it's easy to reach all of the main shaft bearings and to otherwise service the rotor. A real bonus is that the top of the tower can still be used for a conventional HAW. I'm sure that there are other answers to the problem of how to get the VAW "up there", so use the ole noggin.

HAW and VAW Generators

There are some essential differences in the generator requirements for the HAW and VAW; this could be best expressed as a difference in the operating position of the generator itself and perhaps the normal operating speed.   Let's take 'em one at a time.

The HAW will usually employ a generator which has its shaft also horizontal; this will allow a more efficient and easier transfer of power from the aeroturbine to the generator (if the shaft is not outright one in the same between the two). The VAW will also want the generator shaft to be parallel to the aeroturbine shaft, so it'll be mounted vertically, with its shaft perpendicular to the ground. Not hard and fast with either, though. I've seen some HAW's using a car axle to transfer the power to a vertical shaft so that the generator can be mounted at the base of the tower (beware of leaking oil). And some VAW drive shafts are coupled to a 90° gearbox so the generator can be mounted horizontally. I don't necessarily recommend either. . . but becuz there are very few generators designed for vertical mounting, a 90° gearbox is quite understandable and probably necessary. If you want to mount a generator or alternator vertically and it's designed to be (or is normally mounted) horizontal, understand that you might burn out its bearings and otherwise damage it. Know what you are doing.

Any type of aeroturbine (whether a VAW or a HAW) will rotate over a range of RPM. The bottom end will be zero (unless you've perfected a perpetual motion machine) and there's a design RPM beyond which damage or destruction is a certainty. Somewhere in between these two is the normal "operating" range and this will be on the lower end, the cut-in speed (where the windplant begins charging) and on the upper end, the cut-out speed (where the governor activates to limit generator output). If you averaged the operating ranges of all the different types of HAW,

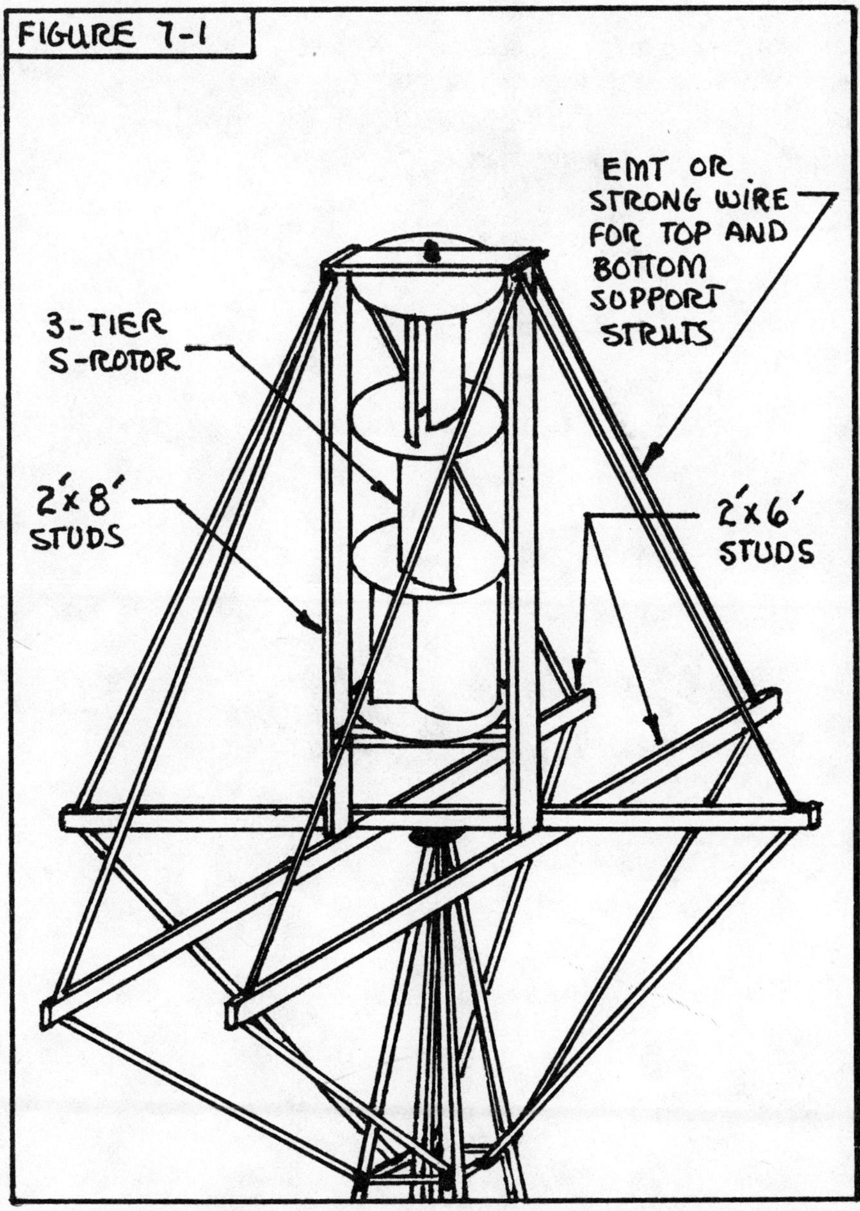
FIGURE 7-1
EMT OR
STRONG WIRE
FOR TOP AND
BOTTOM
SUPPORT
STRUTS
3-TIER
S-ROTOR
2'x8'
STUDS
2'x6'
STUDS

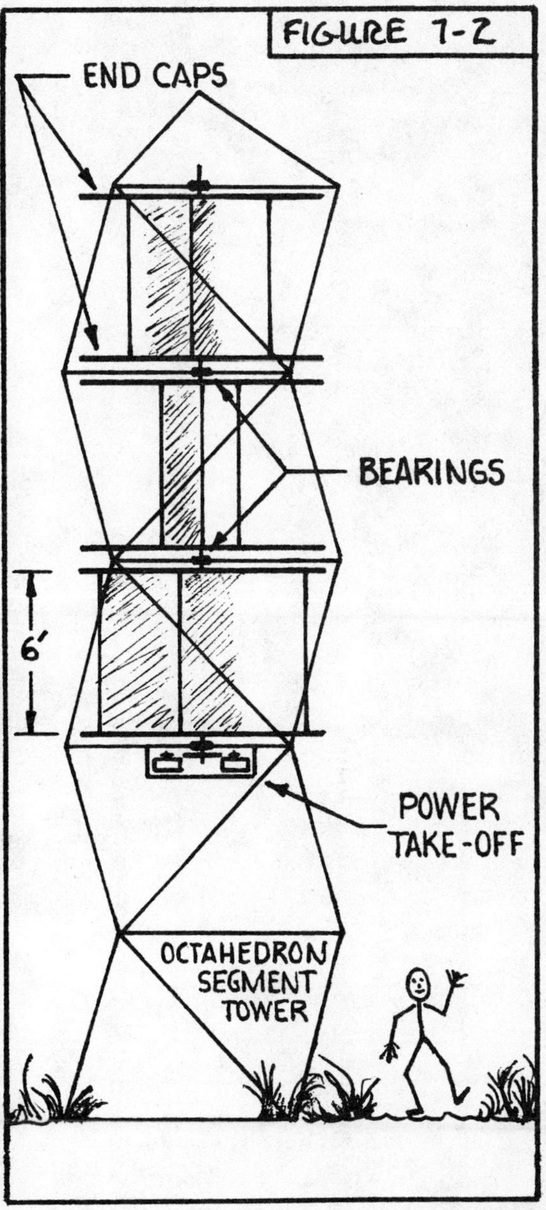
FIGURE 7-2
END CAPS
BEARINGS
6'
POWER
TAKE-OFF
OCTAHEDRON
SEGMENT
TOWER

and then did it for the VAW, you'd probably find a higher value for the HAW than the VAW. So, generally speaking, the VAW will require a lower-speed generator than the equivalent HAW. I reckon that's the same as when MAW SAW PAW RAW in the DRAW and figured it was against the LAW. If gears are used (instead of direct-drive), this won't necessarily be true, but the whole idea is to use the minimum gear ratio (or no gears at all) and employ a slower speed generator.

With proper gear ratios you can match the operating RPM of the aeroturbine with the generator's operating RPM. Unless this is done correctly, however, you won't be matching the torque curves for each and the mismatch will mean increased gear heat, alternator eddy current, and power losses. The ideal situation is to match the generator with the aeroturbine so that they can be directly coupled (no gearing). The next section deals with doing that if you've a mind to try and construct your own prototype.

Which to use--a generator or an alternator--is sumthin' you're gonna have to decide fairly early. The major advantages and disadvantages of each are well outlined in Wind and Windspinners.

Low Speed Alternator

What the wind energy world needs is a good low speed, high-wattage direct-drive alternator for windplants. Upcoming manufacturers will unquestionably pursue this idea if they're interested in selling a wind machine that will last the proverbial lifetime (or longer). The reason is not difficult to grasp. The inherent features of the alternator -- low mass, stationary power-producing coils, smaller physical size, etc. -- make it an excellent choice of design over the generator. As well, low speed means less wear and tear on the moving parts and direct coupling to the aeroturbine.

If you have an inkling to try building one for yourself, here's some info I've run across becuz I'm interested too. I'm not much of a generator design man, but if you are, this may help.

Standard alternators must turn fast in order to have the stator windings cut (or be cut by) enuff lines of electromagnetic force (around the fields); this is, in any electricity-generating device, the action that produces voltage. With the proper number of stator windings, you get the desired voltage and, provided the wire size is correct, you can get it at a desired current. The most easily-scrounged alternator comes from an automotive system. The problem with it is that it was designed to turn at a relatively high speed to produce its rated power. Oh sure, you can rewire the alternator for lower speed operation (one way is to use a 24-volt alternator and re-wind only the stator with twice the turns of smaller wire. See biliography for another possibility). But while this will produce more output at this lower speed, it is not without decreasing the maximum output of the alternator at top speed. Not a bad return but unacceptable for higher power wind machines. There isn't any space in a standard alternator to increase the electromagnetic field (field wires) or the number of stator wires that are cut by the flux (lines of force), so you can't do it that way. So . . . what's got to give?

Why, the diameter of the alternator, of course. If you can understand that voltage (and power) is dependent on the number of lines of magnetic force cut by a given amount of wire in a specified period of time, it should make sense that if you do increase the rate (or speed) at which the lines of force are cut, you'll be increasing voltage and power. But if you don't want to increase the rotational speed, you can enlarge the diameter of the alternator to increase the peripheral speed instead.

If this is not perfectly clear, consider Fig. 7-3; here we have two alternators. One has a field diameter of 6 inches and the other, an effective field diameter of 2 feet; the second, therefore, is 4 times larger in diameter than the first. Both are operating at 300 RPM. Notice the two points marked at the gap between the outer edge of the field winding (which rotates) and the inner edge of the stator coils (which are stationary). The question that needs answering is: how fast is point A moving past point B? Fig. 7-3 gives the actual computation but the answer is, as you probably already suspected, that point B is moving 4 times as fast in the larger alternator. Which means the field's lines of force will cut the stator coil wires 4 times as fast. In order to achieve this result in the smaller diameter alternator we would have to speed it up to 4 times the test RPM, or 1200 RPM. The larger diameter not only gives a larger periphery speed, but it enables the insertion of more field coils and stator coils; this will be necessary to get a minimum of four times the power. So, if it's so simple, why isn't it being done yet? The answer is simple: you run into a whole set of problems that have to be worked out. The generator people I've talked

(1) Earthmind's 3-tier S-rotor, (2) a mobile test stand helps further research here, (3) Mark hangs onto his own wind machine prototype, (4) the author and friend are dwarfed by a monster hybrid (S-rotor and Eggbeater), (5) the author balances a WC air-brake and (6) adjusts it on the machine. (7) Mark checks it out, (8) we raise the machine and (9) inspect the wreckage of a miscalculation.

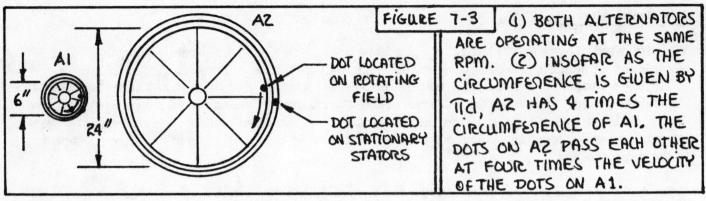

FIGURE 7-3 (1) BOTH ALTERNATORS ARE OPERATING AT THE SAME RPM. (2) INSOFAR AS THE CIRCUMFERENCE IS GIVEN BY πd, A2 HAS 4 TIMES THE CIRCUMFERENCE OF A1. THE DOTS ON A2 PASS EACH OTHER AT FOUR TIMES THE VELOCITY OF THE DOTS ON A1.

to think the idea is sound, but there hasn't been much application before the resurgence of interest in wind power. Can such a device be used in a windplant? Yes! A VAW alternator is not plagued with any problem of size since it will normally be located below the aeroturbine. Application to the HAW might seem to pose a problem, but not so. The center portion of a propeller is ineffectual at power extraction even if there isn't a governor entirely filling the space along with the alternator. It could probably be three feet in diameter without affecting anything.

I mentioned 300 RPM as a design speed but I think 200 is a better one to shoot for if you're going to do a prototype. While an alternator design allows for relatively light weight for the power produced, you will have weight and, consequently centrifugal forces to deal with. The particular thing to watch for here is stretching of the materials used to form the rotating frame for the field coils. Any material will stretch; for most, this will be admittedly, very little. However, when working with alternators, you want to keep the gap between the fields and the stators as small as possible for full efficiency. If the field coil frame elongates under high RPM, you're going to close that gap, and the two will touch, and you're gonna have sparks, heat, fire, and boat-anchor material.

A word here on using permanent magnets instead of the electromagnetic field coils. Avoid them on large machines unless you have a dependable governor and an alternative means of preventing battery overcharge. The biggest problem here is control. It's too bad becuz their use would simplify the design of the alternator we've been talking about. If you can't control the magnetic field, you have to rely on mechanical or other electronic controls. Additionally the slip-rings and brushes used for the field connections in an alternator are not high failure items even in the high speed alternator. So don't rule out the possibility of using them for that reason.

Other things to consider in this low speed alternator-equipped windplant. Bearings, lubrication, cooling, the type of field control, etc. You'll find, as you move into the project, that you are continuously discovering new things which will require your attention and creativity. Move slowly. You are creating, touching, and building; learn the patience and relish the fever, the excitement, and the discovery. It will be a reflection on you and your work.

A word of advice for the homebrew-oriented individual. Stay realistic. A little bit of knowledge is dangerous. If it doesn' t outright cost you a wind machine, some other stuff in the local vicinity of a windplant, or a life, it can lose you a lot of personal energy and put you on an anti-wind energy trip. I'd rather see most people try to build their own wind machine or wind-electric system but I've recommended to some that I've come across to buy one or get someone else to build it. Sure, anybody can learn something. Only problem with that idiology is that it's just that -- the way it can be, which isn't the same as the way it is. I've met some folks that would kill themselves if they tried it. And if I encouraged 'em they might be crazy enuff. If they prove me wrong, more power to 'em; proving me right is what I'm worried about.

About hardware. We'd all love to dig in there and wire our own generator, cast our own generator housing, and manufacture our own bearings. But that's not going to happen with all but a rare few. So, check out what's around you before you try to fabricate something yourself. Anybody that tries to "rough it" when they go back to the land is headed for big trouble. It may look like some (that you've seen) are doing just that, but remember: you're comparing their lifestyle to your own and you haven't been around long enuff to really know. Sure, these folks are living a simpler life, but they're not stupid; they've put to use everything they know that will help. After all, they don't do something the hardest way they can think of, just what's most sensible for the situation. Approach wind machine construction that way; if you have to use a gearbox, see if you can find something (that will do the job) that's readily available. And don't just look at the price and get turned off. Figure the time, skills, tools, parts, and the amount of energy you're going to have to manifest to do it yourself.

BRUSH INSTALLATION INSTRUCTIONS FOR JACOBS WIND ELECTRIC PLANTS - ALL MODELS
- 15 Degree -

There are Two Kinds of brushes used on each Jacobs Direct Drive Wind Electric Generator. When removing old brushes, be careful not to loosen the set screw that holds the brushholder to the shaft. The locking nut on the set screw holds the lug on the brush connecting wire and is loosened to remove the old brush, but never allow the set screw to loosen or the brushholder will not remain at the correct angle and may later cause commutator trouble. The same brushes and arrangement are used on Models 45 (1800 watt) and 60 (2500 watt - 32 volt).

On 32 volt the three brushes marked A-10 are to be installed in the two positive holders which are the upper and lower on right side when standing back of generator looking toward propellers and in the upper left holder (negative). Install the one brush marked 400 N.C. in negative holder (lower left). Be sure to set tension spring at third notch, to give correct pressure to the brushes. All plants have same size brushes - 1-1/2 in. wide, 3/8 in. thick and 1-3/4 in. long.

The double commutator 110 volt plants use 8 brushes; the one 400 N.C. brush is to be installed in the lower left hand brushholder facing rear of generator and the other 400 brush in the lower left hand brushholder, when facing the front of the generator. The A-10 brushes are to be installed in the remaining brushholders. Replace with above brushes, regardless of kind removed.

Make sure the brush fits loosely in the brushholder and slips up and down easily. When fitting new brushes, first place the strips of sandpaper on the commutator with the sanded surface out and with one end of the sandpaper lapped 1/2 turn so that the sandpaper can revolve when plant turns without the end catching on the brushes. Then insert the four brushes and put the spring tension arm against each brush. This will hold sufficient pressure against the brushes so that the sandpaper will grind them to fit. Handle the sandpaper carefully as it cannot be used if it is cracked.

Allow the plant to run slowly (turn it partly out of wind if necessary) and start the sandpaper to moving with the fingers by pressing it against the commutator for a turn or two. Once it starts to revolve, it will turn satisfactorily. Each brush must be sanded or ground to a full 100% fit, as brushes on slow speed generators do not wear in. They must be ground to fit at the start. A brush that does not have a full fit over the entire surface will begin to burn and arc, causing the commutator to become rough, and a rough commutator will soon grind away the brushes.

Slip each brush out of the holder and be sure that it has a perfect full fit before the sandpaper is removed. (It sometimes requires 2 or 3 strips of sandpaper to properly fit the brushes). After grinding all the brushes to fit properly, then remove the sandpaper and blow away any loose sandpaper dust that may be sticking to the commutator. A cloth wiped lengthwise with the mica insulation between each bar, is very effective to clean the sandpaper dust out of the space between the commutator bars.

After the brushes are completely fitted and the commutator is cleaned and ready to go, be sure the pigtail attached to each brush is bent so that it is directly above each brush, otherwise it may touch the brushholder as the brush wears down and this would soon ruin the brush because it would prevent it from sliding down easily in the holder.

Only by following these instructions can you properly install and fit new brushes on your plant. If during brush replacement a brushholder becomes loose and turns, or the stud on which it is mounted turns, so as to set the brush at the wrong angle to the commutator, put the old brush back in holder and adjust angle of brushholder so that the brush fits the commutator correctly. Then after brushholder is tightened in correct position remove the old brush and install the new one as explained above.

A brush Angle Gauge (15 degree) can be secured from the factory to properly set the brush holders at the correct angle to fit the brushes. All brushes must be set at the same angle. If the new replacement brushes are not ground to the same angle as the old ones when received from the factory, then a gauge should be used to reset all the brushholders to fit the new brushes so that future replacements will also fit correctly.

To change old style 30 degree brush angle to new 15 degree, loosen brushholder frame clamp bolt, move frame with armature rotation (clockwise) about 1/8 inch (one commutator bar width). Be sure to retighten clamp bolt and see that frame has not slipped forward to rub any brushholders on commutator riser bars. Chisel or punch new position marks on generator frame.

To change "0" degree to 15 degree move holder against rotation 1/8 inch. Reset brush holders before sanding in new brushes. To check or reset angle always use a factory brush gauge.

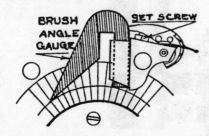

BRUSH ANGLE GAUGE   SET SCREW

HOW TO USE BRUSH ANGLE GAUGE

Insert the gauge as shown. The right side edge of gauge must touch the brush holder body full length (not brush guard). Loosen set screw to shift angle of brush holder. Retighten firmly, using gauge to maintain proper angle. Check all brush holders with gauge when installing new brushes.

BEARING SPECIFICATIONS	GENERATOR (FRONT & REAR)	GEARCASE		TURNTABLE
		FRONT	REAR	
WINCHARGER 1500 WATT	NEW DEPARTURE 8504	NEW DEPARTURE 88507	FAFNIR 205K or HOOVER 205	TIMKEN 13685
WINCHARGER 1000 or 1250 WATT	FAFNIR 204 KTT	FAFNIR 206T or HOOVER 99206	FAFNIR 205K or HOOVER 205	UNKNOWN
JACOBS 1800 or 2500 WATT	NEW DEPARTURE 88508	N/A	N/A	TIMKEN 395-S

GENERATOR SADDLE ASSEMBLY
AND
COLLECTOR BRUSH UNIT

NEG. WIRE (WHITE)
FIELD WIRE (SMALL)
POS. WIRE (BLACK)

IRON WASHER AND COTTER PIN

Zerk Fitting - Grease turn-table when installing. (Swing plant around when greasing, and grease every six months).

½ x 1¾ CAP SCREW

GENERATOR SADDLE

BALL BEARING TURN TABLE

GENERATOR SADDLE TUBE

WEATHER PROOF IRON RING

FELT WASHER

UPPER COLLECTOR BRUSH CASTING

LOWER COLLECTOR BRUSH CASTING

Bolt lower tube support (upper collector brush casting) in position, (The weather proof iron ring and felt washer must be placed on saddle tube when tube is installed.) then install generator saddle and supporting tube unit, being sure first to remove the collector brushes sliding the tube down from the top through tower cap. Grease tube slightly where it enters lower bearings. Check to see that tube turns freely, if it does not, it indicates that the collector brush holder casting is not level and is binding on the steel tube. To correct, loosen corner bolts that hold collector assembly, and shift one side up or down, again tighten the bolts.

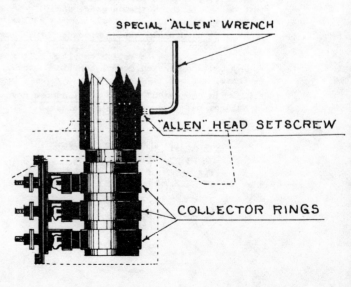

SPECIAL "ALLEN" WRENCH

"ALLEN" HEAD SETSCREW

COLLECTOR RINGS

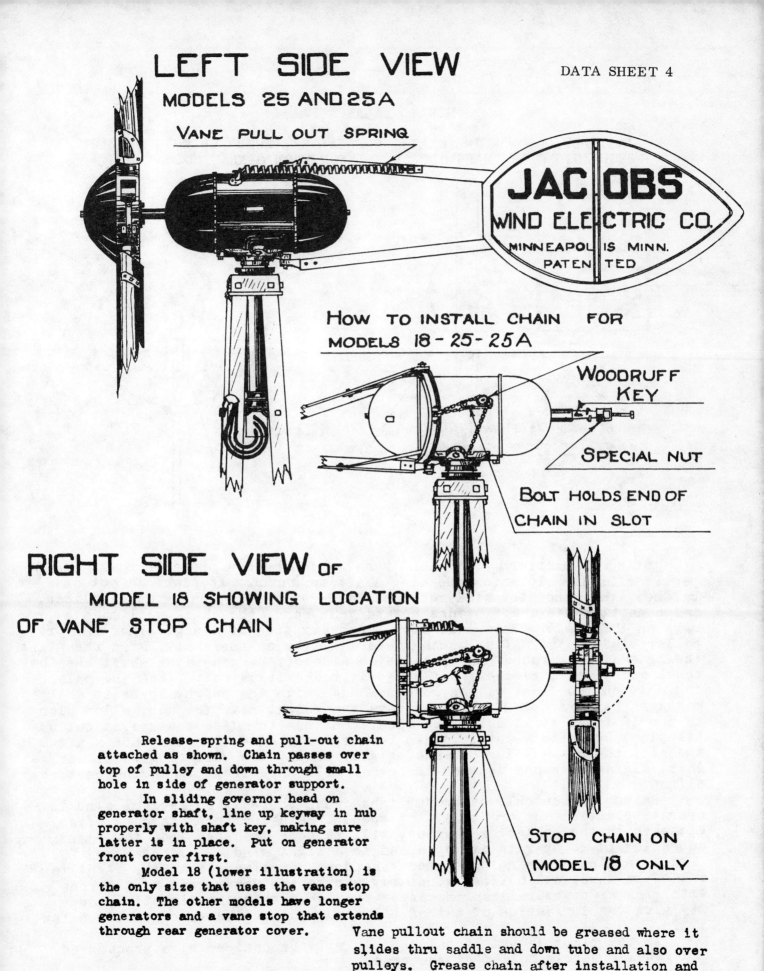

LEFT SIDE VIEW
MODELS 25 AND 25A

VANE PULL OUT SPRING

JAC OBS
WIND ELE CTRIC CO.
MINNEAPOL IS MINN.
PATEN TED

HOW TO INSTALL CHAIN FOR
MODELS 18 - 25 - 25A

WOODRUFF KEY

SPECIAL NUT

BOLT HOLDS END OF
CHAIN IN SLOT

RIGHT SIDE VIEW OF
MODEL 18 SHOWING LOCATION
OF VANE STOP CHAIN

STOP CHAIN ON
MODEL 18 ONLY

Release-spring and pull-out chain
attached as shown. Chain passes over
top of pulley and down through small
hole in side of generator support.

In sliding governor head on
generator shaft, line up keyway in hub
properly with shaft key, making sure
latter is in place. Put on generator
front cover first.

Model 18 (lower illustration) is
the only size that uses the vane stop
chain. The other models have longer
generators and a vane stop that extends
through rear generator cover.

Vane pullout chain should be greased where it
slides thru saddle and down tube and also over
pulleys. Grease chain after installation and
not before.

HOW TO BALANCE PLANT

INSTRUCTIONS FOR INSTALLING SPECIAL BALANCING UNIT IF A PLANT
SHOWS SIGNS OF BEING OUT OF BALANCE WHEN OPERATING.

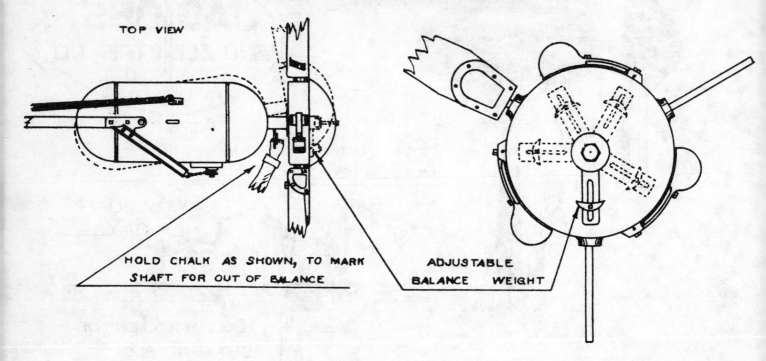

TOP VIEW

HOLD CHALK AS SHOWN, TO MARK
SHAFT FOR OUT OF BALANCE

ADJUSTABLE
BALANCE WEIGHT

Stand on platform with plant running and hold a piece of chalk (lead
pencil will do) close to generator shaft as shown. If plant is out of
balance, the generator will rock back and forth as shown by dotted lines,
and each time the shaft swings toward your hand, the chalk will make a
mark on the shaft. This indicates the heavy side of the governor and propeller blade unit. After making several marks on the shaft, stop the plant
(swing the vane around) and note which side of the generator shaft has the
chalk marks; then remove front cone cover and large nut, place the balancing unit on the front of the governor head with the weight opposite the
chalk marks on the shaft. First have the weight near the hub, allow plant
to run if it is still out of balance, continue to slide the weight out until plant operates smoothly, then be sure to tighten large nut on shaft
and also the nut holding balance weight, moving the balancing weight arm a
short distance to one side or the other, will show if it is in the best position.

Balancing can only be accomplished when there is sufficient wind to
operate plant at top or nearly top speed. Removing both charging wires
attached to the collector brushes, will release the load from the plant
and allow it to operate at top speed in a light wind.

A rocking or swinging of the vane does not always mean the plant is
out of balance, as shifting winds may strike the upper part of the vane
with greater pressure than the lower part when changing direction, and
may give the impression of out of balance, because the vane wabbles a few
times.

If the plant is out of balance, it will be noticed by a pronounced
and regular wabble motion of the vane.

BIBLIOGRAPHY

Most of the folks involved in alternative energy research or education are over-worked and have little money to spend on postage and free literature. In requesting further information, consider how much you are asking for, and the value of that information. The response you receive is likely to be proportional to the money or the information that you offer them. A self-addressed stamped envelope is the absolute minimum. Technical questions should be specific. Give some idea of YOUR background in the subject.

WIND POWER DIGEST -- This new quarterly is already one of the best news and information exchange bulletins available. Issues one and two contain reviews on almost every wind electric system available in manufactured, kit and plan form (old and new) as well as up-and-coming designs, water-pumpers, interviews with windworkers, photos, diagrams, construction plans, and book reviews. Subscription (one year, $6) and back issues ($2 each) are available from Jester Press, 54468 CR 31, Bristol, Indiana, 46507.

ALTERNATIVE SOURCES OF ENERGY-- a magazine of practical technology for a decentralized society. Energy sources, agriculture, architecture, transportation, and communication for the home-builder. 4 worth-it issues per year, $5. Issues 1-10 are reprinted in A.S.E. BOOK ONE, $4. Issue 17-- Spectrum: An Alternate Technology Equipment Directory, $2. Rt. 2, Box 90A, Milaca, Minn. 56353.

WIND AND WINDSPINNERS: A Nuts 'n Bolts Approach to Wind Electric Systems-- an Earthmind publication (by Michael Hackleman), this book-length treatment of wind, wind electric systems, and components covers such subjects as: Wind Energy--efficiency, average energy in the wind, power derivation and formulas, etc.; Generating Electricity--theory, the generating unit, voltage regulation, finding an alternator, transmission; Batteries-- fundamental principles, cpacity, charging/discharging properly for longer life, testing and finding batteries; Control-- aeroturbine/alternator/battery storage control, control circuits and examples, loading effect, increasing power capability, adjustments; Using Electricity--inverters, determining use, cutting down, auxiliary power; The S-rotor-- gathering materials, choosing a design, simple construciton instructions. Supplement, Newsletter One is now sent with book (28 pages). 115 pages, $7.50 (bulk mail price USA), $9.50 (airmail USA) and $10.50 (foreign), from Earthmind.

ENERGY BOOK #1: Natural Sources and Backyard Applications-- A well-chosen selection of articles from many sources. Full of practical hints and good ideas. #2 is coming soon. 112 big pages, $4, or $4.25 postpaid from Running Press, 38 S. 19th St, Philadelphia, Pa. 19103.

ENERGY PRIMER: Solar, Water, Wind and Biofuels-- Complete and concise introductions by various competent authors on natural energy utilization, including food production, architecture and integrated systems. Theory and applications, references, and sources. Put together by the Whole Earth Catalog people. A good place to start. 200 big pages. $4.50 from Portola Institute, 558 Santa Cruz, Menlo Park, Ca, 94536.

SIMPLIFIED WIND POWER SYSTEMS FOR EXPERIMENTERS by Jack Park-- Designing a wind machine is an engineering project. Jack has written an engineering handbook that you can use by applying no more than simple arithmetic and graph-reading to problems of aerodynamic, structural and mechanical design. Includes a good run-down on construction methods and materials for vertical and horizontal axis machines. (Even a page on how to read graphs!) 80 pages, $6.50 from Earthmind.

LEJAY MANUAL-- This vintage classic (1945) describes the processes of rewinding automotive generators for use in direct-drive wind machines and other applications. How to make arc welders, soldering irons, an electric scooter, electric fence, small wind generators, an insect-zapper, trans- formers and an armature-growler, all from salvaged materials. Ask any old-timer about this one. $1.75 from Le Jay Manufacturing Co., Belle Plaine, Minn, 56011.

THE STORAGE BATTERY, LEAD-ACID TYPES: Its Fundamental Principles, Operation and Care-- $1 from Exide Power Systems Division, ESB Inc. Philadelphia, Pa. 19120.

PLOWBOY INTERVIEW: MARCELLUS JACOBS-- Required reading if you are designing, building, or buying a windplant. This interview outlines many of the problems and solutions involved in manufacture and use of the Jacobs Wind-Electric Plant. More than worth the price of either The Mother Earth News issue #24, or The Mother Earth News Handbook of Homemade Power-- 374 pages, $1.95 from The Mother Earth News, P.O. Box 70, Hendersonville, N.C. 28739.

WIND ENERGY BIBLIOGRAPHY-- Wind, Windmills, Aerodynamics, Electrical, Towers, Storage, Conversion, Hydrogen, Catalogs, General Reading. 60 pages, $3 from Windworks (see PLANS).

EARTHMIND'S BIBLIOGRAPHY-- reviews, sources, and references of wind, solar, methane, hydro, and other energy sources. Publication B-1, 4 pages, $1.50

JACOBS OPERATOR'S MANUAL-- this is a reprint of the original installation and operations manual accompanying a Jacobs wind machine. A must for the owner (or prospective owner) and quite useful to any wind energy enthusiast for the info it contains. Earthmind publication W-5, 18-pages, $3.

WINCHARGER OPERATOR'S MANUAL-- similar to above. Earthmind publication W-6, 18 pages, $3.

RADIO INTERFERENCE BULLETIN (from Wincharger Corp.) Earthmind pub. W-8, 6 pages, $1.25.

DELCO LIGHT PLANT TECHNICAL SERVICE MANUAL-- See text, page 160. $3 from Earthmind.

PLANS FOR WIND-ELECTRIC EQUIPMENT (All are 12-volt systems)

WINDWORKS' 12 FOOTER PLANS-- A sophisticated down-wind machine. Max. power: 2000 watts at 25 MPH. Paper-honeycomb/fiberglass blades. Octahedron module tower plans included, $15.

30 FOOT OCTAHEDRON MODULE TOWER PLANS-- See text, page 97, $3 from Windworks, Box 329, Route 3, Mukwonago, Wis. 53149. Send $1 for further information (including synchronous inverter data).

HELION 12/16 PLANS-- A sophisticated down-wind machine. Power: 1000 watts (12') or 1100 watts (16') at 20 MPH (increases at higher wind speeds). Spar-and-rib aluminum blades. Engineering data and plans, $10 from Helion (Jack Park) Box 4301, Sylmar, Ca. 91342.

LANDING'S WIND-DRIVEN GENERATOR PLANT-- Max. power: 600 watts. 12', 3-blade wood prop. Automatic side-facing. An easy-to-build design. See Popular Science , April '75. Poorly drawn but complete plans, $3.60 from Bob Landing, 182 Cortsen Rd. Pleasant Hill, Ca. 94523.

SENCENBAUGH 750-14-- Max. power: 790 watts at 18-20 MPH. 12', 3-blade wood prop. Automatic side-facing. Plans, finished, or semi-finished kits available. Send $1.10 for brochure. Other plans, including Alternator rewinding, no longer available. Sencenbaugh Wind Electric, PO Box 11174, Palo Alto, Ca. 94306.

SAVONIUS ROTOR WIND-ELECTRIC SYSTEM-- Power: 500 watts at 25 MPH (with light-weight design). See text, pages 181-184. Listed under Wind and Windspinners.

SOURCES of HARDWARE

Burstein-Applebee, 3199 Mercier, Kansas City, Mo. 64111. Electronic parts, inexpensive. Catalog free.
Surplus Center, PO Box 82209, Lincoln, Neb. 68501. Electronic bargains. Catalog free.
Dwyer Instruments, Michigan City, Ind. 46360. Inexpensive but accurate windspeed indicators.
Jopp Electrical Works, Rt. 2, Princeton, Minn. 55371. Repair, remanufacture, or replacement parts for Jacobs and other wind-electric plants.
Aero Power Research Co. PO Box 2001, Burlingame, Ca. 94010. Wood blades for wind generators.